Disorders of Simulation

Disorders of Simulation:
Malingering, Factitious Disorders, and Compensation Neurosis

Grant L. Hutchinson, Ph.D.

Psychosocial Press
Madison   Connecticut

Library of Congress Cataloging-in-Publication Data

Hutchinson, Grant L.
    Disorders of simulation : malingering, factitious disorders, and compensation neurosis/Grant L. Hutchinson.
        p. ; cm.
    Includes bibliographical references and index.
    ISBN 1-887841-36-9
        1. Malingering—Diagnosis. 2. Deception. 3. Factitious disorders.
    4. Compensation (Psychology) I. Title.
        [DNLM: 1. Malingering—diagnosis. 2. Diagnosis, Differential.
    3. Factitious Disorders—diagnosis. 4. Neurotic Disorders—diagnosis.
    W 783 H976d 2001]
    RA1146 .H88 2001
    616.85′2—dc21
                                                                    2001019598

With gratitude and passion, I dedicate this work to my wife, my partner in all things.

Table of Contents

Acknowledgments

Writing a book is a vast undertaking that cannot easily be accomplished alone. I had the good fortune to have the support and love of my family during the long hours I spent away from them, tied to a word processor. For all the opportunities missed and good times never had, I especially thank the forbearance of my children, Stan and Katie. My dear wife, Karen, not only ceaselessly encouraged me to write but also was a source of great inspiration and help. Her own work in the complex area of object relations theory was of paramount importance and she spent many long hours reading and rereading the manuscript.

I was also fortunate to enlist the services of two very astute and critical professionals, Drs. Nikki Varzos and Dana Olson. They made many excellent editorial and content suggestions that resulted in far greater clarity than was present in the original manuscript. It is also important to mention the staff at the University of California Davis Medical School Library for their tireless search when asked to obtain ''just one more'' article from an obscure journal.

Introduction

Malingering is a subject upon which I have sometimes
thought of writing a monograph [Sherlock Holmes].
(Doyle, 1894b, p. 941)

Malingering, Factitious Disorders, and Compensation Neurosis
all have in common the false or grossly exaggerated presentation
of symptoms, or false causal attribution of physical or mental
disorders, in a fashion indicating that the patient displays some
degree of intentional or volitional control. Unfortunately, the
psychodynamic boundaries of Disorders of Simulation are vague
and ill defined since, in one way or another, all diagnoses of
simulated illnesses require the diagnosis of nonillness. Health sciences are universally concerned with the opposite: the detection
of genuine illness. In Disorders of Simulation, the very theorists
and clinicians most concerned with real disease and its cure must
turn to *the study of simulated disease* and its detection. Moreover,
a peculiar distinction applies when real and false illness must be
separated; the clinician must distinguish not only between health
and illness, but also between health imitating illness and illness
imitating health. This is a formidable undertaking for pathology-
based health disciplines since the diagnosis of simulated disease
seems to require the impossible: the diagnosis that no real illness
exists; the proof of the null hypothesis; the existence of the "non-
disease" of disease simulation.

Knowledge about Malingering, Factitious Disorder, and
Compensation Neurosis is incomplete, inadequate, and more often than not, defined by default. Diagnosis by exclusion is the

rule rather than the exception. The difficulties inherent in diagnosis by a process of elimination have the added negative effect of directing researchers' attention to other, more attractive, and "legitimate" diagnoses. Despite extensive discussion in the clinical literature for many years, only recently have diagnosticians and taxonomists accorded recognized stature in the official nomenclature to some "simulating diagnoses." However, these conditions remain, for the most part, the illegitimate children of genuine illness, relegated to the orphanages of appendices, addenda, footnotes, corrigenda, and the passing mention. They are without papers or pedigree, mentioned briefly, rarely discussed, the last to be considered and the first to be rejected.

Malingering has been subject to little theoretical attention and even less experimentation as can been seen by a cursory review of the literature. Reported studies are often long on moralizing and short on dispassionate analysis.

Factitious Disorders, although presumably less common than Malingering, have received greater theoretical and clinical attention; the literature is replete with case reports but deficient in empirical studies. Abundant clinical data indicate that Factitious Disorders constitute a fascinating area for clinical study. All the requirements for a tantalizing clinical enigma are present: the symptoms are outstanding (e.g., fabricated complaints, self-induced illness, *pseudologia fantastica, Vorbeireden,* induction by proxy, etc.). The endless variations are intriguing, and the patient is usually assumed to suffer from a serious emotional disorder.

Compensation Neurosis is a vague, ephemeral, and elusive condition, existing in an ill-defined twilight region between true mental disorder and the motivating circumstances of elevated secondary gain. The published articles on Compensation Neurosis are often contradictory and sometimes nonsensical.

A PERSONAL VIEW

As a health care professional, my training required that I take a patient's request for help very seriously. My task was to discover the pathology and treat the patient or, in the event the patient mistakenly thought he was ill, reassure him about his state of mental health. Initially, I viewed illness simulation as not applicable to my own patients. People who solicit health care are invariably bona fide patients with genuinely held beliefs that they are ill, whether or not such beliefs have a basis in verifiable reality. Thus a hypochondriac is as genuine and real a patient as is a stroke victim, despite the fact that the latter has palpable physical illness and resultant mental deficits while the former has solely emotional distress. Both these patients are deserving of health care since, at a psychological level, their complaints are heartfelt and genuine.

I was not taught to expect patients to present with a disguised purpose that was foreign to my humanistic concern for their emotional welfare. Certainly, during training and in clinical practice, I observed an occasional patient who feigned complaints for an obvious purpose such as avoiding military draft, escaping punishment, or obtaining benefits not rightfully owed. However, such observations were noxiously incongruent with my perception of the humanism of caregiving and the time I spent contemplating the simulation of mental disorder was therefore fleeting.

If I suspected simulation, my first impulse was to question my own perceptions and quickly conclude that the patient had a novel but genuine problem which simply defeated my experience and training. Indeed, the tendency to place the patient's complaints within the context of a familiar diagnostic taxonomy is so strong as to leave the caregiver blind-sided to false symptom presentation (Rosenhan, 1973); fortunately, patients usually do not stand on the blind side.

Very few patients try to feign major mental or physical problems and, when they do attempt to deceive, they are usually seriously disturbed and desire to feign mental health in the interest of ego preservation or evading treatment. This dissimulation of health seems more palatable than the simulation of disease since attempts to hide mental illness are often a legitimate symptom of the patient's pathology.

However, if I became convinced that a patient was truly simulating pathology, my impulse was to dismiss him as an illegitimate nonpatient, an undeserving pretender who was playing false with my humanitarian concern. Why should I waste my time and clinical resources on an individual whose only "pathology" was hostility or avarice?

Eventually, I began to think of simulators as bona fide patients and dealt with my own obvious countertransference issues. As I examined my own reactions to patients who simulated, I began to spend more time with them and, much to my surprise, I found an unexpected richness and diversity of human motivation and perception. I discovered that Disorders of Simulation are far more complex than I had ever imagined. In the course of my practice, I also developed the perception that the actual simulation of disorder has become more prevalent.

Initially, I wondered if my perception of increasing simulation among my patients might be erroneous, resulting from my changed perception of the simulator as a patient rather than an illegitimate pretender. A review of several hundred patient charts, however, quickly convinced me that awareness of my own negative countertransference and subsequently changed perceptions was an inadequate explanation for my observation. I also thought that perhaps the increase I perceived in simulation was due to changing referral sources such as more insurance defense work, or to my becoming unconsciously jaded, burned-out, and pessimistic about human nature. Yet, when I checked my perceptions with some colleagues, I found that they also reported a similar upswing in cases where they suspected or actually found symptom falsification. Further, in my own practice, this increase also seemed to be related to a perceived increase in the drama of litigated cases in which the liability was slight, the injury difficult to document, and the claimed loss disproportionately high. Again, some colleagues shared the same experience of increased simulating behavior and drama amongst patients seen for treatment and evaluation.

I estimate that 5 to 10% of patients simulate in some fashion, based upon my clinical practice which is exclusively diagnostic, heavily forensic, modestly hospital based, and therefore probably positively skewed toward encountering simulation. In therapeutic practice it is unlikely that the proportion would be so high, although estimates of Malingering in the literature usually run from 1 to 5% with respect to most patient populations (Flicker, 1956; Mills & Lipian, 1995).

This book is the result of my own consternation when confronted with the simulating patients who presented in my practice. Not only was I ill-trained to troll for symptom falsification in the murky depths of the psyche, I had no guidelines at all about what to do if I actually caught a patient simulating. I sometimes had the feeling of being a Sunday afternoon angler who finds himself with a monstrous fish on the line; the ensuing struggle leads to philosophical reflection about who has really caught whom? When I suspect simulation, what should be my next step? Should I carry on with a standard or modified evaluation? What modifications should I make? Should I confront the patient? How will I know if my suspicions are wrong? What constitutes legiti mate proof and how much is enough? How can I be sure the patient is consciously faking? Since I usually had to prepare a report of my findings (often for forensic purposes), these questions were more than merely academic.

In part, this book results from the confusion engendered by the *Diagnostic and Statistical Manual's (DSM)* exhortation to diagnose mental disorder accurately while, at the same time, providing inadequate definitions, minimal criteria, and vague standards at best for the three Disorders of Simulation: Malingering, Factitious Disorder, and Compensation Neurosis. Standard reference works are also of little help. For example, while contributing authors in the sixth edition of the *Comprehensive Textbook of Psychiatry* (Kaplan & Sadock, 1995) devote more space to Malingering and Factitious Disorders than do most texts, this expanded discussion is of little additional assistance in areas of differential diagnosis, treatment, or prognosis.

Rogers (1988) edited the first text exclusively devoted to the *Clinical Assessment of Malingering and Deception* since Jones and Llewellyn's landmark work in 1917, and reviewed a great deal of the extant literature, reorganizing some relevant concepts in the area. He proposed that simulation is "an adaptive response to adverse circumstances which may best be understood in the context of decision theory" (p. 27). That is, deception does not necessarily imply psychopathology or criminality but rather is an act in which almost any person may engage under certain circumstances. Yet, upon careful inspection, this important book primarily recapitulates, reorganizes, and summarizes prior methods for detecting deception rather than fundamentally reconceptualizing and innovatively reformulating the concept of simulation.

Nowhere in the literature have Malingering, Factitious Disorders, and Compensation Neurosis been adequately developed in theoretical terms. Although Disorders of Simulation are unique and, as such, have received passing mention in standard reference works, they are rarely discussed in depth. Many sources do not address the issue at all. Hall and Pritchard (1996) compiled a variety of methods for *Detecting Malingering and Deception*, labeled *Forensic Distortion Analysis* (FDA), a behaviorally based view that labels simulation as adaptive and situation specific. Like Rogers, Hall and Pritchard (1966) view deception as a behavior that is "adaptive and both cross- and intra-situation specific" (p. xxiv). Their FDA model takes a "sign approach" involving identification of target symptoms to achieve a certain goal and the production of response patterns for "concealing the real or presenting the fake" (p. xxiv).

Other than to note Braverman's (1978) study in which he identified a category labeled *Hysterical Malingering*, Hall and Pritchard do not directly address the difficult issue of separating the hysteriform processes from simulation. They simply state that "generally, nondeliberate distortion needs to be ruled out or taken into account before deception is considered. Ground truth may be misrepresented by both nondeliberate and deliberate deception" (p. 31). However, even if the evaluator is sure that the patient is deceptive, Hall and Pritchard rightly note that:

> The diagnostic label "malingering," for example, does not distinguish between conscious exaggeration of a genuine problem and total fabrication of the problem; it does not distinguish between honest reporting of one problem and distorted reporting of another problem; it does not distinguish between honest reporting of a problem on one instrument and distorted reporting of the same problem on another instrument; it does not distinguish between accurate, replicate indicators of distortion and inaccurate, experimental indicators. It is therefore preferable to avoid summary labels in clinical communications and to use succinct descriptive statements instead. (pp. 260–261)

Despite recent efforts, a rigorous psychodynamic, motivational, and behavioral conceptualization of Disorders of Simulation remains elusive. Each practitioner must diagnose and treat these Disorders without benefit of clear standards and criteria.

The clinician has only a general yardstick to use when he suspects Factitious Disorder much less a finely calibrated diagnostic ruler. It exists in a peculiar category, incompletely specified, and without linkages to either "genuine disorders" or other simulating disorders. In the case of Malingering, a diligent search of the literature reveals only the barest diagnostic rules of thumb. Compensation Neurosis is even more ambiguously defined. Nowhere is it clearly distinguished from Malingering on the one hand and "legitimate" diagnoses such as Somatoform Pain Disorder or Psychological Factors Affecting Physical Condition on the other, despite an attempt to do so by Hyler, Williams, and Spitzer (1988).

Without a robust and uniform system of diagnostic guidelines, individual practitioner standards may vary widely. Some may ignore Disorders of Simulation and never diagnose them while other examiners may be very suspicious and make the assumption of faking with alarming frequency. Without clearly defined standards, how will the clinician judge whether a patient is simulating and, if so, whether the perception of simulation is apparent rather than real, perhaps as the result of countertransference issues or conflicts in moral values? How can an evaluator distinguish between the subtle shadings of the manifold hysteria-based disorders and abject simulation, particularly in the traditional sense of hysteria that includes many somatoform disorders and dissociative phenomena as well as hysteroid personality processes? What ethical issues are inherent in labeling patients as pretenders? What does it mean professionally, personally, and therapeutically if the therapist becomes the "whistle-blower" on a simulating patient? How should the clinician approach the ethical dilemma created when the best interests of the patient and society collide?

The present book also results from my dissatisfaction with the currently conflicting and incompletely specified standards for Malingering, Factitious Disorder, and Compensation Neurosis that pose formidable forensic as well as clinical obstacles to the application of consistent guidelines. Attorneys in trial and deposition often ask the question: "Is the patient faking?" and, whatever the answer, follow up with probing questions: "By what standards did you determine that the patient was (was not) faking? What references did you use? How do you support your opinion? How do you distinguish between simulation and hysteria?"

Finally, this book results from my unabashed intellectual curiosity about the range and scope of simulation, its effective detection, and the reasons why patients feign illness in the first place. Are Disorders of Simulation such simple phenomena as is suggested by the literature? Are they simply "adaptive" behaviors that almost anyone may display if the circumstances are ripe? Or, as I have come to suspect, are they only as simple and unitary as were the concepts of "schizophrenia" or "brain damage" before considerable theory development and experimental work was devoted to understanding these varieties of behavioral anomaly? Is it not possible that Malingering, Factitious Disorder, and Compensation Neurosis, singly and as a group, constitute multidetermined, multiaxial, and multipolar phenomena that defy the simple rubrics for detection and diagnosis mentioned in the literature? My opinion is the latter and it is in that belief that this book was conceived. Indeed, it is the theme of this book that Disorders of Simulation are behavioral syndromes capable of definition in the same systematic fashion as are other *DSM-IV* (APA, 1994) disorders.

1

Definition, Phenomena, and Taboo

> Good Lord, what madness rules in brainsick men.
> (Shakespeare, *King Henry VI*, Act 4, Scene 1)

The notion of simulation has a long and convoluted history. From the earliest times, clinicians have been concerned not only with distinguishing between illness and health but also with determining whether the simulation of illness by the healthy is illness, and whether the camouflaging of illness by the ill is health. These distinctions have never been easy and, in recent times, have been further hampered by multiple changes in the standard diagnostic nomenclature, fluctuating definitions of the simulating disorders, and even disagreement over the existence of some.

Terms used in the discussion of Disorders of Simulation need clear definition. This is no easy task since few conditions have been so labeled, relabeled, and mislabeled as Malingering, Factitious Disorders, and Compensation Neurosis. The definitional problem is made worse by terms that overlap with disorders where simulation is presumably not an issue. Nevertheless, clinical diagnosis of simulation has proceeded despite the fact that theoretical conceptualization is scant, conflicting opinions are prevalent due to the paucity of empirical support, and controversy rages over the legal and financial implications.

DISORDERS OF SIMULATION

Disorders of Simulation have in common the gross exaggeration, fabrication, or wrongful attribution of mental or psychological

1

disorder, including its causes, symptoms, and effects. Symptom production or attribution by the patient is invariably associated with some degree of willful, conscious effort, ranging along a continuum. At one end, the Malingerer overtly falsifies, the Factitious patient is partially aware, while those suffering from Compensation Neurosis exist in a state usually viewed as partaking both of secondary gain and vague, twilight consciousness of symptom exaggeration. Dissociative, Anxiety, and Somatoform Disorders, of course, are the anchor points at the psychodynamic end of the continuum since they are wholly unconscious and therefore not classified as simulation.

Most simple definitions easily distinguish Disorders of Simulation from other categories of illness at conceptual levels but a clear differential diagnostic decision in clinical practice is far more complex. Simulation is a very complicated notion and is composed of several ingredients similar to those noted by Weintraub (1989). In the context of defining "lying," he listed four criteria that, with just slight modification, are equally relevant for the definition of Disorders of Simulation.

False Behaviors

First, some part of the verbal or physical behaviors demonstrated by the patient must be false by the patient's own intention and recognition. Weintraub's definition of intention as "willful design or purpose" refers to a theoretical construct since it occurs entirely within the patient's mind and is therefore invisible to others. This is, of course, the difficult issue of conscious awareness and is not easy to define much less make operational in a clinical or experimental setting. At a practical level, *demonstrating intent in the clinic is as difficult as proving fraud in the courtroom;* in both cases it can only be perceived if the patient overtly states his intent or if all reasonable observers agree that the patient's behavior bears no other sensible interpretation.

Volitional Action

Second, simulation must be the result of some volitional action. That is, without action the patient has no more than a thought or plan and merely having the thought is not only insufficient to define simulation but also impossible to observe. Thus, in order for simulation to be present, some observable, behavioral action must occur which, in turn, a clinician must interpret as representative of simulation. Adequacy of interpretation is the major obstacle to practical application of this portion of the definition since no objective standards exist, customary guidelines are generally inadequate, and the distinction between hysteria and simulation is formidable.

False Presentation

Third, some part of the patient's presentation must actually be false. That is, the complaint must be either entirely false or else represent significant and substantial symptomatic exaggeration or causal misattribution of an actual disorder from which the patient currently suffers. Obviously, the disorder in question may be mental, physical, or some combination of both but, in whatever combination, cannot be wholly genuine. At a practical level, it is not always easy to determine whether a patient is genuinely ill or well, much less, whether he is feigning sickness or health.

Nontrivial Consequences

Fourth, the simulation must have nontrivial consequences. Of course, the definition of "nontrivial" can be as controversial as the definition of simulation itself, but Weintraub's intent is important to note. In the literature, it is possible to find discussions where untruthful but trivial statements such as, "Not tonight Dear, I have a headache" (Yudofsky, 1985), are not only cited as examples of simulation but also of the difficulty determining when fabrication reaches significant levels of clinical importance. Clearly, the clinician should avoid labeling little white lies, face-saving social excuses, and insincere compliments as examples of simulation, if for no other reason than doing so avoids trivial diversions and maintains the focus upon the real issues.

As examination of Weintraub's four criteria suggests, the distinction between true disorder and simulation is much easier to define in theory than to demonstrate in practice. In addition, these criteria, while describing simulation as an individual act, do not define a coherent syndrome. Motivation is important to consider and, since simulation is largely if not solely an interpersonal phenomenon, the interpersonal quality implies personality organization and developmental object relations levels. Further, in addition to Weintraub's four essentials, Disorders of Simulation must be described in terms of associated features, age at onset, course, impairment, complications, predisposing factors, and prevalence.

PRIMARY DEFINITIONS

A number of terms have been used more or less interchangeably to describe Disorders of Simulation. Largely as a result of the influential *DSM* series, Factitious Disorders are now quite restricted in definition but were less discretely defined in the past. For example, Factitious Disorder was previously interchangeable with Munchausen Syndrome although the latter is really a subset of the former. In the *DSM* and elsewhere, definitions are not so clear concerning Malingering and Compensation Neurosis. Upon review of the literature, many different labels exist for the same phenomena as well as the same label for different phenomena.

Malingering

The term *Malingering* customarily refers to the intentional, voluntary production of symptoms that simulate physical or psychological disorder. The symptomatic complaints may result from exaggeration of genuine disorder, complete fabrication, causal misattribution, or some combination of these elements. Most definitions state that symptom production is motivated by external gain, secondary gain, or external incentives, such as "avoiding military duty, avoiding work, obtaining financial compensation, evading criminal prosecution, or obtaining drugs" (*DSM-IV*, APA, 1994, p. 683). A few authors have acknowledged that Malingering may result from internal motivation without reference to an obviously recognizable external goal (Travin & Protter, 1984). Generally, antisocial personality types are linked with Malingering

(Mills & Lipian, 1995), but some reviews of the literature also mention the borderline spectrum of disorders (Travin & Protter, 1984). Glossary Table 9.1 lists many of the "synonyms" for Malingering. Some labels are more emotionally laden and less well defined than others; all should be avoided as synonyms for Malingering.

Factitious Disorder

The term *Factitious Disorder* used generically refers to the inten-tional but involuntarily compulsive production of symptoms that simulate physical or psychological disorder. Apparently, the disorder exists for no motivation other than assuming and maintaining the patient role. This motivation is known as internal gain, primary gain, or internal incentives. *DSM-IV* (APA, 1994) indicates that factitious patients are unique in that they are unable to restrain themselves from symptom production, even under circumstances that may lead to complications such as discovery of the patient's fabrications or the imposition of serious physical injury through unnecessary treatments. It is widely believed that Factitious Disorder requires a very substantially disturbed psyche—customarily a severe Borderline Personality Disorder—upon which to engraft itself, particularly in view of the fact that not only may nonexistent injury be falsely reported but also such patients frequently cause painful genuine injury or disease to the self or others (Bools, Neale, & Meadow, 1992; Ehlers & Plassmann, 1994; Haddy, Diamond, Black, Upshaw, & Curry, 1987; Jacoby & Hyslop, 1979; Jones, 1995; Justus, Kreutizger, & Kitchens, 1980; Marsh & Johnson, 1983; Nadelson, 1979; Schreier & Libow, 1993).

Factitious Disorder with Predominantly Physical Signs and Symptoms

First named Munchausen's Syndrome by Asher (1951), who described the well-known variant of the disorder characterized by the production of predominantly physical symptoms, Factititous Disorder with Predominately Physical Signs and Symptoms is often accompanied by *pseudologia fantastica.* Chertok (1974) coined the label *mania operativa* and others have shown similar creativity in penning humorously titled articles such as "Fraudulent Feculent Fever in a Female Fabulist" (Raff, Stodghill, & Royal, 1975). These labels and descriptors are problematic since they imply not only ill-defined or controversial etiologic and motivational factors but also a sense of moral judgment and condemnation. The seemingly endless variety of labels noted in Glossary Table 9.2, applied to the seemingly endless variety of Factitious Disorders with Physical Symptoms, ought to be avoided in the interest of clarity.

Factitious Disorder with Predominantly Psychological Signs and Symptoms

The term *Factitious Disorder with Predominately Psychological Signs and Symptoms* refers to the variety of disorder characterized by the production of false psychological symptoms, usually simulating psychosis or dementia, although some authors have reported false Posttraumatic Stress Disorder (Rosen, 1996). A limited number of articles have occurred in the literature and thus the proliferation of colorful descriptors has been restricted. Nevertheless, in the interest of clarity, it is best to avoid the synonyms listed in Glossary Table 9.3.

Factitious Disorder with Combined Psychological and Physical Signs and Symptoms

This Factitious Disorder is listed in *DSM-IV* (APA, 1994) for the primary purpose of categorizing the common occurrence of Factitious Disorder with both types of symptoms. Although most Factitious Disorders present with both physical and psychological symptoms, only one synonym has been used in the literature, Dual Factitious Disorder (Merrin, Van Dyke, Cohen, & Tusel, 1986).

Factitious Disorder Not Otherwise Specified (NOS)

This category of Factitious Disorder is reserved for cases not meeting the above criteria, such as Factitious Disorder by Proxy, a specialized diagnosis, mentioned in *DSM-IV* Appendix B (APA, 1994, pp. 725–727) as requiring further study but commonly reported in the literature (Bools, Neale, & Meadow, 1992; Feldman, 1994; Krupinski, Tutsch-Bauer, Frank, Brodherr-Heberlin, &

Soyka, 1995; Ostfeld & Feldman, 1966; Schreier & Libow, 1993). The designation "by proxy" means that one person fabricates illness in another, usually a female adult in her child. In some cases, the adult actually causes injury or illness in the child, although the pathology may be limited to false symptom reporting by the parent, without actual induction of trauma in the child. Virtually all reported cases of Factitious Disorder by Proxy involve physical symptoms, but it is certainly conceivable that some cases may also display factitiously generated psychological symptoms concurrently, predominantly, or exclusively. There is report of at least one case in which both the patient and the victim presented simultaneously with factitious symptoms (Feldman, 1997). The labels in Glossary Table 9.5 have been used in the literature, often with the risk of confusion.

Compensation Neurosis

Never well defined and lacking in other distinction, Compensation Neurosis probably deserves recognition as the most ambiguous but widely discussed concept in psychology, law, and medicine. Miller (1961a, 1961b) has been the most prominent modern proponent of the diagnosis. The terms noted in Glossary Table 9.5 are of unexplicit origin, indefinite meaning, involving equivocal levels of intention or volition, and represent a nearly infinite number of "synonyms" that have been used to describe mental phenomena ranging from Hysteria to Malingering. The indices of *DSM-III* (APA, 1980) and *DSM-III-R* (APA, 1987) imply that Compensation Neurosis should be redefined as a variety of Psychological Factors Affecting Physical Condition although the text does not discuss how Compensation Neurosis fits into this diagnostic category. In *DSM-IV* (APA, 1994), however, the diagnosis is not mentioned or discussed.

From the general psychiatric standpoint, some authors suggest that Compensation Neurosis is the perpetuation of a disabling condition, at least partly under volitional control, which often resolves coincident with termination of the legal case (Andreasen, 1985; Hyler & Spitzer, 1978; Miller, 1961a, 1961b). Barton (1985), in his plaintiff-oriented manual, indicates that Compensation Neurosis is a subconscious, genuine, disabling, and compensable condition although defense-oriented attorneys maintain just the opposite. Most authors comment on the prospect of secondary gain (usually financial) as integral to the concept but it seems that the intentional and volitional elements are variably attributed depending upon both the context and expert queried.

Recent research casts doubt upon the long-held belief that the symptoms resolve upon termination of the patient's legal case (Mendelson, 1982; Tarsh & Royston, 1985; Woodyard, 1982). Previously, Slovenko (1973) noted that the usual interpretation is "neurosis developing from an injury caused by another person, which is complicated by factors in compensation and litigation; but compensation is not an essential element in the etiology of the neurosis" (p. 294).

Hyler, Williams, and Spitzer (1988), however, deny that Compensation Neurosis exists as a separate category and indicate that when it is suspected, the patient must be rediagnosed as suffering either from Malingering or some variety of legitimate mental disorder. The broad-spectrum, easily abused, and eminently ambiguous "synonyms" listed in Glossary Table 9.5 should be carefully avoided.

ASSOCIATED DEFINITIONS

The term *simulation*, and its opposite, *dissimulation*, as well as synonyms for both labels, have been subject to considerable misuse and misinterpretation in the literature. At times, even *defensiveness* and *denial* have been confused with words that signify the overt, conscious processes of symptom manipulation. Thus, it is important to define the terms used to describe the degree of awareness displayed by patients in their presentation of false symptoms, before undertaking discussion of such psychodynamically convoluted concepts as consciousness and unconsciousness.

The term *simulation* refers to the behavioral act of symptom creation, exaggeration, or misattribution with a clear intentional or volitional component. Glossary Table 9.6 lists many terms used generically in the literature to denote simulation. None of them signifies a specific diagnosis although they generally convey a quality of moral disapprobation.

The term *dissimulation* is often used interchangeably with *simulation* in the literature but is, in fact, its polar opposite. As careful authors have long noted, dissimulation refers to the concealment of illness by feigning health while simulation is the feigning or exaggeration of illness. The *Oxford English Dictionary* (1971) confirms this point in addition to indicating that the dissimulation of health must be, in part, intentional or volitional. In the literature on simulation a careful reading of context is frequently necessary in order to determine whether the author is discussing the feigning of health or pathology. For example, the term *dissimulation index* is often identified as a scale for detecting faking bad but it technically refers to detection of symptom suppression (faking good) rather than the simulation of illness. Diamond (1956) opines that, in comparison with malingered insanity, "much more prevalent is the simulation of sanity [dissimulation of insanity]—the concealment of delusional systems and other psychopathology even in the face of the death penalty" (p. 165). The "dissimulation of insanity" is equivalent to the "simulation of sanity" since both refer to the concealment of mental disorder by an insane patient who wishes, for whatever reason, to appear sane. Although simulation and dissimulation have "faking" in common, the concealment of illness by simulating health may imply a different set of psychological mechanisms, motivations, strategies, and prognoses as well as methods for diagnosis and treatment. Terms often used synonymously with dissimulation, at the risk of further clouding the definition, include those noted in Glossary Table 9.7.

Defensiveness is unconscious resistance to self-examination which, in turn, usually results in the production of defense mechanisms as a barrier against the experience of anxiety. When defensiveness is involved in symptom concealment, it occurs without intention or volition since it is impossible to effectively hide problems from the self if the process of doing so is conscious. While defensiveness is customarily reserved for the notion of unconscious processes such as repression and denial, some authors have used it interchangeably with dissimulation or even with simulation in the generic sense (Rogers, 1988). In the extreme case, defensiveness reaches the proportions of dissociation or symptom denial and the patient simply ignores some aspect of reality. In essence, defensiveness is "unconscious dissimulation" and takes many forms, customarily described by referring to the defense mechanisms employed by each patient.

Hysteriform processes are the polar opposite of defensiveness, at least concerning symptomatic presentation. These processes, a constellation of fully unconscious disorders, protect the patient against the experience of anxiety by converting mental conflicts into physical symptoms. Formerly a group of related psychopathologies including Briquet's Syndrome, Hysteria, Hypochondriasis, Neurasthenia, Conversion Reaction, Dissociative Disorder, and others, the hysteriform processes have been subdivided and distributed throughout several diagnostic categories beginning with *DSM-III* (APA, 1980). In effect, hysteriform processes are the "unconscious simulation" of disease, disorder, or distress. Figure 1.1 illustrates how the two "conscious" response styles of simulation and dissimulation compare with each other as well as with the two fully "unconscious" styles of defensiveness and the hysteriform process in psychopathology.

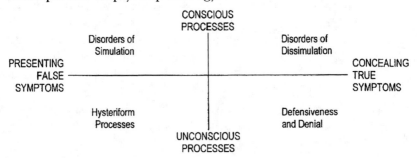

Figure 1.1. Types of response styles arranged along the axes of conscious-unconscious processes and presentation-concealment of complaints.

Conscious versus unconscious processes are psychodynamically useful concepts when discussing customary mental disorders, but several authors (Jonas & Pope, 1985; Pope, Jonas, & Jones, 1982; Rogers, 1988) have rightly noted that these terms pose enormous problems when analyzing simulation. Since consciousness and unconsciousness are theoretical constructs (intervening variables), they are also inferential and unavailable for direct inspection. Insurmountable difficulties obviously occur whenever a diagnostic system, in order to function effectively, requires observation of the degree to which specific emotional or physical behaviors are the result of mental activities that can only be inferred, intuited, or implied.

The dimension of consciousness is therefore best avoided in operational definitions although it may be fruitfully applied as a molar concept or final judgment that is contingent upon synthesis of molecular data such as clinical behavior samples, process test observations, records review, interdisciplinary consultation, and the results of standardized assessment. Molecular data may thus be produced by operational methods from which ultimate molar conclusions may be drawn regarding the relative balance of conscious versus unconscious processes. Two important molecular dimensions are those of intention and volition. When design and display of an illness, injury, or stressor are crossed in a two-by-two matrix with intention and volition (Figure 1.2), the theoretical position of Simulating Disorders as compared to traditional disorders is readily apparent.

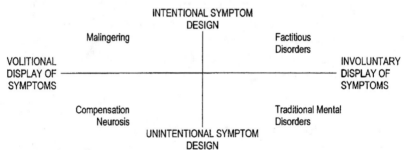

Figure 1.2. Disorders arranged by intentional-unintentional design versus volitional-involuntary display.

Intentional versus unintentional design refers to the mental act of planning, engineering, and design. When intention is present, the patient plans with awareness and purpose in mind. The planning need not be complex. For example, a simple mental set to unartfully reply "I don't know" to many of the examiner's questions is sufficient. In contrast, some Factitious Disorder patients carefully and elegantly craft their plans so that, even on sophisticated medical testing, the thoughtful artifices by which they designed their "illness" remain hidden. Unintentional design, however, is the product of unpremeditated processes and there-fore often has classically symbolic value. In this instance, the de-sign process is natural and reflexive such that the meaning of the symptoms is usually more mysterious to the patient than to the observer. For example, the symbolic value of hysterical blindness, as a way of preventing the patient from seeing something forbid-den, is readily evident to the clinician but remains a mysterious, physical symptom to the patient.

Volitional versus involuntary display defines a dimension in-volving the physical act of production, demonstration, and dis-play. When the patient engages in voluntary behavior, he has some degree of control of presentation. With the notable excep-tion of Weintraub (1989), few authors have drawn a distinction between symptom design and symptom display, a distinction that appears crucial to understanding Disorders of Simulation. Thus, a patient may choose to display symptoms at one moment and not the next, depending upon his assessment of the situation. Other patients—notably those with Factitious Disorders—per-form in a compulsive, driven manner and seem to be involuntary in their demonstration of pathology. Generally, involuntary pro-cesses are probably the least negatively tainted of all the descrip-tors, implying the operation of accepted psychological mechanisms such as repression and denial, reaction formation, projection, dissociation, and blocking.

Functional is a term of indefinite meaning, used loosely to refer to disorders of bodily or mental function that are without known organic basis and often incorrectly equated with psy-chogenic or emotional disorders. Campbell (1981) points out that, while all psychogenic disorders are functional, not all func-tional disorders are psychogenic; some may be the result of physi-cal events. One is a subset of the other; the terms *psychogenic* and *functional* are not synonyms. It is generally true that no imputa-tion of simulation necessarily applies, although some of the roughly equivalent expressions found in the literature do have a distinctly negative aura. Glossary Table 9.8 lists terms often used synonymously with *functional.*

Organic is the opposite of functional and indicates that the problem, whether mental or physical, results from physiological as opposed to psychological etiology. Purely used, the term *organic* means that the patient's symptoms and complaints are attributable to lesions, metabolic disturbance, neuropathology, or other manifestations of disordered physiology. However, it is true that secondary emotional, behavioral, or motivational problems often occur in reaction to physical pathology. Consequently, many physical problems are complex because they result from a combination of functional and organic causes, particularly the Somatoform and Organic Mental Disorders. Glossary Table 9.9 lists terms often used as equivalents.

Gain refers to motivation or incentive, commonly on two levels but occasionally with a third added. All three levels are important to consider in Disorders of Simulation. *Primary gain* refers to relief from anxiety or other intense, conflictual emotion through the unconscious invocation of defense mechanisms often resulting in apparent illness of symbolic value. Blinder (1973) views primary gain as a precipitant of psychological illness and *DSM-IV* (APA, 1994) appears to use the term synonymously with internal gain or incentives. *Secondary gain* refers to unconscious protraction of disorder in order to obtain the practical benefits and satisfactions, such as money and dependency gratification, that accrue following primary gain. Thus, as Blinder (1973) notes, secondary gain is a perpetuating rather than precipitating influence which is present in cases of Compensation Neurosis. Synonyms include external, epinosic, method, and morbid gain as well as external incentives and illness by advantage. *Tertiary gain* has been proposed for benefits that accrue to others rather than to the patient when such advantage is based upon the patient's apparent illness (Campbell, 1981) but this term is not frequently encountered in the literature. However, in the diagnosis of Factitious Disorder by Proxy, it may be appropriate to describe the motivational factors active in the inducing party as tertiary gain.

Confabulation refers to the replacement of memory traces lost as the result of partial amnesia with new, fabricated memories. Generally, confabulation occurs because the patient finds himself unable to adequately recall the answers to questions about specific persons, places, events, or situations. This mental process differs from pathological lying or *pseudologia fantastica* because the patient is involuntarily compensating for organically based memory deficit rather than attempting to deceive. However, the distinction can be quite difficult, especially when the confabulation appears to have functional as opposed to organic origins.

Pseudologia fantastica, often labeled *pathological lying,* occurs when the patient truly believes a fantasy description, at least momentarily. Campbell (1981) indicates that the patient quickly drops the fantasy on confrontation but, in the context of Factitious Disorder, many clinicians note that the fantastic stories seem both uncontrollable in production and unshakable on confrontation. The patient may steadfastly deny that he is anything but truthful, making it difficult to determine whether the patient intends to deceive, is distorting reality, or both (Linn, 1985). *Pseudologia fantastica* should be distinguished from confabulation. Campbell (1981) maintains that patients who confabulate will stick to their stories on confrontation while the patient with *pseudologia fantastica* will not. There is, however, considerable evidence against relying upon this distinction.

Folie à deux is sometimes termed *double insanity* such that two individuals manifest identical symptoms of psychosis, most customarily two members of the same family who reside together. It is important to distinguish this condition, when it occurs in an adult–child combination, from Factitious Disorder by Proxy. For example, a mother and child may both share a psychotic delusional system about bodily symptoms but this is clearly different from a mentally disturbed factitious mother who induces or misreports physical symptoms in a healthy child.

Vorbeireden (talking past) was introduced by Moeli (1888, cited in Enoch & Trethowan, 1979) to specify a notably wrong near-miss response by the patient to a clearly understood question. Ganser (1898) used a similar term, *Vorbeigehen* (to pass by), in partial description of the syndrome which now bears his name. Both terms have generally been used to indicate that the patient has clearly understood the question but is giving approximate answers that just avoid adequately responding. In the classic example, when asked to state the number of legs on a dog, the patient replies "five." The answer indicates he has probably understood the sense of the question but the response is relevantly bizarre. Since a variety of patients may "talk past the point," *Vorbeireden* does not imply a specific disorder although it does narrow the range of probable diagnoses and is common in but not unique to Ganser's Syndrome, some varieties of Factitious Disorder, and Malingering. It may also occur in Somatoform Disorders, Hysterical Dissociation, Toxic–Organic Mental Disorder, Schizophrenia, and Epileptic Twilight States (Lehmann, 1985). A moderate number of synonyms have been used in the literature as illustrated in Glossary Table 9.10.

Prevalence

Clinically derived estimates of Malingering frequency range from rare to moderately common in cases where compensation is in the balance, but no data are available in substantiation. Diamond (1956) suggested that the dissimulation of mental health is more frequent than the simulation of mental illness. Factitious Disorders are rare, although the frequency of case reports in more recent literature has increased slightly (Sussman & Hyler, 1985). Much has been written in a general way about Compensation Neurosis but actual cases are rarely reported in the literature, perhaps as befits a constellation of symptoms whose independent existence has been challenged by some observers (Hyler, Williams, & Spitzer, 1988).

Careful studies of prevalence are rare to nonexistent. This is obviously true for Malingering since, by definition, *successfully simulating individuals go undiscovered* and thus actual prevalence in the patient population is not only difficult to measure but also undoubtedly somewhat greater than clinically estimated. Conversely, Factitious Disorder patients make multiple medical visits, and it has often been assumed (but not clearly demonstrated) that prevalence is significantly inflated by overreporting the same patients as they traipse from hospital to hospital and doctor to doctor. The prevalence of Compensation Neurosis is completely obscure since the syndrome has never been sufficiently well described to allow operational definition for epidemiological or research purposes.

Although prevalence rates are obscure, the faking of symptoms or disease entities has always been fascinating, leading to the accumulation over the years of a considerable volume of case study reports on Disorders of Simulation. But, since it is true that rare phenomena often prove to be highly interesting, the frequency of reports in the literature may be disproportionate to clinical frequency, as reflected in the enormous published interest in the infrequent diagnosis of autism, for example. Therefore, frequency of citation in the journal literature is a poor index of prevalence for any disorder, even for disorders that are far more carefully defined and less ambiguously diagnosed than Disorders of Simulation.

Although the clinical syndromes of simulation are relatively rare, accurate diagnosis is no less essential as in the more common mental disorders. Treatment formulation depends upon accurate differential diagnosis, although this axiom is difficult to apply when patients suffer from Disorders of Simulation since they seek to emulate genuine mental or physical disorder. They are the great imitators and, like mockingbirds, have no song of their own but rather steal phrases and melodies from the pathological songs of others. To further compound the problem, patients who fabricate symptoms may have genuine underlying mental or physical problems that they have elaborated or exaggerated rather than entirely fabricated. Thus, just as the presence of bona fide disease or trauma does not rebut simulation, so the diagnosis of Malingering, Factitious Disorder, or Compensation Neurosis does not rule out coexisting physical or mental illness.

Motivation

Various theories have been advanced to explain why patients fabricate mental or physical illness and the literature contains a broad range of hypotheses. At one end of the spectrum, Menninger suggested that any form of deception represents illness in the patient (Menninger, Mayman, & Pruyser, 1963) although some patients, such as those suffering from Factitious Disorder, are more disturbed than others. Of course, the opposite explanation has been offered; simulating patients are just problem children requiring discipline rather than diagnosis. Discussion of simulation spans the range from atheoretical description to psychodynamic etiology, and the roots of simulation have been identified in contexts as diverse as the fertile depths of the unconscious to rampant poverty, social disadvantage, and the emergence of workers' compensation laws. Description of patients runs the gamut from lost souls to artful dodgers, and discussions reflect attitudes from empathic understanding to accusatory moralizing.

THE NEED FOR DIFFERENTIAL DIAGNOSIS

Civil Law

There are indications that our society is becoming more litigious and, while Disorders of Simulation are certainly not limited to the arena of personal injury litigation, some varieties occur in the courtroom in significant numbers. The courts are clogged with cases, insurance companies have objected to the notion of large settlements from their deep pockets, and the popularity of personal injury suits for almost any real or imagined wrong appears to be growing. Various municipalities and cities have found it either impossible or exorbitantly expensive to obtain insurance. Malpractice suits have become commonplace amongst service providers and even attorneys have become the targets of malpractice as "officers of the court" find themselves no less vulnerable than any other category of service provider.

The factors involved in the glut of civil suits are undoubtedly complex. The public, more that ever before, is aware that service providers and manufacturers have an obligation to do no harm and to make their products or services as safe and predictable as possible. With the enormous emphasis Americans place on health care, a multibillion-dollar health industry has established itself within our society. The consequent increase in health services provided and the number of service providers necessarily means that there will be at least an absolute—possibly a per capita—increase in errors, omissions, malpractice, and product defects. It is important that legal redress be available for protection of both the individual patient and society as a whole. Nevertheless, just as the complex growth of the health care industry must result in more professional and product deficiencies, so it must result in more spurious claims of harm where none have occurred. As never before, it has become important to determine which claim is real and which claim is false.

Although the progress of medical science has made it possible for severely damaged patients to survive who would have died just a few years ago, minor injuries have always been common as, for example, the rear-ender with the patient complaining of "whiplash." Since objective medical signs are infrequent in minor cases and since pain is so ephemeral, it is difficult to discriminate between real and feigned injury. Indeed, chronic pain and disability syndromes are not only widely experienced at genuine levels but also easily simulated. The principal problem is that as the number of objective signs of injury decrease, the opportunities for simulation increase, as does the burden upon the clinician to tell real from feigned complaints. The matter is even more complex because it is certainly possible to have bona fide musculoligamentous injury and serious pain without demonstrable physical findings on medical examination.

Some have pointed to the increase in the number of attorneys to explain the popularity of personal injury suits. Competition among large numbers of hungry attorneys ensures that clients with questionable injuries—often in product liability cases where the defendant has substantial financial resources to pay settlement demands—will have little trouble finding legal representation in the hopes of at least a nuisance settlement and perhaps more. Again, it is important to separate false from genuine claims.

The current glut of civil lawsuits may also involve the press of economics and the widening financial gulf between the upper and lower classes. Some patients experience a sense of despair and hopelessness over the prospect of ever "getting ahead." The televised real estate get-rich-quick schemes, the growth of state lottery systems, and the ever-popular gambling industry illustrate the common hope that fortune will smile and bestow a munificent answer to life's problems. Other individuals, fearful of the risks, change, and effort necessary to stay even in life (much less move ahead) hope for a ready economic solution by holding someone else responsible for their own resistance to success. In either case the individual, wishing to be indemnified against the complex difficulties and risks of living, spawns within himself the belief that life's obstacles and failures must be the fault of someone else. Obviously, it is important to recognize when the patient's complaints represent unintentional distortion and when they reflect a volitional intent to deceive and wrongfully benefit, no matter how self-justified the explanation.

Workers' Compensation Law

Workers' compensation is a special area of administrative civil law, designed to evaluate, treat, and rehabilitate injured workers. Largely determined by regulation within broad, legislatively established guidelines, the workers' compensation rules of evidence and proof conform to civil standards within reasonable limits, but there are important differences. As Lasky (1980) notes, psychiatric and legal terminology are often at odds, determination of residual mental disability in the workplace is a special consideration, and the issue of legal liability for emotional damage is complex. In many ways, the added convolutions and ambiguities in workers' compensation cases make the system particularly ripe for abuse. Further, a large number of patients find themselves prisoners of the workers' compensation system where returning to work often ensures a minimal settlement and, in some cases, a plague of questions as to whether the worker was ever truly injured.

The size of the applicant's award is determined by a complex set of rules involving the nature and extent of the injury, periods of partial and/or total disability, residuals that reduce competitiveness in the marketplace, and apportionment of prior disability. In California, employers' costs were over $6 billion in 1996 and the system paid out almost $7 billion in benefits (California Workers' Compensation Institute, http://www.cwci.org). Obviously, it is important to assess accurately the applicant's mental and physical state since falsification or exaggeration by even a small percentage represents a significant misallocation of resources.

Criminal Law

The need for discrimination between true and feigned mental illness has been of considerable importance in criminal law for years. Issues in this area span the entire criminal forensic process

from arrest to sentencing. Was the defendant-in-custody competent to understand and waive his Miranda rights? Is he mentally
competent to stand trial? Did he commit the acts while suffering
from mental illness leading to diminished capacity or diminished
actuality? Was the defendant insane at the time of commission
of the offense and is he sane or insane now? Are there factors in
the defendant's background, personality, and mental functioning that should be taken into consideration in sentencing?

Unusual mental problems sometimes occur in institutional
settings in response to intense stress and prolonged incarceration. It is in the context of involuntary confinement that Ganser's
Syndrome was originally identified (Moeli, 1888, cited in Enoch &
Trethowan, 1979; Ganser, 1898). Obviously, it is critical to discriminate between genuinely impaired defendants and those who
willfully simulate in order to wrongfully claim exculpatory physical or mental impairment.

Military Service

The evasion of military conscription or attempts to secure early
discharge from the service is also an area long recognized as ripe
for Malingering (Clark & Campbell, 1948; Eckert, 1977; Freemon,
1993; Gavin, 1843; Mauran, 1995; McMahon, 1984). Historically,
the notion of Malingering first emerged when conscripts attempted to simulate illness, trauma, or other disability in order to
avoid dangerous assignments or avoid military service altogether
(*Oxford English Dictionary*, 1971). Malingering was generally more
prevalent in those branches of the armed forces that relied upon
conscription and less prevalent in branches that depended upon
voluntary enlistment. While Malingering was quite infrequent
amongst seasoned soldiers, the emergence of "combat fatigue"
pressed for a distinction between the real and feigned variety of
what is now termed Posttraumatic Stress Disorder. In times of
relative peace, the issue of simulation in the military is largely
quiescent but in times of conflict it is important to determine
which conscripts are feigning illness so that the sparse resources
in wartime are not misallocated (Lorei, 1970).

Health Care

From the standpoint of health care, *DSM-IV* suggests that Malingering must be distinguished from other "V Code" nondiagnoses such as Adult Antisocial Behavior as well as genuine diagnoses such as Antisocial Personality and Somatoform Disorders. Unfortunately, the literature provides little help about how an evaluator ought to undertake such differential diagnosis or know which criteria distinguish Malingering from other diagnoses. In text and reference books as well as the *DSM-IV*, discussion of Malingering is brief, unelaborated, oversimplified, without prognostic or treatment recommendations, and mentioned only in passing as is deemed to befit the illegitimate offspring of a bona fide physical and psychological disorder.

Factitious patients share the feature of conscious symptom production with Malingerers but appear compulsively driven and are therefore thought to be less voluntary in their simulation of illness. Despite this observation and the fact that Factitious Disorder is presumably rare, the patient nonetheless falsely induces or reports symptoms. Thus, precisely the same reasons apply for discriminating between Factitious Disorder and other diagnostic categories where symptoms are either genuine or unconsciously fabricated as in some Somatoform Disorders.

In addition, Factitious Disorder is a rather remarkable phenomenon in the literature of mental abnormality and a more comprehensive understanding of its underlying psychic mechanism may be not only of academic interest but also of practical significance. Understanding the dynamic and motivational cross-linkage between the Factitious symptom complex (which appears to be associated with serious underlying personality psychopathology) and other diagnostic categories is probably essential to the understanding of simulation.

Factitious Disorder included Ganser's Syndrome according to *DSM-III* (APA, 1980) since it supposedly involved some simulation. In *DSM-III-R* (APA, 1987), Ganser's Syndrome underwent taxonomic change to a diagnostic category not involving simulation. However, the syndrome is only mentioned in passing under the category of Dissociative Disorder Not Otherwise Specified, without diagnostic criteria. The current definition of the syndrome as "the giving of approximate answers to questions . . ." (*DSM-IV*, p. 491) is inadequate with respect to this controversial collection of symptoms, particularly in view of the fact that the distinction between Malingering, Ganser's Syndrome, and Factitious Disorder is critical.

For example, as simple as "approximate answers" sounds, there are at least two types of "talking past the point" or *Vorbeireden* in response to any question: near-miss and far-miss. The differential implications of each type are important in attempting to discriminate entities like Ganser's Syndrome from simulation. In addition to the two types of approximate answer, patients may make genuine errors that do not involve *Vorbeireden*. For example, asked to change six quarters into dollars and cents, one patient may reply with $1.49, another states the answer is $30.00, and a third proposes $1.25. All three answers suggest that the patient understood the question in a general sense and each answer constitutes an approximate response, although in remarkably disparate ways. In the near-miss instance, the answer of $1.49 suggests the patient has correctly calculated the answer and then perversely made slight modification to avoid being correct, as may occur in Disorders of Simulation. The far-miss answer of $30.00 suggests the patient has grossly misperceived the question or is responding to internal stimuli irrelevant to the question, and suggests a gross mental disorder such as Dementia. The third answer of $1.25 suggests a simple arithmetic or aphasic auditory reception error since the patient has obviously multiplied by five rather than six. The distinction between near-miss, far-miss, and genuine error is important since it stresses the mechanism of response formulation in *Vorbeireden* and allows the inference of different psychological mechanisms in each patient.

Compensation Neurosis continues to be a diagnostic conundrum. The index to the *DSM-III-R* directs the reader to Psychological Factors Affecting Physical Condition, a change from *DSM-III* where Malingering and Psychogenic Pain Disorder were also cross-referenced. *DSM-I* (APA, 1952), *DSM-II*, and *DSM-IV* have no listings for Compensation Neurosis at all. Yet, the topic is discussed in the psychiatric literature with some frequency.

Economic Issues

Several authors (McCahill, 1995; Reich & Hanno, 1997) have noted the financial cost of some Disorders of Simulation, most notably of the Factitious variety. Many of these patients sustain multiple hospitalizations with administration of costly and dangerous medical tests and treatments. There is record, for example, of one patient scoring at least 124 hospitalizations with multiple surgical procedures at a total cost obviously running into the tens of thousands of dollars (D'Souza, Bharucha, & Shah, 1977). Another Factitious patient not only sought treatment from 35 doctors for nonexistent cancer but also alleged negligence and promptly filed suit for $14 million. She sued all the physicians—and several hospitals as well—for failing to cure her of a disease she did not have, receiving $315,000 in an out-of-court settlement (Lipsitt, 1986).

In Malingering and Compensation Neurosis, it is obvious that to the extent simulated or exaggerated complaints receive compensation, someone must fund the award. In addition, litigation consumes valuable court time, plaintiff and defense attorneys are expensive, and a broad range of supportive services are needed whether the case goes to trial or settles out of court. Malingered claims can also lead to the diversion of funds from public assistance agencies such as Social Security Disability, Welfare, Medicare, and Workers' Compensation.

TABOO

It is certainly remarkable that, in most major medical and psychological textbooks, there is no more than brief mention of Disorders of Simulation. As a review of the literature suggests, the dearth of research information is compelling despite over 3200 published articles. Legal texts are unexpectedly even more bereft of comprehensive discussion. Indeed, the more diligent the search for solid data about Disorders of Simulation, the less is found. Most articles moralize at some level or caution the practitioner against moralizing but in neither case have authors conducted much research. The paradox of scarce research but frequent moral philosophizing in largely scientific journals certainly requires some explanation. One assumption is that a general taboo exists regarding research into and diagnosis of Disorders of Simulation. The reasons are legion with the sense of moral outrage and anger occupying the front ranks.

Moral Outrage

When a patient simulates mental or physical disorder, he seems to be engaging in unscrupulous behavior akin to cheating, lying, and stealing. These behaviors elicit moral condemnation from most caregivers as well as society's formal institutions. The patient's actions generate concern that the mutual basis of faith and trust upon which civilized order depends is under siege. The sanctions for such behavior customarily range from disapproval to disapprobation or even social ostracism. Unless the simulator commits demonstrable fraud, however, the penalty exacted rarely results in stiff legal action. Thus, the emotions of moral outrage and condemnation are society's primary form of judgment. Although caregivers are no less subject to judgmental moralizing than are the laity, judicial bodies, or society at large, health professionals are taught that all patients must be given expert diagnosis and treatment. The risk of violating this fundamental precept is great when Disorders of Simulation are not carefully diagnosed or researched. "Failure to notice" illness fabrication may protect caregivers from the unpleasant emotion of moral outrage but it does so at the cost of increasing the taboo against looking closely at an important area of human behavior.

The fact that simulation carries with it more than a hint of moral corruption probably has subtly polarized the diagnostic perception of health care professionals. Malingerers and, to a lesser extent, Factitious Disorder and Compensation Neurosis patients, are held in general disrepute. It would be surprising if caregivers found themselves free of all moral condemnation toward those who simulate illness. Indeed, it may be that the greater the tendency to moral judgment, the greater the risk that complex diagnostic issues will be seen in bold, black-and-white relief. Thus the clinician may be led to view a patient simply as either Malingering or not, Factitious or not, Antisocial or not. Those found morally lacking may be readily dismissed since they deserve less attention than a bona fide patient. Yet, simulation is a complex area of human behavior requiring just as much diligence and clinical acumen as does the differentiation of depressive phenomena, for example. Clear observation is possible only when the clinician suspends moral judgment and persists in viewing even obvious simulators as genuine patients who pose a clinical, theoretical, and forensic challenge.

Anger and Rage

For many clinicians, the patient who deceives evokes powerful feelings of anger and rage. The patient meets attempts to help with resistance, counters sympathetic concern with arrogant selfishness, parries genuineness with fraud, and causes the clinician to squander his skills upon the investigation of deceitful symptoms. Most clinicians feel supremely impotent when faced with simulating patients who defeat the diagnosis, render the treatment irrelevant, and implicitly ridicule the whole health care process. It is, therefore, little wonder that anger results when doctors feel duped by simulating patients. In order for the caregiver to retain a sense of compassion and caring, the clinician must contain his angry exasperation through repression, denial, and outright suppression. Anger, the anathema of good bedside manner, is swept under the clinician's emotional rug with the result that the taboo against acknowledgment of Disorders of Simulation is reinforced. Menninger et al. (1963) pointed out that Malingering is irritating to doctors, largely because it represents an act of aggression. Malingering "elicits first solicitousness, then treatment, then chagrin and finally anger and even vindictiveness. He [the physician] feels deceived, teased, challenged, ridiculed, 'taken in' " (p. 209).

Naivete and Gullibility

Effective health care requires the assumption of a genuine and reciprocal doctor–patient relationship. Violation of faith and trust is simply not anticipated by most caregivers and, while the expectation of patient honesty is mandatory at the inception of each case, this attitude approaches naïveté and gullibility if un-checked in the face of contrary evidence. In order to be detected, simulation must first be suspected and then assessed, but most clinicians have not been schooled in Disorders of Simulation and, in any case, there is very little information available with which to school them. Assessment requires careful sifting of the clinical evidence as well as a thoughtful differential diagnostic workup. This process may fail to occur because of lack of knowledge, cred-ulousness, gullibility, inexperience, or lack of professionalism. In any case, the taboo is reinforced.

Fear of Suit

In this litigious society, professionals fear suit, and most patients take offense at being called less than genuine. Hence, evaluative reports may contain the euphemistic phrase "the patient's symp-toms, the results of clinical examination, and laboratory assess-ment do not conform to any known diagnosis." This phraseology presumably confers forensic immunity against the dreaded sub-poena for court appearance as a litigant rather than as an expert witness. However, a perceptive, knowledgeable, and aggressive attorney, unhindered by fear of suit, is quite able to pose ques-tions that make the doctor's half-hidden opinion uncomfortably visible and, again, the taboo is reinforced.

Time Constraints

The issue of diagnostic certainty, the need for comprehensive review of records, the prospect of lengthy paperwork and reports for documentation, responses to subpoenas, requests for more information, and the likelihood of deposition or court testimony all conspire to make diagnosis of Disorders of Simulation a time-intensive process. The clinician's reasoning process may approxi-mate the following:

> I am sure that this patient is faking an injury to gain workmen's compensa-tion; however, if I accuse the patient of malingering, extensive documenta-tion will be required, there will be time-consuming legal challenges, the patient will certainly become angry, and there might even arise counter-accusations that may damage my reputation. Perhaps it is easier to just look the other way. (Yudofsky, 1985, p. 1862)

Such thought processes reward the clinician for failing to notice Disorders of Simulation and the taboo is reinforced.

Concurrent Illness

Another variable that may account for reluctance to diagnose Disorders of Simulation, is the omnipresent problem of concurrent illness. That is, a patient may engage in symptom fabrication while simultaneously suffering from bona fide mental or physical illness. Most professionals are realistically concerned over the ethical, moral, and humanistic (not to mention legal) dilemma of mistaking genuine but rare or unknown disorders for mere fabrication. In some cases, once the examiner has identified a bona fide illness or trauma, he is reluctant to pursue the question of simulation or may even discard the issue as relevant. The presence of any genuine illness provides welcome relief when the clinician faces even obvious symptom fabrication in a patient. Relief reinforces taboo.

Research Obstacles

By definition, Disorders of Simulation are truly effective only when the patient evades detection. Therefore, the classic and successful examples of simulation remain unseen and it is difficult to research an invisible problem. When patients are unavailable who clearly demonstrate the problem under study, it is important to find alternative subjects and methods of study. The alternatives fall into three unsatisfactory general classes: analogue studies, clinical reports, and contaminated symptom patterns. A fourth category—natural process research—holds promise but is uncommonly difficult to design.

Analogue studies usually involve "normals" or patients with a defined physical or mental disorder who volunteer to "fake bad" under a variety of test and interview conditions or who are paid to do so. Obviously, such studies fail to truly address the problem of simulation since normals instructed to deceive or fabricate are undoubtedly psychologically different from those patients who truly simulate. As Rogers and Cavanaugh (1983) noted, "The research paradigm presents a paradox in asking subjects to *comply* to instructions to *fake* in order to study subjects who *fake* when asked to *comply*" (p. 447).

Clinical reports focus upon one or more identified cases of the phenomena under study but such reports involve only identified cases, usually collected in nonrandom and statistically biased fashion. While this strategy is occasionally acceptable in clinical description, it obviously involves only the discovered or admitted and therefore predominantly unsuccessful cases of simulation.

Contaminated symptom patterns occur when the disorder under study is not the only problem from which the patient suffers and statistical attempts must be made to "factor out" the contaminating influence. When used to extract the essence of behavioral syndromes from contaminated data, statistical purifying procedures have questionable validity. Although factor loadings and analyses of covariance may reach acceptable levels of significance, the error variance is often too great for the results to be of practical, daily, clinical significance.

Direct empirical or natural process research is a fourth, very satisfactory class of study (Shontz, 1965). Unfortunately, studies falling into this category are very difficult to design, expensive, laborious to execute, and therefore exceedingly rare in the literature. In this research design the experimenter does not manipulate variables but rather identifies natural situations in which the phenomena of interest occur and are measurable in an unobtrusive manner. In any case, the lack of empirical research serves to reinforce the taboo. Many clinicians feel substantial discomfort over diagnosing Disorders of Simulation backed only with "research" that is long on philosophy but short on data.

Collegiality

It frequently occurs that some patients, in whom a clinician suspects simulation, will have a history of treatment on the assumption that their symptoms are bona fide. Indeed, it is common to identify falsification in a patient who, by virtue of enduring treatment and multiple previous evaluations, has attained the status of a proven sufferer. Problems may occur when the patient's other treating or evaluating parties are caregivers in the same geographic area. To render a diagnosis of simulation is, by proxy, to indict a colleague's diagnosis and professional acumen. There are obvious reasons for concern over offending associates within the same community upon whom one's professional life and economic welfare may depend. Again, the taboo is reinforced.

Aversion to Trickery

Finally, some authors have noted that the diagnosis of Disorders of Simulation is more in the province of an insurance investigator, detective, or hidden cinematographer than health care provider. Most clinicians feel uncomfortable resorting to trickery and artifices designed to outwit the simulator. Such feelings arise because clinicians find Disorders of Simulation to be morally noxious and outside the proper scope of the health sciences. Again, the taboo is reinforced.

SUMMARY AND CONCLUSIONS

For many reasons, rendering a diagnosis of simulation is difficult for health care professionals. However, such matters are common concern in the law and no taboo is detectable when attorneys raise the specter of simulation in tort litigation, insurance investigation, workers' compensation law, or criminal justice. It seems improper, unprofessional, and hazardous for caregivers to remain compliantly ostrich-like and allow criminal and civil law to take the lead in the definition of clinical syndromes. All varieties of human physical and behavioral affliction are the defined province of health care professionals and Disorders of Simulation must not be excepted. Research is sorely needed; it is always appropriately scientific to devise clinical "tricks" that cause an illness to reveal itself as long as the professional follows ethical standards, clarifies the diagnosis, and withholds moral judgment of the patient.

Behavior and behavioral syndromes should be grouped and classified by the mental health professions according to established taxonomic principles; the moralizing may be left to others. Other disciplines will inevitably make some decisions about the broader social and fiscal implications of Disorders of Simulation but this is no reason why the suspension of moral judgment by mental health professionals must also result in abandonment of efforts to provide clear and coherent taxonomic classification. Failure to do so will simply allow Disorders of Simulation to be defined by the legal profession or some other group, uneducated in human psychology, unsophisticated in classificatory systems, and oblivious to the distinction between science and social judgment. It serves no purpose to deny that simulation exists or that it partakes of behavior outside the provenance of those who study mental disorder. Past disclaimers by clinicians have not resulted in the abandonment of the derogatory terms and labels for simulation listed in the Glossary, but rather, for lack of clear definition, in their proliferation, perversion, and misuse by both clinicians and nonclinicians alike.

The present contradictory attitude of diffident neglect but moral opprobrium toward Disorders of Simulation must be reversed. The spell must be broken and the clinical taboo shielding Disorders of Simulation lifted. Medicine and psychology must display vigorous responsibility for discovering origins, operationalizing definitions, reporting demographics, conducting research, making differential diagnoses, establishing prognoses, prescribing treatments, and observing outcomes. These responsibilities are no less relevant for Disorders of Simulation than "legitimate" diagnoses.

2

A Short History of Simulation and Deception

> All these conditions the laity think ought to be discovered and distinguished from one another by the doctors? (Claudius Galenus, 150 A.D.)

Although the true etymology of *malinger* is obscure, W. F. Gorman (1982) suggests that the origin is the Latin *maleus ager*, or evil disposition. However, Shipley (1961) indirectly attributes derivation to the combination of the Latin noun *male* (illness) and the verb *gignere* (to beget). The *Oxford English Dictionary* (1971) indicates that the word *malingering* is probably a derivation from *malingre*, the French word for ailing.

ANIMAL INSTINCT

The origins of feigned illness are entirely unknown but it is clear that human beings are not the only species to engage in simulation. Irrespective of etymology, it is likely that somewhere in the dawn of hominid development, early man took notes from his animal contemporaries and simply applied to himself the techniques of simulation he observed in other creatures. For example, the cat pretends to sleep to avoid frightening the mouse; the fox feigns death in order to turn away the pursuing dog; if flight is impossible, the opossum and the snake act dead when in danger; and the killdeer feigns a broken wing, dramatically limping away

31

from her nest to distract predators. Other animals use trickery or camouflage to defend themselves or their young—the chameleon changes color to blend with its background. Because of their numbers, ancient origins, and diversity, the insects have developed the widest range of deceptive illusions in the interest of self-protection. Deceptive devices include matching the pattern of their background, imitating a nasty-tasting creature, a variety of techniques to make themselves look larger and more fearsome than is actually the case, and even sonar-jamming capacities to confuse predators.

HUMAN ORIGINS

Historically, only the very severely mentally disturbed were assumed to have some form of psychic illness and, even then, they were usually seen as lunatics, possessed by Satan, pestered by gods, bewitched, bedeviled, or enchanted. Those suffering from lesser disorders of the spirit without clear organic etiology were presumed to be shamming illness. That is, before the development of modern notions regarding the role of the unconscious in mental disease, malingering was a symptomatic complaint in the absence of verifiable physical disorder. Not only did this definition ignore claims of mental distress less obvious than total madness, but also mislabeled the symptoms of many genuine but undiscovered physical and mental disease processes as resulting from chicanery and subterfuge.

GREEK CONTRIBUTIONS

According to myth, Ulysses, not wishing to go to the war, feigned madness. Two versions of the story are extant. In one, when Ulysses pretended to act insane, Palamedes, the King of Ithaca, followed him, snatched his infant son from its mother, and drew his sword as if to kill him. In his fear for the child, Ulysses confessed that he pretended madness in order to avoid military service (Pseudo-Apollodorus, *Library*, E3:7). The second and more usual story is that Ulysses simulated insanity by yoking an ox and a horse together, plowing the seashore, and sowing salt instead of grain. While he acted insane, Palamedes saw through the deception, and laid Ulysses' infant in front of the plow, whereupon the father at once swerved around his son and thus betrayed his sanity. Ulysses' actions were of sufficient interest to arrest the attentions of Sophocles in *The Mad Ulysses* (*Fragments of Sophocles*, II:115).

Deception, of course, has been part of warfare since ancient times. Other than in the Homeric works, instances of military deception occur in the writings of Diodorus, Perseus, and Xenophon. The latter historian composed two technical handbooks on matters of practical knowledge dealing with military matters. In *On the Cavalry Commander*, Xenophon (5:15) noted that: "Another ruse that proves highly effective at times is to *feign* excess of caution and reluctance to take risks. For this *pretense* often lures the enemy into making a more fatal blunder through want of caution. Or once come to be thought venturesome, and you can give the enemy trouble by merely sitting still and *pretending* that you are on the point of doing something" (emphasis added).

Herodotus recorded the use of deception, as a military strategy, against the barbarians in *The Histories* (VII:211). The barbarians were lured on when the Lacedaemonians pretended to flee only to find themselves the victims of a trap: "The Lacedaemonians fought memorably, showing themselves skilled fighters amidst unskilled on many occasions, as when they would turn their backs and *feign flight*. The barbarians would see them fleeing and give chase with shouting and noise, but when the Lacedaemonians were overtaken, they would turn to face the barbarians and overthrow innumerable Persians" (emphasis added).

Apparently, physicians were not above aiding and abetting simulation of illness when it suited some political purpose. Demosthenes recorded that the physician Execestus certified Aseschines' false illness but the deed was undone when the patient, out of avarice and greed, later forgot to act ill:

> Now to decline an appointment on affidavit with no reason alleged was a strange move and very suspicious. "What do you mean? Are you declining the embassy? Are you not going to Macedonia to realize all those grand benefits which you announced yourself?" However, he had to remain. What was to be done? He pleaded ill health and . . . *taking Execestus the*

physician with him . . . made affidavit of the illness, and received the appointment himself. . . . [later] He forgot that he had sworn that he was too ill
to travel; forgot that another ambassador had been chosen in his stead,
and that the law visits such conduct with death. . . . Nevertheless, he was
so excited, his appetite for moneymaking and bribe-taking was so keen,
that he put aside and ignored all these obstacles, and off he went. (Demosthenes, *On the False Embassy,* 19:124-127; emphasis added)

In another example, according to Demosthenes, the coward Meidias might have malingered in order to avoid service in the cavalry as well as to enrich himself. In this passage, Demosthenes
refers to Meidias' attempt to use his nominal service with the
cavalry in order to secure the profits of a tax collector.

But not so our cavalry-officer Meidias. He deserted the post assigned him
by the laws, and this, which is a punishable offense against the State, he
is prepared to count as a meritorious service. Yet, good heavens! What
name best befits such a trierarchy as his? Shall we call it patriotism, or tax-
jobbing, two-per-cent-collecting, desertion, *malingering,* and everything of
that sort? Unable in any other way to get himself *exempt from service* with
the cavalry, Meidias has invented this new-fangled cavalry-collectorship.
(Demosthenes, *Against Meidias,* Oration 21:166; emphasis added).

BIBLICAL DECEPTIONS

The Bible is rife with references to deception. As early as Genesis,
Satan hoodwinked Eve with the "big lie" when, in a serpent's
guise, he falsely assured: "You will not surely die" (Genesis 3:4).
Abraham feigned kinship with Sarah so that, as her brother, his
life would be spared (Genesis 12:13). Isaac led people to believe
that his beautiful wife was his sister fearing that, because others
lusted after her, he might be killed (Genesis 26:7).

The litany continues with Jacob impersonating Esau (Genesis
27:6–23) and Jacob's sons deceiving their father by dipping Jo-
seph's robe in sheep's blood and stating that he had been de-
stroyed by wild beasts (Genesis 37:29–35). Ehud deceived Eglon
in order to slay him (Judges 3:15–30), and Delilah pulled the
wool over Sampson's eyes (Judges 3:15–30). Tamer fooled Am-
non by feigning sickness (2 Samuel 13:6–14), Hushai misled Absalom (2 Samuel 16:15–19), Sanballat tried to deceive Nehemiah

(Nehemiah 6), and Absalom engaged in deception when aveng-
ing his sister (2 Samuel 13:24–28) and again when he began a
conspiracy (2 Samuel 15:7). Other deceptions include those of
the old prophet, Gehazi, Job's friends, Doeg, Herod, the Phari-
sees, chief priests, a lawyer, and Ananias and Sapphira.

Simulation of insanity was also a Biblical event. David feigned
madness rather spectacularly in First Samuel.

> And David . . . was sore afraid of Achish the king of Gath. And he changed
> his behavior before them, and *feigned himself mad* in their hands, and
> scrabbled on the doors of the gate, and let his spittle fall down upon his
> beard. Then said Achish unto his servants, Lo, ye see the man is mad:
> wherefore then have ye brought him to me? Have I need of mad men,
> that ye have brought this fellow to play the mad man in my presence? (I
> Samuel 21:12–15; emphasis added)

To obtain help for her son, the wife of Jeroboam pretended to
be someone else, a fact that did not go unnoticed by the Almighty:
"Behold, the wife of Jeroboam cometh to ask a thing of thee for
her son; for he is sick: thus . . . when she cometh in, that she shall
feign herself to be another woman. And it was so, when Ahijah heard
the sound of her feet as she came in at the door, that he said,
Come in, thou wife of Jeroboam; why feignest thou thyself to be
another?" (Kings I, 14:5-6; emphasis added).

THE ROMAN WAY

Claudius Galenus wrote an early text on malingering in civil life
(Brock, 1929). Upon reading Galenus' work, *On Feigned Diseases
and the Detection of Them,* it is clear that the struggle to distinguish
between simulation and hysteria, known by whatever names were
popular at the time, is as old as medicine itself. Roman soldiers
reportedly cut off thumbs or fingers to render themselves unfit
for military duty. Galenus may not only have been acutely perceptive in the diagnosis of Malingering but also adept at performing
it as well (Veith, 1955). When he wished to remain at home rather
than suffer the danger and inconvenience of traipsing off as sur-
geon to Marcus Aurelius' army during an expedition against the
Germans, Galenus falsely asserted that his family god Asklepios

had appeared in a vision and commanded that he remain in Rome. Fearing to alienate the gods by disobeying their wishes, the Emperor excused his favorite physician from active duty.

MIDDLE EASTERN TEXTS

In the Koran, the faithful are cautioned against swearing falsely and promised severe punishment as the wages of simulation: "Have you not seen those who befriend a people with whom Allah is wroth? They are neither of you nor of them, and they *swear falsely* while they know. Allah has prepared for them a severe punishment; surely what they do is evil. They make their oaths to serve as a cover so they turn away from Allah's way; therefore they shall have an abasing chastisement" (*She Who Pleaded*, 58: 14-16; emphasis added).

Much like the protagonist in Leonid Andreyev's *The Dilemma* (1910), a malingerer shall have his simulations visited upon him according to The Talmud. "If a man is not lame, blind, or halting, and he feigns to be as one of these, he will not die in his old age before he actually becomes as one of these" (Mishnah Peah, VIII:9).

SHAKESPEARE

In *Julius Caesar* (Act II, Scene II), Calphurnia begged her husband, the emperor, to simulate illness and avoid danger rather than attend the senate house where Brutus planned to strike a fatal blow. Caesar decided that "Mark Anthony shall say I am not well; And, for thy humour, I will stay at home." But, upon the false advice of Brutus, Caesar decided it would be ignoble to feign sickness. "How foolish do your fears seem now, Calphurnia! I am ashamed I did yield to them. Give me my robe, for I will go." In this instance, of course, Caesar would have been wiser to simulate.

WITCHCRAFT TO REFORMATION

Classic examples of illness as due to forces other than organic disease or physical injury may be found in *Malleus Maleficarum* or the *Witches' Hammer* (Sprenger and Kraemer, 1487) where such unexplained phenomena are defined as the work of the devil. They note that if no medical reason for the illness can be found or "if the patient can be relieved by no drugs, but rather, seems to be aggravated by them, then the disease is caused by the devil." Of course, the satanic explanation of disease processes held little comfort for patients who were tortured or burned at the stake.

By the 1500s, some nonreligious descriptive work began to appear although the focus was primarily upon severe mental disorders such as mania and melancholia. Plater, in *Praxis Medica*, attempted classification of mental as well as physical diseases but made the general assumption that "most mental diseases were due to some sort of brain damage; he explained sexual fantasies, nonetheless, as the result of possession by the devil or punishment by God" (Alexander & Selesnick, 1966, p. 75).

Weyer's (1563) monumental *De Praestigiis Daemonum* (The Deception of Demons) held that witches were mentally ill rather than bewitched, and he suggested treatment by physicians rather than ecclesiastic interrogation. He also documented an example of simulation. A 16-year-old girl maintained that Satan filled her stomach with all manner of common objects. However, upon examining a piece of cloth which she apparently regurgitated, he found it saturated with saliva rather than gastric fluids, thus proving her a malingerer. He also refuted the teachings of *Malleus Maleficarum*, a critique that Reginald Scott (1584) closely followed in *The Discoverie of Witchcraft*.

MIND VERSUS BODY IN THE AGE OF REASON

Hysteria

In 1697, Thomas Sydenham published an interesting treatise which, in the fashion of the time, was almost as instructive in title as in content: "*Discourse Concerning Hysterical and Hypochondriacal Distempers: Dr. Sydenham's Complete Method of Curing Almost All Diseases, and Descriptions of Their Symptoms*" to Which Are Now Added *Five Discourses of the Same Author Concerning the Pleurisy, Gout, Hysterical Passion, Dropsy, and Rheumatism.* Sydenham precisely described the symptoms of hysteria and was fully aware that it was a great imitator of other diseases. Despite his acute observations, however, he remained convinced that "animal spirits" were the etiologic agents. He noted: "the frequency of hysteria is no less remarkable than the multiformity of shapes which it puts on. Whatever part of the body it attacks it will create proper symptom of that part. Hence, without skill and sagacity a physician will be deceived; so as to refer the symptoms to some essential disease of the part in question, and not to the effects of hysteria."

Alexander and Selesnick (1966) commented upon psychiatry in the 1700s: "Although the mentally sick had not been tortured at the stake for a considerable period of time, their condition during the century of the Enlightenment was still agonizing. If they were not hospitalized, they wandered through the countryside, scorned, beaten, and ridiculed" (p. 114).

Primarily, only very severe mental illness attracted the attention of physicians in the 18th century with one outstanding exception. Cheyne (1733) wrote a text on *The English Malady* that was among the first attempts to investigate neurotic phenomena. The "English Malady" refers to melancholia, a constellation of symptoms within which early writers included "crankiness from an overloaded stomach, to lowness of spirits, the spleen, vapours, melancholy, hysteria, hypochondria, and insanity of the melancholic type." Although he abandoned the customary etiology of an excess of black bile, he attributed the malady to exogenous effects such as the weather, rich food, a sedentary life, and crowded cities. Whytt (1777) took up the challenge and segregated three types of neurosis from the body of what was loosely called mental illness in his work, *Observations of the Nature, Causes and Cure of Those Disorders Which Have Been Commonly Called Nervous, Hypochondriac or Hysteric.* Whytt refers to "nervous exhaustion," a phenomenon later labeled by Beard (1880) as "neurasthenia."

During the same time, in the early days of the American Colonies, the popular attitude toward individuals who complained without demonstrable physical cause was not always charitable. "At that time scurvy and beriberi were rampant among the colonists and produced lassitude, fatigue and inability to work. This condition was not recognized as disease but was regarded as evidence of laziness" (Veith, 1955). Since only those who worked earned food, malnutrition compounded the problem.

Battie's (1758) *A Treatise on Madness* distinguished between exogenous and endogenous mental disease although exactly how external causes led to madness remained obscure. Battie noted:

> From whence we may collect that Madness with respect to its cause is distinguishable into two species. The first is solely owing to an internal disorder of the nervous substance; the second is likewise owing to the same nervous substance being indeed in like manner disordered, but disordered *ab extra*; and therefore chiefly to be attributed to some remote and accidental cause. The first species, until a better name can be found, may be called *Original*, the second may be called *Consequential Madness*. (p. 44)

Thus, the stage was set for sculpting "disorders of the spirit," without obvious physical correlates, as legitimate diagnoses rather than Malingering. It remained only to find some sensible cause.

Throughout the 19th century, somatic and mental complaints without apparent organic cause were cataloged loosely as "nervous" in nature. Generally, physicians were skeptical about nervous conditions and they remained in the shadows of medical respectability, accepted as genuine phenomena by only a handful of practitioners. "The lack of causal explanation, the absence of morphological change and the apparent presence of an influence of the mind on biological functions gave 'nervousness' a pseudo-scientific stigma" (McMahon, 1984, p. 16). The publication of an enormously interesting volume by Mackay (1852), *Extraordinary Popular Delusions and the Madness of Crowds*, signaled greater popular acceptance of the notion that hysteria could induce all manner of symptoms in otherwise apparently normal individuals.

Nervous Indisposition and Brain Fever

The popular acceptance of hysterically based somatoform phenomena developed gradually amongst medical men but more so in the laity since it occurred with frequency in everyday life and was even codified in widely read literature. "Brain fever," an old synonym for neurasthenia, occurs in several of the Sherlock Holmes stories. Who can fail to be impressed by the eloquent description of the sudden attack of "brain fever" suffered by the nervous and effete young diplomat, Mr. Percy Phelps? After he discovered a top secret alliance between England and Italy had been stolen from his desk at the Foreign Office in *The Naval Treaty* (Doyle, 1894c), Phelps languished for weeks before recovering enough strength to rouse himself from his sickbed and call for the services of Sherlock Holmes and Dr. Watson, to whom he lamented:

> It was evident to all that I was in for a long illness, so Joseph was bundled out of this cheery bedroom, and it was turned into a sickroom for me. Here I have lain, Mr. Holmes, for over nine weeks, unconscious, and raving with brain fever. If it had not been for Miss Harrison here and for the doctor's care, I should not be speaking to you now. She has nursed me by day and a hired nurse has looked after me by night, for in my mad fits I was capable of anything. Slowly my reason has cleared, but it is only during the last three days that my memory has quite returned. Sometimes I wish that it never had. (p. 454)

As Watson recalls, the patient spontaneously recovered from his nervous prostration when Holmes melodramatically presented the reclaimed treaty in a covered breakfast dish.

> Phelps raised the cover, and as he did so he uttered a scream and sat there staring with a face as white as the plate upon which he looked. Across the center of it was lying a little cylinder of blue-gray paper. He caught it up, devoured it with his eyes, and then danced madly about the room, pressing it to his bosom and shrieking out in his delight. Then he fell back into an armchair, so limp and exhausted with his own emotions that we had to pour brandy down his throat to keep him from fainting. (p. 466)

This description reveals the popular late Victorian view of nervous indisposition since Sir Arthur Conan Doyle, a physician turned storyteller, was certainly aware of what most laymen would recognize as the symptoms of "brain fever." His description of the syndrome is probably a reasonably accurate portrayal of the public view. In one of Doyle's few medically based volumes, *Round the Red Lamp* (1894a), one story, "A Medical Document," finds a trio of physicians discussing their cases after dinner. One remarks, "Then there is the mysterious malady called brain fever, which always attacks the heroine after a crisis, but which is unknown under that name to the text books" (p. 200).

Yet, the physical hysteria or hypochondria of the nineteenth century remained but a thinly guised synonym for Malingering amongst most of the medical profession. As Beard (1880) noted: "The time was when the symptoms of insanity were believed to indicate, not disease, but the possessing of an evil spirit; so now, very many of the symptoms of neurasthenia have been regarded by men of science as imaginations of patients, proofs of hypochondria—a vague term which, in this generation, covers all symptoms which the physician either doubts or misinterprets" (pp. 5–6).

Triumph of the Unconscious

Jean-Martin Charcot was a leading neurologist, physician in charge at the Salpêtrière in Paris, and, by the account of some historians, a consummate showman as well (Naish, 1979). Amongst the thousands of patients under his care in the 1880s, he became intrigued with those who appeared ill but who did not display organic pathology. With remarkable clinical insight, he grouped these patients together as suffering from hysteria, although he was unaware of unconscious etiology and believed that hysteria was an organic disease process of the nervous system (Alexander & Selesnick, 1966). While Charcot felt that malingering—in the sense of unconscious or preconscious symptom exaggeration—was part of hysteria, other observers remained unconvinced. Most clinicians believed hysteria was synonymous with conscious symptom fabrication and thus this diagnosis was not yet ready to be extracted from the matrix of malingered illness.

One of Charcot's students, Pierre Janet, took the next step and proposed that unconscious mental processes, in conjunction with constitutional physical weakness, predisposed the patient to the development of hysteria, especially with the onset of acute stress. He believed that trauma may lead to dissociation or splitting-off of disquieting feelings from consciousness such that the patient then acted upon motivations unknown to his aware mind. The theory of a split in consciousness seemed to be confirmed under hypnosis when many patients recalled specific traumata seemingly related to the nature, type, and onset of the symptomatic complaint. The fact that a significant number of these patients seemed "cured" by discovery of the traumatic event under hypnosis remained a mystery both to Janet and his competitor, Josef Breuer (Alexander & Selesnick, 1966).

After the preliminary work of Charcot and Janet at the Salpêtrière, as well as the contemporaneous publication of *Studies on Hysteria* (Breuer & Freud, 1893–1895), Freud began his landmark research into the expansion of the role of the unconscious. Through free association, Freud was able to duplicate much the same revelation of past trauma and subsequent cure through verbal abreaction as Janet and Breuer had demonstrated through hypnosis, a discovery he labeled *psychoanalysis* in 1896. Although acceptance was neither immediate nor universal, Freud's work soon made it quite clear that a whole system of human motivation existed below the level of conscious awareness and that this unconscious system could produce complaints of illness and genuinely perceived symptoms that had no objective physical etiology. Over the years, more and more syndromes were discovered, documented, and diagnosed as mental illness rather than Malingering (nonillness). Steadily, the spectrum previously considered to be malingered illness was reduced in breadth.

The last years of the 19th century were clearly pivotal for the conceptual development of psychology and psychiatry. Charcot gave birth to the concept of somatoform disorder and, ably assisted by Janet and Breuer as midwives, the infant soon developed hysteria. Freud inoculated the child with unconscious processes, repression, and denial as well as an enormous complexity of inner life. Transference and abreaction soon followed and, by the first part of the 20th century, the notion of mental disorder, unconsciously produced, and richly expressed in a broad spectrum of psychic and somatic symptoms, grew to young adulthood. No longer were patients suffering from hysterical and somatoform disorders necessarily viewed as Malingerers simply because their symptoms could not be verified as having organic origins.

The Emergence of Forensic Medicine

In forensic areas, before the mid-1800s, only raving, fulminating insanity would serve to absolve guilt in criminal cases. The French and Prussian criminal codes embodied a tripartite notion consisting of imbecility, madness, and dementia. The English common law originally recognized only two: idiocy and lunacy (Ray, 1838). As quoted by Pritchard (1835) in *A Treatise on Insanity*, a lunatic, opined Blackstone, "is properly one that hath lucid intervals; sometimes enjoying his sense, and sometimes not, and that frequently depending upon the state of the moon." To be judged insane, there could not be the slightest vestige of rationality and the defendant had to "be a man, that is totally deprived of his understanding and memory, and doth not know what he is doing, no more than an infant, than a brute, or a wild beast." In an opinion, as quoted by Ray (1833) in *A Treatise on the Medical Jurisprudence of Insanity*, in 1723, Mr. Justice Tracy found Mr. Arnold sane in the shooting of Lord Onslow and sentenced the defendant to death. Lord Onslow, who survived the assassination attempt, thought Arnold was clearly insane, intervened, and managed to have the sentence commuted to life imprisonment. Obviously, it was not easy to receive exculpation from crime based upon a definition of insanity that required the presence of fulminating madness and unmistakable mental *illusions*. The subsequent notion of "moral" insanity (insanity due to *delusions*) was prevalent but not encoded into law: "I must first observe that no such disorder [moral insanity] has been recognized in the English courts of judicature, or even admitted by medical writers in England. In general, it has been laid down that insanity consists in, and is co-extensive with, mental illusion" (Pritchard, 1835, p. 380).

Yet, the presence of lunatics and their insane delusions could not be denied and, with the M'Naughten decision of 1843 as a major turning point, the formal mental defense emerged. The M'Naughten decision was excessively complete and compulsively long-winded. Had it taken half as long for the bullet to leave the gun barrel as it took the learned justices to describe this action, M'Naughten's victim would surely have dodged the missile and spared us the agony of the insanity defense. In any case, avoidance of the penalty for crime was now possible, signaled by the judiciary's reluctant acceptance of M'Naughten: if an individual presented with delusional symptoms for which no obvious physical correlates existed, with a level of sanity greater than that of a mad dog, he may be adjudged insane and therefore not responsible for his actions.

Even after M'Naughten, however, a mental defense had to be based on disorder of unquestionably major proportion. A physical illness or simple hysteria, for example, was not a sufficient defense for murder. As might have been anticipated, as soon as the presence of major mental symptoms earned exculpatory value in courts of law, it became justifiable to suspect Malingering when defendants claimed insanity. Indeed, even prior to M'Naughten, the concern over simulated insanity was sufficiently great to occupy a significant portion of an early text by Ray (1838) on medical jurisprudence.

Recent Military History

The issue of feigned illness is widely reported to have emerged in the context of military service (*Oxford English Dictionary*, 1971). One of the earliest literary references occurred in 1820 (Luscombe): "Formerly, it was ulcers of the legs which were most usually produced by artificial means by soldiers. . . . disposed to malinger" as noted in *Practical Observations and Means of Preserving Health in Soldiers* (*Oxford English Dictionary*, 1971). Despite occasional mention in medical texts and rather dramatic literary accounts, the military implications of "physical hysteria" or malingering was the focus of attention. Most publications from ancient times to the middle part of the 19th century dealt with the question of malingering in the military. Virtually all authors on military medicine agree that the simulation of illness is much more common in times of war and involuntary conscription than during peace (Freemon, 1993; Gavin 1843; Good, 1942; Mauran, 1995). The combat soldier who complained of symptoms uncorrelated with physical disease was shirking his duty, promptly diagnosed as Malingering, and returned to duty or, more rarely, mustered out of the service.

During the Civil War in the United States, malingering was an important issue. Keen, Mitchell, and Morehouse (1864) indicate that the soldiers whom they suspected of malingering were intent upon being discharged from the service or avoiding combat, but there are also indications that financial gain as well as relief from unpleasant or dangerous duty may have occasionally accompanied symptom falsification. At the time of the Civil War, the armed services paid bounties for enlistment. Malingering soldiers, after being paid the enlistment bounty, would shortly thereafter feign some sort of illness to obtain discharge (possibly with a pension) only to reenlist and repeat the process elsewhere in the Union.

A second and less common strategy was dissimulation. That is, the patient would conceal the fact that he was genuinely ill, enlist in the service, obtain the bounty, and subsequently reveal his illness. The soldier would then be discharged (again possibly with a pension) only to repeat the cycle elsewhere. Generally, however, financial motivation was not an early source of gain for Malingering since, with the exception of military bounty, there were few opportunities to exact money through simulation of illness prior to the period of social reform and workers' compensation laws in the late 1800s.

One observation made on the battlefield proved most puzzling to physicians during the Civil War: apparently genuine concussion by cannon without observable physical injury. In the heat of battle, one side directed withering volleys of cannon and mortar fire toward the other, resulting in horrible mutilation and carnage. However, some wounded soldiers seemed to suffer genuine concussion without a mark—not even a bruise—anywhere on their bodies. Exactly how this could happen was a source of great controversy since the notion of hysteria had not yet attained respectability. Otherwise learned army medical officers proposed outrageous explanations for this conundrum. Some opined that the cannon ball actually struck the soldier but because of its rapid rotation, rolled around the body thus leaving no mark. Others felt that if the missile passed very close to the soldier but did not strike him, the force of wind created by the cannon ball could be the cause of concussion (McMahon, 1975). Feeling that many of these "concussed" Civil War soldiers were truly suffering and not Malingerers, treating physicians required some explanation for patients who presented as mentally comatose yet physically undamaged. Though they now seem nonsensical, the quasi-physical explanations involving the "wind of the cannon ball" were the best physicians could muster at the time given that hysteria had not yet attained respectable status in medical texts.

WORLD WARS I AND II

Malingering was a significant issue during World Wars I and II. In general, the published literature was highly theoretical or clinical, nonempirical, tinged with moralizing, and scantily scientific at best. Confusion was evident with a proliferation of descriptions, definitions, redefinitions, and variations on the diagnostic theme. Some wrote of neurotic reactions in psychopaths (MacLean, 1947) or Hysterico-Malingering, others of pure or partial Malingering Neurosis (Gill, 1941), still others of Constitutional Psychopathic Inferiority (Brussel & Hitch, 1943) and Opportunistic Malingering. Despite thousands of mental and medical evaluations during two devastating World Wars and the diligent attention of some of the best minds in psychiatry and psychology, knowledge about Malingering did not advance much in comparison with Galenus' writings just after the death of Christ.

THE SIMULATING DISORDERS EMERGE

Ganser's Syndrome

In 1888, Moeli (cited in Enoch & Trethowan, 1979) described how some of his prisoner-patients responded to simple questions with nonsensical or approximate answers (Weiner & Braimann, 1955), a phenomenon he labeled *Vorbeireden*. Ten years later Ganser (1898) wrote his classic monograph reporting on a short-lived and rare syndrome involving not only approximate answers (*Vorbeigehen*) but also hallucinations, disorientation, clouded sensorium, sensory disturbance, memory loss, and profound lack of insight. Aware of the newly discovered hysterical conditions and with revelation of the unconscious mind well underway, Ganser appropriately labeled his syndrome as "an unusual hysterical confusional state" (*Uber einen eigenartigen hysterichen Dammerzustand*).

Other observers were also aware of the new discoveries, and it is not surprising to find that Ganser's Syndrome was quickly relabeled as hysterical pseudo-stupidity, hysterical pseudo-dementia, and prison psychosis. Although Ganser was certain his patients were not Malingering, others were not so sure. In addition to Malingering, Ganser's Syndrome has been labeled through the years as Factitious Disorder with Psychological Symptoms (*DSM-III*, APA, 1980), organic brain dysfunction (Whitlock, 1967), psychosis (Ingraham & Moriarty, 1967), and even Adjustment Disorder of Adult Life (*DSM-II*, APA, 1968). Debate raged over the precise etiologic processes involved in Ganser's Syndrome—and whether it was truly a syndrome or just Malingering—for nearly 70 years until Cocores, Santa, and Patel (1984) persuasively argued for its classification as a variety of Dissociative Disorder. Thus, with its new designation in the *DSM-III-R* (APA, 1987), another syndrome was freed from the matrix of Malingering.

Compensation Neurosis

With the advent of the industrial revolution, first Prussia and then other states implemented workers' compensation legislation to protect those injured while on the job. Chancellor Otto von Bismarck introduced state-mandated workers' compensation in 1884 that he hoped would create "a strong partnership between employers and employees."

Britain introduced a version of workers' compensation in 1897 to replace its older, Hammurabi-style code. Up to the mid-1800s, the value of the item that caused the industrial fatality was the gauge for the compensation awarded for death by injury. For example, if a collapsed stack of timber buried an employee, his family received the equivalent of the worth of the timber involved. Thus, the code was similar to Hammurabi's, symbolically replacing an "eye for an eye." However, the notion of contributory negligence in British law made it uncommonly difficult for a worker to effectively prosecute his case in court. The final British version was, like its Prussian progenitor, essentially a "no fault" system as long as the injury occurred in the course of work duties. The laws were predicated on a doctrine of strict liability or liability without fault where the applicant need not demonstrate that the accident or illness was caused by his employer, only that it happened on the job. The increasingly hazardous nature of the industrial revolution workplace and the growing number of injuries sustained created a public clamor for reform of the remedies available to injured workers. Concepts were desperately needed to categorize the broad and rapidly proliferating variety of alleged work injuries, many of which seemed significantly less severe to those paying the claims than to those making them. Although perpetually ill defined, the notion of Compensation Neurosis was readily accepted when it first appeared in the literature. The financial fears of employers and insurance carriers encouraged the diagnosis, a condition which some viewed as Malingering, others as genuine injury albeit with legal complications, and still others as intermediate between feigning and true injury.

Since the early years of this century when Compensation Neurosis was first "identified," confusion has reigned and there is probably no diagnosis, mental or otherwise, that has engendered more heat and less light among honorable people in law, mental health, and medicine. Four editions of the *DSM* are inconsistent, definitions from respectable sources vary widely, and clinicians have designated the syndrome as falling anywhere from genuine mental disorder to abject fabrication. By *DSM-III* (APA, 1980), the status of Compensation Neurosis was no less muddled than was true in the early years of the century. The diagnosis is completely ignored in *DSM-IV* (APA, 1994) and currently remains inextricably embedded in the "matrix of malingering and disorders not yet identified."

With the passage of time, legislative action, regulatory guidelines, and judicial decisions made it clear that an ever-increasing spectrum of plaintiff injury was at least partly compensable. Thus, the workers' compensation statutes that emerged from social legislation around the turn of the century established a system that gradually became increasingly favorable to the applicant. If the worker was not disabled prior to an injury but became so afterwards (irrespective of the seriousness of the injury or the existence of prior pathology in all but a few instances), the worker's entire disability was deemed the temporary responsibility of the employer. Employers were required to restore the worker to his preaccident state or, if such restoration could not be accomplished, compensate the injured party for loss of competitiveness in the open labor market. Insurance companies, their claims adjusters, and attorneys became increasingly apprehensive that they were being required to underwrite some claims spawned by avarice and counterfeited by Malingering or Compensation Neurosis.

Workers' compensation was extended from physical to mental injury and the mid- to late 1980s resulted in a flurry of stress and harassment claims by employees against their employers. Between 1980 and 1986, the number of stress-related mental claims submitted in California grew 430% with average benefits rising from $7,500 in 1987 to the range of $10,000 to $13,000 by 1989 (California Workers' Compensation Institute, http://www.cwci.org). In these mental injuries, it seemed less relevant that the stress or harassment actually took place as alleged by the worker than the worker was judged to truly believe the offensive events occurred as he or she perceived them. In California, the enormous growth of stress-related claims during the early and mid-1980s prompted revision to curb abuse. The mere perception of the patient, however genuine, was no longer sufficient to validate a stress claim. In 1989, the changes in the statutes required that a worker actually have a mental disorder that, in turn, must be the result of verifiable stress. That is, the examiner must now consider the perceptions of coworkers, supervisors, and the inherent nature of the workplace as well as be able to cite actual, specific, identifiable events during the course of employment that are responsible for at least 51% of the causation.

Civil law has a long history of compensating loss with financial settlement and, as the philosophy of monetary awards for injury expanded through the evolution of workers' compensation, the opportunities for Compensation Neurosis increased as well. Even acts of overt simulation might induce some compensation in the form of nuisance settlement, especially when the defendant had liability exposure based on the "social fault doctrine." The "social fault doctrine" arose as the result of the view that employers are in the most favorable position to prevent accidents and forestall disease. Therefore, the notion of strict liability where the employer is responsible for accidents or illness that arise as a consequence of the workplace, provides an obvious economic incentive for the employer to protect the best interest of the workers.

Upon formulation of the *DSM-III* (APA, 1980), Hyler and Spitzer (1978) thought it possible to reclassify many persons who presumably had Compensation Neurosis as suffering from some variety of Somatoform Disorder or other bona fide illness. They reflected upon the traditional monetary motive and indicated that patients whose pain symptoms did not go into remission after settlement of compensation claims were somatoform; those whose complaints disappeared were Malingerers. Unfortunately, this *post hoc* formulation is like waiting to see if the patient dies before diagnosing the illness. Further, a great deal of evidence has accumulated to suggest that most patients remain symptomatic long after financial compensation issues have been settled. Nevertheless, Hyler, Williams, and Sptizer (1988) later attempted further reclarification by defining Compensation Neurosis out of existence—at least as far as *DSM* is concerned—and declared that patients suspected of suffering from this diagnosis were either Malingerers or genuinely mentally disordered. Thus, for one reason or another, Compensation Neurosis has never fully broken free from the matrix of Malingering.

Posttraumatic Stress Disorder

The novel concept of the unconscious process was obviously important in the debate over whether Ganser's Syndrome represented mental illness or Malingering. Similarly, the new theories of unconscious mental processes were developed just in time so that, during World War I, an explanation became available for a variety of suspected simulation that had plagued soldiers since ancient times: Posttraumatic Stress Disorder.

Although early known as Malingering, then shell shock, combat fatigue, and later as traumatic neurosis, unconscious processes were ultimately held accountable and the patient declared innocent of Malingering—at least by some. Paradoxically, the psychodynamic explanation of "war neuroses" convinced other observers that Malingering was involved. As McMahon (1984) states: "Whether the 'wish' was conscious or not, it carried the same implication." Thus, at the same time as the concept of Compensation Neurosis, initiated by the workers' compensation legislation, rose like an illegitimate Phoenix, reborn from the ashes of the

Freudian revolution, the unconscious psychodynamics of Post-traumatic Stress Disorder were being examined and validated as genuine. Other, similar terms soon followed including such labels as *semimalingering, hystericomalingering, neuroses of covetousness,* and the oxymoronic *unconscious malingering.* The distinction between Malingering as fully conscious and Compensation Neurosis as partially conscious was never robust and quickly became entirely confused. Fortunately, Posttraumatic Stress Disorder emerged from these concepts and eventually attained the status of a genuine diagnosis.

Factitious Disorder

With the confusion and dispute surrounding the status of Traumatic Neurosis, Compensation Neurosis, and Malingering in the early years of the 20th century, it is little wonder that, as McMahon (1984) stated, "By the 1930's, the definition of Malingering was so confused as to be scarcely informative." Attempting to bring order where chaos prevailed, Asher (1951) noticed that some patients who simulated physical disorder and who were presumed to be Malingering, did so without displaying the motivations customarily associated with Malingering or Compensation Neurosis. He described a syndrome where the patient presented with apparently serious medical complaints, a history of multiple prior hospitalizations, and a plausible but quite dramatic history that invariably proved to be false. Asher named the syndrome after the widely traveled raconteur, Karl Fredrich Hieronymus, Freiherr (Baron) von Munchausen (1720–1797). As Saluki (1978) noted, the Baron, while "maintaining a straight face would narrate the most amusing and absurd tales. They may have had a slight basis in truth but were embellished by the invention of his vivid imagination" (p. 287). Actually, the Baron was an accomplished raconteur who created stories based upon vivid elaboration of his adventures as a soldier, sportsman, and hunter. It was Rudolf Raspe who, in 1785, anonymously published a group of wildly exaggerated and apocryphal stories that he attributed to the Baron (Raspe, 1948). In any case, the frequency of *pseudologia fantastica* in Asher's classically factitious patients inspired him to name this new syndrome based on the Baron's acquired reputation for spinning extraordinarily fantastic tales.

Asher identified several additional diagnostic features associated with Munchausen Syndrome, a disorder first catalogued in *DSM-III-R* (APA, 1987) as Factitious Disorder with Physical Symptoms. The patient often had a multiplicity of abdominal scars (gridiron abdomen), was truculent, evasive, and noncooperative in manner, presented with an acute and harrowing history, had great familiarity with insurance claim forms, and a litigious demeanor. He cautioned that just as there may be a shred of truth underlying the patient's fantastic stories, so the patient may also have genuine medical illness, whether natural or self-induced. Well-known varieties, according to Asher, were the acute abdominal type (*laparotomophilla migrans*), the hemorrhagic type (*haematemesis merchants*), and the neurological type (*neurologica diabolica*).

The most puzzling aspect of Munchausen Syndrome was the absence of obvious motivation. While the Malingerer seeks to avoid pain, the Munchausen invites it; the Malingerer desires money or exculpation from danger, the Munchausen seemingly cares not; the Malingerer recognizes when it is advantageous to lie, the Munchausen compulsively lies even when doing so may lead to his discovery. Asher (1951) speculated on motivation, including a desire to be the center of attention, a grudge against doctors and hospitals, a desire for drugs, hope of escape from the police, and need of free room and board. He wisely added that "Supplementing these scanty motives, there probably exists some strange twist of personality."

By the 1970s an additional variety of Factitious Disorder involving largely psychological symptoms was codified in *DSM-III* (APA, 1980). While the physical type customarily presented with somatic complaint, the psychological type complained of psychotic symptoms, depression, bereavement, Posttraumatic Stress Disorder, memory complaint, and similar problems with *Vorbeireden* present in some cases.

In the decade of the 1970s, Meadow (1977) reported a variant: Factitious Disorder by Proxy. In this particularly insidious mutation, an adult—usually a female parent—falsely reports or actually creates illness in her young child. This disorder is, as

Meadow noted, truly "the hinterland of child abuse" where the parent's typically narcissistic or borderline personality psychopathology leads to actions that often endanger the child, sometimes in fatal measure.

Evidence has slowly been accumulating that some instances of Sudden Infant Death Syndrome (SIDS) are actually Factitious Disorder by Proxy cases taken to the extreme of homicide (Artingstall, 1999). Further variations have continued to emerge including the Cinderella Syndrome (Goodwin, Cauthorne, and Rada, 1980), a reverse Factitious Disorder where children feign abuse and neglect, complain to the authorities, and thus bring undeserved retribution upon innocent parents or caregivers. There is also evidence that Munchausen by Proxy abuse has been extended to family pets (Sheridan, 1995).

The process of sculpting true disorder from Malingering has always been long and arduous. Asher's observations on the nature of Factitious Disorder in 1951 were important but, since these patients seemed to engage in some degree of conscious symptom presentation, several decades were to pass before Factitious Disorder became firmly distinguished from Malingering.

Psychological Factors Affecting Physical Condition

As Hyler and Spitzer (1978) note, *DSM-III* (APA, 1980) was an attempt to reclassify many traditional disorders including those labeled as the "hysterical neuroses." Disorders suggesting physical illness but due instead to psychological factors were distributed throughout the new *DSM* taxonomic system rather than grouped together. In the process of reclassification, some disorders were reformulated, others were modified based upon review of recent literature, and one wholly new diagnosis was added to the general roster of Somatoform Disorders: Psychological Factors Affecting Physical Condition. While including the spectrum of psychophysiological disorders, the new diagnosis also included physical conditions where unconscious psychological factors were involved in the initiation, exacerbation, or maintenance of the patient's pathological physical condition.

As with undiagnosed physical illness, Somatoform, Anxiety, and Factitious Disorders, it is important to distinguish Psychological Factors Affecting Physical Condition from the volitional symptom initiation, exacerbation, or maintenance found in simulation. Hyler and Spitzer apparently intended the reformulation of hysterical disorders in general, and the addition of Psychological Factors Affecting Physical Condition in particular, to provide a sufficiently robust taxonomy so that the vague diagnosis of Compensation Neurosis could be discarded. That they did not fully succeed is demonstrated by the need for a second article in response to persistent queries over how Compensation Neurosis should be defined in *DSM-III-R* (Hyler, Williams, & Spitzer, 1988).

IMMORALITY, NOXIOUS BEHAVIOR, OR ILLNESS?

In the 1960s, social, political, and moral upheaval was rife. Mental health did not emerge untouched by 10 years of social iconoclasm, polarization, rebellion, and acrimony. Confusion begets contention and contention presages change; this was never more true than in the psychiatric thrust and parry of Thomas Szasz and Karl Menninger over the status of Malingering.

Malingering as Immorality

In his important but controversial work, *The Myth of Mental Illness*, Szasz (1961) devoted a great deal of attention to Malingerers, especially with regard to Charcot's early reclassification of many such individuals as suffering from hysteria. He found it disturbing that, over time, the psychodynamic theories of hysterical conversion had the side effect of absolving sufferers from responsibility for their actions. Szasz rebelled against the school of thought in psychiatry that held Malingering, like hysteria, to be a form of mental disorder. Thus, he noted, emerged a "logical dilemma—the dilemma of the existence of an alleged entity called 'mental illness' which, even when deliberately counterfeited, is still 'mental illness' " (p. 11).

To make his point Szasz painted three portraits of Malingering based on historical review: as simulation of illness, as conscious imitation of illness, and as actual mental illness. In the view of Malingering as simulation of illness, he discussed patients who were actually suffering from Factitious Disorder. He took exception to the prevalent view that such patients are sufficiently disturbed as to require confinement in a mental institution. This point makes sense for those diagnosed as Malingerers but Szasz quotes Chapman (1957) who was actually reporting on Munchausen's Syndrome (Factitious Disorders) as "peregrinating problem patients." It was not uncommon—even after Asher—to confuse Malingering with Factitious Disorder and this confusion dilutes Szasz's point since patients with the latter diagnosis are, on the average, the more substantially disturbed.

Malingering as conscious imitation of illness, according to Szasz, resulted from psychiatric attempts to distinguish "unconscious malingering" or hysteria from "conscious malingering." He was perfectly correct in asserting that the distinction between hysteria and Malingering has been historically difficult, fraught with value-laden judgment, and poorly specified criteria.

Finally, he was of the opinion that Malingering as mental illness posed the ultimate paradox: only a crazy or sick person would malinger. Szasz (1961) eloquently summed up the position against which he rebelled: "When simulation of mental illness is itself regarded as a form of mental illness, the rules of the medical (or psychiatric) game are so defined as to explicitly exclude the class 'counterfeit illness.' . . . . *Counterfeit illness, or malingering, is now a species of illness. The good imitation of a masterpiece is redefined as itself a masterpiece*" (p. 48).

Szasz suggested that the distinction between conscious and unconscious deception had been a complicating rather than clarifying factor in discussions of Malingering, hysteria, and related problems. Rather than continuing to rely upon attempts to distinguish the level of consciousness, he suggested differentiation between goal-directed and rule-following behavior on one hand as opposed to indifferent mistakes on the other. Not only was his proposed change ignored, Szasz himself continued to refer to the distinction between the conscious and unconscious in his subsequent discussion of impersonation.

The point of Szasz's somewhat labored and unidimensional approach was his contention that persons usually designated as mentally ill are impersonators of behaviors such as helplessness, hopelessness, weakness, and bodily illness although they are actually in frustrating, perplexing, and unhappy conflict of ethical, social, and interpersonal varieties. The diagnostic problem became even more confused when Szasz conceptualized psychiatrists and psychoanalysts as actors impersonating physicians and playing the role of medical therapist. In sum, both Malingering and mental illness are simply "problems in living."

While intellectually and theoretically quite challenging, the arguments and positions advanced did not lend themselves to practical implementation except within a rarefied Szaszian atmosphere. Since the potent social ether of politics, philosophy, and medicine is quite stable and resistant to change, few practitioners opted for the cumbersome life-support gear needed to live in the Szaszian climate. Important daily issues in patient care and forensic transactions depended upon the distinction between hysteria and Malingering as well as conscious simulation versus unconscious symptoms. Szasz warned that the fumes of our traditional psychological conceptualizations were potentially noxious but, in turn, his views were so radical as to be potentially paralyzing. Clinicians simply could not breathe deeply of his philosophical anesthetic and get their daily work done.

Malingering as Mental Illness

Karl Menninger, in *The Vital Balance* (Menninger, Mayman, & Pruyser, 1963), argued for a position diametrically opposed to Szasz's and began with the assumption that concealment and escape by dissimulation is almost universal amongst living creatures. Again, the term *dissimulation* requires caution. The proper definition of feigning health makes no sense in this context since Menninger appears to be using it in a generic sense as a synonym for hiding or running away. He viewed Malingering as an example of acute discontrol under the general rubric of frozen emergency reactions or personality deformities. Malingering is compulsive, aggressive deception involving a fraudulent personality that he distinguished from inadequate, infantile, schizoid, cyclothymic, narcissistic, negativistic, and addictive personalities. Fraudulent personalities involve such characteristic behaviors as lying, check forging, and Malingering.

For a fraudulent personality, lying is a way of life emanating from a compulsion to deceive. Since the Malingerer does not believe he is ill but tries to persuade others that he is, Menninger opines that he must, in fact, be ill. He asserted, "No healthy person, no healthy-minded person, would go to such extremes and take such devious and painful routes for minor gains that the invalid status brings to the malingerer" (p. 208).

His statement, of course, implies that Malingering is mental illness; an example of the circular thinking against which Szasz had cautioned just two years earlier. He described a case to illustrate his point but it is clear, even in his brief vignette, that the patient is Munchausen rather than Malingering. Although he failed to distinguish between Malingering and Factitious Disorder—despite Asher's seminal contribution to the literature 12 years earlier—his point of view represented the logical but extreme application of the unconscious process: *Malingering is mental illness.*

The views of neither Szasz nor Menninger have fully prevailed although the mental health disciplines are richer for having heard the debate. While Szasz's views on mental illness as myth have not been widely accepted, he certainly made a telling point on the seeming paradox of Malingering as a diagnosis. Menninger's argument that Malingering is mental illness proved equally untenable but the torch still sputters as in Schneck's (1970) analysis of Leonid Andreyev's *The Dilemma* (1910). The *DSM-IV* (APA, 1994) takes an intermediate position by designating Malingering as a "condition" in the "V Code" section, halfway between Menninger's diagnosis of true disorder and Szasz's notion of simple cheating.

Malingering as a Behavior

Some authors have labeled Malingering as a behavioral response style determined by analysis of "perceived risks and benefits" (Rogers, 1988, p. 300). Others view it similarly as a behavior which is "adaptive and both cross- and intra-situation specific" (Hall & Pritchard, 1996, p. xxiv). Simulation, when viewed as a discrete behavior resulting from an intrapersonal and informal Baysean calculation of risks and benefits in specific situations, suggests that Malingering is a behavior in which anyone may engage, given a compelling set of circumstances. This notion is attractive since it does away with high-handed moralizing on one side and the notion of complex psychodynamics on the other. The behavioral approach suggests that, with focus upon the patient's specific behaviors in certain situations and with reliance upon a panoply of clinical tests, tricks, and artifices, true disorder may be distinguished from Malingering. One might expect that such a philosophy would encourage the proliferation of simple, "one-shot" tests for simulation and, indeed, this appears to have happened. The number of "tests" for Malingering on the market has never been greater, each promising to detect simulation quickly and efficiently.

MENTAL ILLNESS AND THE MATRIX OF MALINGERING

Disorders involving nonorganic symptoms have always resided in the twilight areas not only of medical respectability but also of psychological and psychiatric theory. In the times before Charcot, Janet, and Freud, it was difficult to imagine why a patient would claim to have physical problems that could not be objectively demonstrated unless the patient was Malingering. Patients simply malingered in order to avoid work, escape conscription, or other noxious circumstances.

Only in 1951 was Factitious Disorder clearly identified, and many more years passed before it was designated as nonmalingering; nearly 70 years passed before Ganser's Syndrome was freed from the matrix of Malingering; Posttraumatic Stress Disorder required that the world experience two devastating wars before it was fully accepted as a genuine emotional condition rather than Malingering.

The primary liberating influence in the emergence of these and other new syndromes was recognition of the somatoform process in hysteria. From the late 1800s through the first part of the 20th century, clinicians gradually realized that the unconscious process held enormous explanatory power. More and more syndromes were discovered, documented, and diagnosed as genuine illness in contrast to the nonillness of Malingering. Therefore, the spectrum of symptomatic presentations previously considered to be malingered illness was steadily reduced. The historical graph (Table 2.1) illustrates how the disorders discussed above were, over the course of years, sculpted free from the matrix of Malingering.

The last entry in Table 2.1 refers to "The Matrix of Malingering *and* Disorders Not Yet Identified" since there can be no assurance that all possible "genuine" conditions have been identified and separated from the matrix of Malingering. Up to the present time, however, Malingering itself has never been an integral, independent syndrome with its own motivations, structure, symptomatic presentation, and psychodynamics. Rather, Malingering has been part of the great rootstock of unknown disorders, presumed nongenuine illness, and fraudulent phenomena. Part of the reason Malingering has never been a syndrome itself is the widely held post-Freudian assumption that unconscious motivation and symptom presentation are prerequisites for true mental disorder.

Since discovery of the unconscious, Malingering has been viewed historically as ground rather than figure, the backdrop against which true disorders are visible, the hole rather than the doughnut, the complex matrix from which genuine pathology must be disentangled. Since "true" disorders must partake of unconscious psychodynamic motivation, Disorders of Simulation—being fully or partially conscious—do not qualify as genuine behavioral syndromes. They are customarily relegated to vague, crepuscular categories, falling between health and pathology such as the "V Codes" of *DSM*, or have been shuttled from one category to another because of frequent taxonomic changes. Theoretically, however, unconsciousness of motivation in mental illness is no more necessary than the belief, in the times prior to Charcot, Janet, and Freud, that demonstrable physical pathology was necessary in order to have genuine illness or injury.

V-Codes, Morals, and Disorders of Simulation

It seems unwise to include some Disorders of Simulation, like Factitious illness, as legitimate yet exclude Malingering as a disorder of morality or behavioral act and either pretend that Compensation Neurosis does not exist or allow it to languish in nebulous

Table 2.1

Emergence of Genuine Disorders from The Matrix of Malingering and Disorders Not Yet Identified

Time Line Symptom Complex	Charcot & Freud		World Wars		APA Diagnostic & Statistical Manuals			
	Pre- 1890	Post- 1890	I 1922	II 1945	I 1952	II 1968	III/R 1980–1987	IV 1994
Physical Illness	G	G	G	G	G	G	G	G
Psychotoform Disorders	G	G	G	G	G	G	G	G
Hysteria[a] and Hypochondriasis	M	G	G	G	G	G	G	G
Posttraumatic Stress Disorder	M	M	E	G	G[b]	G[c]	G	G
Ganser's Syndrome	M	M	E	E	E	G[d]	G[e]	G
Factitious Disorder with Physical Sympt.	M	M	M	M	E	E	G	G
Factitious Disorder with Psychological Sympt.	M	M	M	M	M	E	G	G
Psychological Factor Affect Physical Condition	M	M	M	M	M	E[f]	G	G
Factitious Disorder by Proxy	M	M	M	M	M	M	M	G[g]
Compensation Neurosis	M	M[h]	E	E	E	E	E[i]	M[j]
Matrix of Malingering *and* Disorders Not Yet Identified	M	M	M	M	M	E[k]	M	M

Key: E = Equivocal Disorder   G = Genuine Disorder   M = Malingering

[a] Hysteria as used here is generally synonymous with Briquet's Syndrome.

[b] In *DSM-I* (APA, 1952) the classification of Posttraumatic Stress Disorder was Gross Stress Reaction.

[c] Posttraumatic Stress Disorder was classified as Adjustment Reaction of Adult Life in *DSM-II* (APA, 1968), popularly known as Traumatic Neurosis.

[d] Rather remarkably, Ganser's Syndrome was classified under Adjustment Reaction of Adult life in *DSM-II* (APA, 1968), the same category used for Traumatic Neurosis.

[e] Ganser's Syndrome was classified as a variety of Factitious Disorder with Psychological Symptoms in *DSM-III* (APA, 1980), but is listed under Dissociative Disorder, NOS, in *DSM-III-R* (APA, 1987) and *DSM-IV* (APA, 1994).

[f] In *DSM-II* (APA, 1968) the diagnosis of Psychological Factors Affecting Physical Condition did not exist. Such patients were designated as suffering from a Psychophysiologic Disorder.

[g] In *DSM-IV* (APA, 1994), the Proxy variant is included under Factitious Disorder Not Otherwise Specified as well as in Appendix B: Criteria Sets and Axes Provided for Further Study.

[h] For many years after Charcot, Compensation Neurosis frequently meant hysterical exaggeration and was known by the oxymoron of "unconscious malingering."

[i] In *DSM-III* (APA, 1980), Compensation Neurosis was cross-indexed to Malingering, Psychogenic Pain Disorder, and Psychological Factors Affecting Physical Condition. In *DSM-III-R* (APA, 1987), the first two cross-references were dropped while the latter was retained.

[j] All references to Compensation Neurosis have been dropped from *DSM-IV* (APA, 1994).

[k] In the 1960s two radical viewpoints emerged but have since lost momentum. Szasz contended that, for the most part, mental illness does not exist and Malingering is nothing more than moral condemnation by psychiatry of simple cheating. Menninger opined that only mentally ill people would malinger and, therefore, Malingering is as much a mental illness as any illness malingerers might choose to simulate.

diagnostic regions. Since simulation is abnormal, relatively rare, and an example of obviously disordered behavior, it may be considered mental illness by some. Yet, to consider simulation as mental illness runs the risk of violating Szasz's caution against designating the counterfeit of disorder as disorder itself. In essence, the authors of *DSM-III-R* "solved" this conundrum by: (1) placing Factitious Disorder in a peculiar category which is taxonomically unrelated to other categories since it alone involves some conscious elements; (2) defining Malingering as an isolated behavior of full consciousness and excluding it from the official nomenclature while nevertheless including it as a "condition" in the "V Code" section; and (3) attempting to eliminate the diagnosis of Compensation Neurosis altogether, directing that patients so diagnosed must be rediagnosed as suffering from either Malingering or a "genuine" disorder.

This diagnostic scheme has emerged because simulation is an example of primarily conscious behavior with few unconscious components. We must take a lesson from history: Ganser's Syndrome, hysteria, Posttraumatic Stress Disorder, and Psychological Factors Affecting Physical Condition were considered varieties of Malingering before they were subjected to rigorous study and identified as pathological symptom complexes. The fact that simulation involves a volitional and intentional pattern of behavior does not automatically negate the syndrome factors of motivation, personality configuration, gender ratio, predisposing factors and other such considerations.

Like the disorders to which it has given birth, Malingering may itself represent a robust syndrome of pathology despite skeptics who label it as "problems in living," those who label the simulation of disorder as mental illness, and others who label it as a response style or adaptive behavior.

It is inescapably true that simulation is abnormal human behavior by any standard of measurement. It is fairly rare and thus is statistically abnormal; most people find the conscious simulation of illness to be morally repugnant; it has appeared in taxonomies of mental pathology for at least a century; several thousand articles have been published on the topic in medical and psychological journals. Behavior in general and deviant behavior in particular is the proper province and study of the mental health professions. It seems unwise and inconsistent to define Malingering as a simple behavior, outside the taxonomy of classifiable aberrant syndromes, and representing no disorder at all. The issue is further confounded by listing Factitious Disorder in its own legitimate but highly peculiar category with vaguely specified criteria while Compensation Neurosis withers as an indefinite concept.

There is much to be gained by grouping Disorders of Simulation together and relegating the moral, economic, and legal judgments to the social bodies concerned with such matters. It might be argued that Disorders of Simulation should not be included in the taxonomy of mental syndromes because to do so would legitimize them in some degree as "mental illness," possibly leading to compensation or exculpation in moral and legal arenas. The potential for this occurrence seems slim, however, since the legal standing of Disorders of Simulation is much more likely to be determined by courts of law than by disease classification schemata. For example, Antisocial Personality Disorder was coded as a formal diagnosis, Sociopathic Personality Disturbance, as early as *DSM-I* (APA, 1952). This label changed to *Antisocial Personality Disorder* in *DSM-II* (APA, 1968), a designation that has been retained through *DSM-IV*. Despite its inclusion in the official psychiatric taxonomy, courts have long held that, whether or not it is a mental illness, Antisocial Personality Disorder is not an exculpatory factor when a defendant pleads diminished capacity or insanity.

SUMMARY AND CONCLUSIONS

Freud established that unconscious motivation underlies true psychopathology. From this principle an implicit and infrequently spoken corollary has been derived: *consciously controlled behavior is not psychopathological.* In addition, most traditional diagnoses are *syndromes,* a complex constellation of behaviors and motivations, rather than *a single, isolated behavior.*

These traditional assumptions have ensured that the simulation of illness could not easily be considered a genuine mental disorder since it is neither a syndrome nor involuntary. The lists of "synonyms" for Malingering, Factitious Disorder, and Compensation Neurosis referenced in the Glossary are clear evidence that simulation is held in disrepute. It is because simulation is largely viewed as an individual behavior—unattached to a syndrome, criminal or adaptive in nature, partially or fully intentional, consciously motivated, and under some degree of volitional control—that such an insidious, calculated, statistically rare, aberrant, and socially unacceptable behavior is deemed to reflect no mental disorder whatsoever.

It is important to investigate whether Malingering is part of an identifiable and coherent syndrome. Factitious Disorder—only recently designated as a legitimate mental illness and barely so at that—requires the formulation of conceptual linkages to "fully legitimate" categories of disorder. And, since Compensation Neurosis was vaguely referenced in the literature throughout the 20th century, then it surely deserves close analysis rather than peremptory dismissal.

If a complex, interpersonal, psychodynamic theory can be developed to explain and predict the behavior of individuals who engage in simulation, it is certainly worth the effort to do so. Such a theory, to be robust and have true heuristic value, must obviously account not only for Malingering but also for Factitious Disorder. It must do other things as well: it must resolve the endless problem of Compensation Neurosis; it must not do violence to established nomenclature and taxonomy; it must result in testable hypotheses; and, of equal importance, it must avoid moralizing.

3

Taxonomy and Disorders of Simulation

The taxonomic burden of proof lies upon the entomologist rather than upon the bug.

Malingering is the prototype for Disorders of Simulation since mental health professionals almost universally view it as "nonillness" behavior. Such apparently volitional, deceitful conduct has been only indirectly interesting to most clinicians and thus has not received the attention required to formulate precise classification. Malingering, designated as a *DSM-IV* (APA, 1994) V-Code, is classified as illegal or cheating behavior and therefore only marginally within the province of mental health. Despite this designation, clinicians persist in thinking and writing about Malingering as an "official" diagnosis. Consequently, Malingering has become a variety of disordered behavior, half diagnosis and half moral condemnation, unattached to a syndrome. It is rare yet not uncommon; mentally abnormal yet not psychopathological; morally repugnant yet not a social judgment; both nonillness and nonhealth.

THE MEDICAL MODEL

Part of the problem lies with the medical model of mental illness that assumes the patient to be either sick or well. Diagnostic ambiguity is resolved by assessing the adequacy or completeness of the

65

evaluative technique, insufficient current knowledge of disease processes, or error on the part of the clinician. The medical model works well for physical illnesses in addition to many mental illnesses when a consensus exists that the patient is "sick" or has a heredofamilial disorder. It even works reasonably well for disorders which are presumed to have no more than a minor hereditary component such as those loosely subsumed under the now passé category of "neuroses." Problems with the medical model arise, however, when patients exhibit simulating behaviors about which professionals then render social judgments in the context of "diagnosis."

Even under the assumption that Malingering is a moral rather than medical problem, health care professionals often "diagnose" it and distinguish it from other disorders without clear definition of its boundaries or parameters. It is a kind of "diagnosable nonillness." Obviously, straddling the diagnostic fence by designating Malingering as a V-Code is both unacceptable and dangerous.

BEHAVIOR VERSUS SYNDROME

Disorders of Simulation require systematic description with the same standards of comprehensiveness and systematic description that apply to other diagnostic categories. The current situation is confusing with Malingering as a V-Code Condition, Factitious Disorders isolated in a unique, partially defined diagnostic category, and Compensation Neurosis seemingly eliminated or reclassified under Psychological Factors Affecting Physical Condition or similar diagnoses.

DSM-IV V-Codes

The *DSM-IV* categorization of Malingering as a "V-Code additional condition" is either a euphemism for quasi-diagnosis-without-criteria, a thinly disguised moral condemnation applied to socially opprobrious behavior, or both. Moreover, V-Codes compound rather than clarify the taxonomic problem since very severe and aberrant varieties of human conduct are juxtaposed with rather common and benign behaviors that almost every normal human experiences.

For example, Adult Antisocial Behavior (AAB), Occupational and School Problems, and Uncomplicated Bereavement all coexist as V-Codes. The practice of grouping together disturbed human behavior of the most grievous type—cold-blooded murder—and benignly normal grief reactions as "disturbed human behavior not attributable to a mental disorder" is of questionable validity. By every measure, AAB as practiced by "some profes sional thieves, racketeers, or dealers in illegal psychoactive substances" (*DSM-IV*, p. 684) is grossly pathological. Statistically, morally, psychologically, ethically, and socially, AAB is not only abnormal but also inherently indicative of a very disordered psyche. By what stretch of taxonomic imagination and strain of psychodiagnostic credulity is AAB even remotely similar to its diagnostic V-Code cellmate, Uncomplicated Bereavement?

V-Code Conditions are labels for a broad range of diverse behaviors that do not constitute coherent syndromes. It makes little theoretical or practical sense simply to list individual behaviors not associated with legitimate diagnoses. The list is virtually endless and the behaviors chosen for inclusion or exclusion reveal more about the authors of the text than about the nature of disordered human behavior. Why not also list, for example, "Persistent Bank Overdrafting" or "Deficient Household Maintenance" or "Aerobic Exercise Avoidance" as V-Codes? As now constituted, Malingering as a V-Code is a diagnosis without portfolio, a term that may be used for pseudoscientific labeling of a specific behavior in isolation, without necessary connection to a syndrome.

By listing AAB, Malingering, and other assorted behaviors in the "nondiagnostic" section of the diagnostic manual, the *DSM-IV* straddles the fence, indicating that these behaviors are abnormal in some indefinite sense although not deserving of formal categorization. Thus, the diagnostician may apply his own system of values and valences. To different clinicians, simultaneously and unwittingly, Malingering may be no more than simple cheating, a particularly worrisome and malignant form of swindling, a bona fide indication of a diagnosable mental disorder, or some indefinable combination of all these views.

In sum, V-Code "Conditions" suggest vague abnormality, instances of socially deviant behavior, or normal variations of the human condition, without clear indication of diagnosable psychopathology. Assigning a label from the V-Code section to a single behavior rather than making formal diagnosis of a syndrome opens the door to idiosyncratic interpretation of the worst kind: personal moral judgment cloaked in clinical respectability.

Malingering as a Quasi-Legitimate Condition

It is, at best, gratuitous to indicate through a V-Code nondiagnosis of Malingering that the simulating patient has no clinically significant mental illness but rather suffers from moral deficit. The task of mental health professionals should be to describe individual psychodynamics with appropriate diagnoses rather than render opinion that a defendant's mental condition is legally nonexculpatory, or enter social judgment upon a patient's moral fiber. Like other V Codes, Malingering exists in a murky region: too important a behavioral aberration to ignore and too ill defined as a syndrome to be formally diagnosed.

In part, debate over the diagnostic status of Malingering continues because it is not described as a coherent constellation of symptoms with explicit psychodiagnostic criteria. Rather, as currently defined, it is an isolated behavior involving the exaggeration or creation of false symptoms, motivated primarily by external incentives. This definition relegates Malingering to the status of a specific, behavioral act rather than as one symptom among others within a true mental syndrome or diagnosis.

The problem with the view of Malingering as a behavioral act is generic and applies to any disorder involving simulation. On one side, Szasz erred when he damned all diagnoses—most particularly Malingering—as nothing more than moral condemnation masquerading in psychiatric clothing. Menninger overstepped in the opposite direction, indicating that anyone who would simulate truly must be mentally ill. The middle position holds greater promise; Malingering as a diagnosis requires that simulation be viewed as one symptom amongst others that, taken together, constitute a true clinical entity.

Thus, while the volitional presentation of false pathology is certainly a hallmark of simulation and is obviously a unique symptom, this isolated quantum of objectionable behavior cannot be the only factor considered in diagnosing a syndrome or there is, by definition, no syndrome to diagnose. It runs against the principles of psychodynamics to mention one or two specific behaviors without full analysis of the underlying syndrome.

Simulating Disorders currently are defined largely by exclusion. This situation is no different from the practice before Charcot when entities now defined as legitimate illness (e.g., Hysteria, Somatoform Disorders, and Posttraumatic Stress Disorder) were, by exclusion, considered simulation. These diagnoses became legitimate only after psychological thought advanced to the point where it was no longer possible to view them as simple exaggeration or simulation of true disorder. Therefore, the diagnoses became coherent, unified syndromes rather than as single instances of behavioral falsification. Only in the case of Factitious Disorder, however, has a disorder involving simulation emerged from the shadowy world of nondiagnosis into the daylight of bona fide syndromes, and then only partly, and only recently.

Syndromes are, of course, defined by the systematic descriptive approach first comprehensively codified in *DSM-III* (APA, 1980): essential features, associated features, age at onset, course, impairment, complications, predisposing factors, prevalence, sex ratio, familial pattern, and differential diagnosis. As long as Disorders of Simulation are defined more by exclusion than inclusion, they can never be syndromes and are destined to be little more than a name used to describe a quantum of behavior that is too important to ignore but that represents neither mental illness nor mental health.

To many, the views of "simulation-as-behavior" and "simulation-as-illness" are polar opposites and admit no middle ground. That is, as a behavior, simulation is either immoral action falling outside the province of mental health or, as a mental disorder, it is a traditional illness. It is possible, however, to take the best of both views and consecrate the unlikely marriage of Szasz's demythologizing cautions and Menninger's view of simulation as illness: Disorders of Simulation constitute behavioral syndromes capable of definition in the same systematic fashion as are, for example, Somatoform Disorders or an Adjustment Disorder with Mixed Emotional Features. Whether Disorders of Simulation are "mental illness" or exculpatory in legal settings is, of course, another matter.

Compensation Neurosis: The Illusion of Resolution

Inexplicit or absent diagnostic criteria are not problems solely confined to Malingering. In an attempt to resolve the diagnostic confusion surrounding Compensation Neurosis, Hyler and Spitzer (1978) noted that the designation of psychalgia (Psychogenic Pain Disorder in *DSM-III,* APA, 1980; Somatoform Pain Disorder in *DSM-III-R,* APA, 1987; and Pain Disorder in *DSM-IV,* APA, 1994, may be used to classify complaints of pain unassociated with or unexplained by any physical pathology. "Many persons who have been described as having Compensation Neurosis may now be classified in this category" (Hyler & Spitzer, 1978) and, as an example, they cite the patient who, upon settlement of the legal claim, continues to experience intractable pain. They further noted that "Persons whose complaints of pain disappear soon after settlement of a compensation issue may best be classified as malingerers." Thus, Hyler and Spitzer expunged Compensation Neurosis as a diagnostic category, and reassigned the patient to psychalgia or Malingering, with the litmus test being the presence or absence of symptoms after legal settlement.

Such dichotomous thinking represents a naive and unidimensional view of human motivation and does not take into account the fact that Compensation Neurosis is not invariably connected with financial compensation just as it is not truly a neurosis. The "compensation" in Compensation Neurosis is a psychodynamic variable and may refer to gratification of dependency needs, expression of revenge, passive–aggressive discharge of anger, and other such motivations instead of or in addition to simple avarice.

Some individuals are motivated by the settlement of associated legal claims but others are not and symptoms frequently do not resolve post-litigation. A significant percentage of patients remain dysfunctional, never return to productive life, and continue to suffer irrespective of their forensic success or failure.

To hinge formal differential diagnosis between simulation and psychalgia upon resolution of symptoms following legal suit suggests moral judgment of the *post hoc ergo propter hoc* variety rather than of psychodynamic precision.

In "Where, in DSM-III-R, is Compensation Neurosis'?" Hyler, Williams, and Spitzer (1988) designed a decision tree wherein patients with a compensation claim involving physical and/or psychological symptoms enter at the top and exit with a differential diagnostic formulation in hand at the bottom. The exit diagnosis only may be true physical illness, Psychological Factors Affecting Physical Condition, some variety of Somatoform or Anxiety Disorder, Factitious Disorder, or Malingering. There is no exit diagnosis—by name or by description—that is Compensation Neurosis. Clearly, the authors constructed a "diagnosis-disappearing-machine" that cleverly did away with the problem altogether!

However, the notion of Compensation Neurosis has endured for so long—however vaguely defined—because it has been viewed as a bridge over the chasm between genuine illness on one side and Malingering on the other. Most clinicians have treated or evaluated patients who seemed to display more exaggerated or protracted symptoms than expected in Somatoform or other "legitimate" disorders but who are not accurately described as Malingering. Decision-tree slight-of-hand will not meet the needs of those who are confronted daily with such cases. Admittedly, the vaguely specified category of Compensation Neurosis has been in urgent need of reformulation for decades but Hyler, Williams, and Spitzer's psychodiagnostic legerdemain presents the diagnostician with only the illusion of resolution.

Indices of Suspicion

Another problem in the taxonomy of simulation involves identifying the behaviors, motivations, and personality organizations that define each syndrome. Disorders of Simulation are complex phenomena and, therefore, understanding them requires an equally complex formulation. One attempt to address this complexity has been the proliferation of behavioral lists and indices of suspicion.

Unfortunately, "suspicious behavior" is vaguely defined in the literature and the available lists are generally a combination of observation and judgment, partly clinical and partly moral-social, subject to skew and distortion, and containing behaviors typical of a large number of psychiatric diagnoses. Mood, Somatoform, Ganser's Syndrome, Adult Antisocial Behavior, Posttraumatic Stress Disorder and many others, upon initial presentation or even upon extended analysis, may display unusual features, fail to conform to the prototypical case, present in "suspicious" ways, or otherwise appear unconventional. While lists of suspicious behaviors are useful as a signal to further evaluate the patient, they are not a true test for Disorders of Simulation and are susceptible to misuse. An index of suspicion applied in the absence of differential diagnostic criteria is a hypothesis unconfirmed by examination. The use of lists alone runs the enormous risk of mistaking suspicion for confirmation, hunch for reality and, in the worst case, personal bias for diagnosis.

List Mania

Despite the vagaries inherent in generating lists of suspicious behaviors and motivations, such indices appear with some frequency in the literature. *DSM-IV* provides a short list of four indicia for simulation while other authors have organized more extensive compilations. Glossary Table 9.11 presents a composite list extracted from several major sources.

The latest trend in cataloging simulation is the development of multiple, sometimes competing, lists of criteria for the identification of simulation. Thus, such current authors as Rogers (1984b), Hall and Pritchard (1996), and Mills and Lipian (1995) organize Malingering-like behaviors according to simulation of conditions contained in Table 3.1.

Another approach has been to divide simulation by alleged type or form according to ordinal or nominal scales of great variety as illustrated in Table 3.2.

The issue of motivation, by contrast, has received relatively little attention, and there are no complex schemata or lists extant in the literature. For example, a recent summary of motivations for Malingering is quite superficial with no hint of advancement

Table 3.1

Diagnoses Listed by Various Authors as Frequent Targets for the Simulating Patient, Each Associated with a List of Criteria

Amnesia	Legal Incompetency
Auditory Hallucinations	Mental Deficiency
Cognitive Disorder	Neuropsychological Impairment
Delusions	Pain and Loss of Sensation
Distress Following Trauma	Posttraumatic Stress Disorder
Legal Insanity	Psychosis

Table 3.2

Gradations and Schemes Proposed for Cataloging Simulation and Malingering

Mild Malingering	
Moderate Malingering	
Severe Malingering	Proposed by Rogers (1988)
Moderate Defensiveness	
Severe Defensiveness	
Data Tampering	
False Imputation	
Opportunistic Malingering	Proposed by Yudofsky (1985)
Staged Events	
Symptom Invention	
Other Deceptive	
Mixed Deceptive	Proposed by Travin and Protter
Self-Deceptive	(1984)
Hybrid Responding	
Honest Responding	Proposed by Rogers (1984a)
Random Responding	
Pure Malingering	
Partial Malingering	Proposed by Garner (1965)
False Imputation	

in thinking over the previous decades of this century. Mills and Lipian (1995, p. 1617) summarized the "motivational literature" in just six points presented in Table 3.3.

Lists of the types of personality pathology associated with simulation are virtually nonexistent. The literature simply suggests that such behavior may occur with somewhat greater frequency in antisocial and borderline configurations.

Table 3.3
Motivations for Simulating Behavior

Avoidance of Criminal Responsibility, Trial and Punishment
Avoidance of Military Service or Particularly Hazardous Duties
Financial Gain
Facilitation of Transfer from Prison to a Hospital
Admission to a Hospital
Drug Seeking

Problems with the List Approach

Excessive Simplicity

The lists of suspicious behavior in the literature are incomplete, inconsistent, and, although the broad range of behaviors listed suggests that simulation is a complex problem, the lists per se do not reflect a systematic approach to understanding simulating behavior. Most of the indices make at least intuitive sense (although a few press credulity to the limit and some are contradictory) but a coherent theoretical picture does not emerge from inspection of such lists. The notion, popular amongst authors, that a simple checklist of behaviors will suffice when the clinician suspects a Disorder of Simulation is of limited clinical utility. It is never true that all indicia are present in one patient, and no author has ever been so bold as to indicate how many items from each list are required before making a "diagnosis." Lists that address motivation are also simplistic. Table 3.3 betrays little evidence of psychodynamic factors, object relations capacity, or other time-honored principles of human motivation. In fact, the list of motivations could just as easily have been written by Galenus in 150 A.D. than in the psychologically sophisticated 1990s.

Fractionalization

The use of lists fractionalizes the issue of simulation, encouraging the view that a few simple tests or interview techniques will serve to identify it. Thus, the trend is away from examining simulation in the context of a comprehensive theoretical framework and toward the reductionistic view of simulation as a simple behavior, likely to occur under a wide variety of circumstances, and signaling no particular pathology in the alleged simulator. The ultimate outcome is to reinforce the notion that patients are either suffering from a genuine mental disorder on the one hand or simply simulating in obvious ways for obvious reasons on the other. At present, the major focus seems to be largely upon the elaboration of clinical techniques, tests, and tricks designed to detect instances of simulation rather than upon development of a robust theory of simulation.

Prejudgment

Finally, the notion of a quick, behavioral checklist for simulation runs the risk of encouraging the clinician to prejudge when only a full and complete examination of the patient and all relevant data holds hope of accurate assessment. Closely allied to the list approach is the design and development of psychological tests to detect simulation. Some commercial tests advertise the ability to detect simulation with high levels of confidence. While these tests have the advantage of being inexpensive, quick, and easy to administer, and making intuitive sense, tests for simulation suffer from the same problems as the list approach. Reliance on lists and tests alone increases the chance of Type I and Type II errors. Lists and tests have an important place in the assessment of Disorders of Simulation but should be considered supplementary to differential diagnostic criteria.

Limited Theory

Indices and lists reflect each author's clinical impression of the conditions under which simulation may occur and the methods that they have observed in fabricating patients. While naturalistic data are quite important, it is equally important to measure such observations against theories that discuss why patients simulate. Unfortunately, such theories are scarce. Another problem resulting from the fractionalization of simulation is the lack of focus upon theory linking simulation with "legitimate" disorders. Historically, the distinction between physical disorder and the unconscious simulation of physical disorder led to the full integration of hysteria and the somatizing mental disorders within the corpus of psychological theory. Over the years, robust theoretical linkages developed which served to expand our understanding of the complex psychodynamics involved in abnormal human behavior. In so doing, psychology and psychiatry have largely limited themselves to the study of unconscious dynamics; consciously motivated behavior usually has been defined as "normal"—or at least not formally indicative of psychopathology—and therefore tacitly beyond the scope of mental health. Such normal, conscious behavior commonly falls within the province of ethics, religion, social psychology, sociology, political theory, economics, or other nonpathology based disciplines.

It seems both artificial and arbitrary to define mental disorder as ending where consciousness begins. Just as psychology must examine both the unconscious and conscious process in order to understand the whole person, so it must also examine the linkages between simulated abnormality and abnormality itself. To date, *DSM* identifies only one psychopathological syndrome that partakes of consciousness, although it straddles the line between conscious and unconscious processes; Factitious Disorder. Another, Compensation Neurosis, also partakes of consciousness but is not currently officially accepted while Malingering, of course, involves full mental awareness.

Whether fully or partially conscious, Disorders of Simulation are psychodynamically convoluted and no less complex expressions of human functioning than syndromes believed to be fully unconscious. It is important to uncover the theoretical connections between unconsciously produced disorders and similar mental or physical disorders produced consciously. There is no reason why a robust theory of abnormal human behavior cannot incorporate conscious as well as unconscious mental processes.

THE TAXONOMIC PARADOX

Malingering, Factitious Disorders, and Compensation Neurosis are inadequately defined concepts that often are oversimplified. The more patients in whom a clinician strongly suspects or actually diagnoses the presence of a Disorder of Simulation, the more it becomes apparent that the motivation and methods of simulation are quite diverse and multiform, often subtly blending and shading into each other in a rich array. For example, some patients quite blatantly feign with seeming unconcern about the clinician's reaction to even their most obvious and transparent misrepresentations. Others are very subtle simulators although overt in displaying a need to have their apparent deficits accepted as genuine. One subset is difficult to distinguish from hysteroid patients who display emotionally based overreactivity and unconscious exaggeration of complaints yet do not qualify as having Somatoform Disorder. Another subset significantly exaggerates their injuries but seems to justify doing so based on conscious or preconscious expectations of special privilege.

The current nomenclature does not allow for a diagnostic position between Malingering and bona fide mental disorder. That is, patients who seem to protract their symptomatic complaints and who are motivated by secondary gain must either be diagnosed as having a "legitimate" mental disorder or, after leaping a wide chasm, as Malingering. However, many observers and clinicians have commented on the need for some middle position, a bridge spanning the considerable gulf between true disorder and Malingering. When using the *DSM-IV* as a guide, some patients defy categorization since they neither display classical features associated with Somatoform, Anxiety Disorders, or Psychological Factors Affecting Physical Condition nor the hallmarks of Malingering. These patients pose a diagnostic dilemma, a "taxonomic paradox."

Case 3.1—The Taxonomic Paradox

A 49-year-old family man was questionably injured but presented as seriously impaired. It indeed seemed paradoxical that, during the course of his lawsuit, he abandoned his successful occupation of many years thus incurring severe financial loss that he could never realistically expect to recover no matter how successful his claim. On close examination, it was questionable whether the *DSM-IV* criterion of "external incentives" truly fit this ultimately self-defeating patient who, because of a suit for several hundred thousand dollars, initially appeared to be motivated by the prospect of financial gain. Paradoxically, the "external gain" to which he presumably aspired could only result in enormously less compensation than he would have earned had he simply continued to work. However, on further analysis, neither did he fit the criterion of "internal incentives" such as in a Factitious Disorder with physical or psychological symptoms. Although he had numerous exaggerated physical complaints, there was no Munchausen quality nor did he spin tales reminiscent of *pseudologia fantastica.* He did display some need to assume the patient role insofar as he was erratically attending outpatient psychotherapy but there was neither a history of excessive hospitalization nor multiple, suspicious physician contacts. Although he appeared to feign deficit on some psychological and neuropsychological tests, he did not overtly display evidence of more than highly dependent and passive–aggressive personality traits by *DSM-IV* criteria and had no history of antisocial tendencies. He did not fully qualify for Conversion or other Somatoform Disorder although some features were present. Indeed, there was evidence that he had been a healthy, noncomplaining, upstanding, tax paying, fully employed individual for many years, with no history of problems with the law.

The patient's behavior was ultimately financially self-defeating in the present without evidence for such behavior in the past; his internal and external motivations were in paradoxical conflict; he existed in an ill-defined twilight region somewhere between outright Malingering and an Undifferentiated Somatoform Disorder. The *DSM* does not have a category for such patients but, had Compensation Neurosis been a legitimate and well-defined diagnostic alternative, the patient might have qualified.

Because of cases like the self-defeating patient and other paradoxical or mixed symptom patterns, the standard nomenclature for diagnosis of Disorders of Simulation seems incomplete. It is easy for a clinician to be confused since most simulating patients do not neatly fit the black-and-white distinctions of real versus feigned illness, internal versus external motivation, conscious versus unconscious presentation, and the like. Rather, they frequently and persistently fall into gray areas between these polarized guidelines. The striking absence of intermediate positions, qualifiers, quantifiers, indicators of complexity, chronicity, or prognosis in the diagnosis of simulation is remarkable.

Shades of gray are of measurable assistance to the clinician in other, relatively well-defined diagnostic areas such as the mood disorders. Like many *DSM* diagnostic categories, Organic Mood or Personality changes include requirements that the course or current level be specified through modifiers such as manic, depressed, mixed, or explosive. Affective Disorders may be described with similar terms and are additionally modified by descriptors such as mild, moderate, severe (without psychotic features), or with psychotic features (mood-congruent or mood-incongruent). Terms such as *recurrent, single episode, partial remission,* and *full remission* catalog the course of disorders. The point is that depressive phenomena occur in varying contexts, shades, degrees, complexities, and chronicities.

While perhaps not so complex as depression, the area of simulation is certainly more varied than the vague differentials presented in the *DSM-IV* between bona fide diagnosis in which there is no simulation, three subtypes of Factitious Disorder, and the nondiagnosis (V-Code) of Malingering itself.

DSM-IV contains no modifiers, no descriptors of chronicity, and only minimal discussion of coexisting diagnosis such as emotional or organic disorder. For example, diagnosis of Factitious Disorder occurs only after exclusion of all other possible causes of the behavior, including Malingering. *DSM-III-R* (APA, 1987) states "a diagnosis of Factitious Disorder excludes a diagnosis of Malingering" (p. 360); *DSM-IV* indicates that "External incentives for the behavior (such as economic gain, avoiding legal responsibility, or improving physical well-being, as in Malingering) are absent" (p. 474). However, there are reports in the literature that both Factitious Disorder and Malingering may occur simultaneously (W. F. Gorman, 1982).

Compensation Neurosis is listed in the index to *DSM-III-R* and the reader is referred to Psychological Factors Affecting Physical Condition. Upon turning to the cited page, however, Compensation Neurosis is never mentioned and thus the criteria for diagnosis are apparently left to the reader's fantasy or awareness that Hyler, Williams, and Spitzer (1988) wrote an addendum defining the disorder out of existence altogether. In *DSM-IV* there is no mention of Compensation Neurosis whatsoever. At best, these are glaring oversights in a diagnostic taxonomy that has expanded from 139 to 886 pages during four revisions since 1952.

The incomplete and vague taxonomy for Disorders of Simulation makes it quite difficult to disentangle diagnostic cases where the clinician suspects multiple sources for the patient's behavior such as a combination of real and feigned illness. For example, what diagnosis should apply in patients who simultaneously suffer from Somatoform and Facititious Disorders? Why must a Factitious Disorder preempt rather than coexist with Malingering? Why is it necessary to view the internal versus external motivational factors (which presumably differentiate Malingering from Factitious Disorders) as mutually exclusive? What should be the diagnosis in cases where the clinician suspects both genuine psychiatric or physical disorder and Malingering? The answers to these and related diagnostic questions posed by the frequent "taxonomic paradox" cases are not readily available in the literature and remain unaddressed in *DSM-IV*. The problem is compounded by a bold black-and-white approach without intermediate shades of gray.

The taxonomic paradox case, falling in the psychodiagnostic no-man's land, is distressingly common in clinical practice, and is the result of judgmental, simplistic, and unartful diagnostic nomenclature. According to the rules of taxonomy, the inability to make clear classificatory decisions is always the fault of the classifier or his system and is never the fault of that which is to be classified. That is, the taxonomic burden of proof lies upon the entomologist rather than upon the bug. Therefore, paradoxical cases—those truly falling within the semiconscious, the psychodiagnostic twilight zone—must result from problems with the classificatory system. They are specific exceptions to the "either simulating or genuine" rule and have great value in providing the impetus for taxonomic redefinition.

THE NEED FOR REFORMULATION

Specification of criteria for the Simulating Disorders ought to follow the format employed for "legitimate" disorders. The psychodynamic underpinnings of simulation must be outlined and linkages established with other mental disorders. Despite several major works (Artingstall, 1999; Hall & Pritchard, 1996; Rogers, 1988; Schreirer & Libow, 1993) and review articles, timeworm information about Disorders of Simulation has been largely summarized, reworked, or reframed rather than reconceptualized.

In preference to its current status as a moral violation or psychiatric quasi-diagnosis, clinicians must examine the nature of Malingering as a true syndrome. The diagnostic criteria for Factitious Disorder require some reformulation, primarily in developing linkages with other disorders involving both simulation and genuine pathology. The conundrum of Compensation Neurosis must be resolved, and either defined as illness with specific criteria or dismembered with its parts *fully* assigned to other, established diagnostic categories without resort to verbal sophistry or differential diagnostic sleight-of-hand. Before the laudable goals of reformulation and redefinition can be accomplished, however, a number of basic issues in Disorders of Simulation must be addressed.

BASIC ISSUES IN DISORDERS OF SIMULATION

While the notion of grouping similar problems together based on psychodynamic theory, parsimonious taxonomy, or clinical treatment is not new, much work in this area remains to be undertaken in Disorders of Simulation. At the very least, a truly robust picture of Disorders of Simulation must address three areas in depth: behavioral orchestration, motivation, and personality pathology.

The Issue of Behavioral Orchestration

The greatest confusion rests with the enormous difficulty operationalizing the historical distinction between acts determined by *conscious* versus *unconscious* mental processes. The notions of the conscious and unconscious reflect such complexity and occur in so many different contexts that they are useless for describing observed behaviors. Each term has been used to describe deliberation, action, or both without clear explanation. A potentially useful distinction is the critical difference between *intention and volition* when describing a patient's orchestration of behavior. *DSM-III-R* hinted at the distinction under the heading of Factitious Disorders with the note that:

> The judgment that the symptom is *intentionally* produced is based, in part, on the person's ability to simulate illness in such a way that he or she is not likely to be discovered. This involves decisions as to timing and concealment that require a degree of judgment and intellectual activity suggestive of "*voluntary*" control. However, these acts have a compulsive quality in the sense that the person is unable to refrain from a particular behavior even if its dangers are known. The behaviors should therefore be considered "*voluntary*" only in the sense that they are deliberate and purposeful (*intentional*), but not in the sense that the acts can be controlled. Thus, in Factitious Disorders, behavior that appears to be under

"*voluntary*" control is used to pursue goals that are *involuntarily* adopted. (p. 315; emphasis added)

While the *DSM-III-R* was correct as far as it went, the distinction between the *planning* process involved in designing or engineering the symptoms and the *action* process required to produce or display those symptoms was only briefly stated and rudimentary in formulation. Under Factitious Disorders, *DSM-IV* made a further attempt to operationalize the word *intentional* by use of observation and inference.

> The judgment that a particular symptom is *intentionally* produced is made both by direct evidence and by excluding other causes of the symptom. For example, an individual presenting with hematuria is found to have anticoagulants in his possession. The person denies having taken them, but blood studies are consistent with the ingestion of anticoagulants. A reasonable inference, in the absence of evidence that accidental ingestion occurred, is that the individual may have taken the medication *intentionally*. (p. 471; emphasis added)

While it has been implied that behavioral orchestration must somehow be linked to intention, volition, and complexity or severity, more attention must be directed toward systematizing the complex, multidimensional evaluation of *behavioral orchestration* by the patient when questions of simulation are raised. Analysis of behavioral orchestration must account for a rich, broad, and textured array of false symptoms.

The Issue of Motivation

The reasons why patients fabricate illness are not only critical to an understanding of Disorders of Simulation but also inherently fascinating. External versus internal incentives and primary versus secondary gain are descriptive terms that obviously refer to the reasons why a patient acts as he does, each term reflecting human action from a different perspective.

Incentive, either internal or external, is the motivational label used in *DSM-IV* (APA, 1994). However, this term has the handicap of value-laden associations that suggest investment, return, profit margin, and other economic concepts. It also subtly implies that the clinician must ferret out information that is more in the realm of an economist than a mental health professional. Moreover, the distinction between internal and external incentives is vague and hard to make operational. Most simulating patients do not reveal "obvious external objectives" because it is imprudent for them to do so. Thus, even if the motivational notion of "internal or external incentives" is valid, frequently, it is useless since it is difficult to obtain the differential diagnostic data.

Much of the literature discusses motivation as involving *primary or secondary gain,* terms that suggest the importance of psychological underpinnings. Gain is somewhat more abstract than incentive and, although it too has monetary implications, the concept is somewhat more psychological. Primary gain is similar to the concept of internal incentive but with fewer value judgments. Secondary gain, upon close inspection, is more similar to than different from external incentive and contains some elements of psychodynamic thinking but, unfortunately, does not adequately address the issue of willful simulation.

The classical concept of *motivation* is probably the least value laden of the terms used to describe human action and not only has the most psychodynamic explanatory power but also falls within the realm of familiar investigation by mental health professionals. *Motivation* is a term that avoids concrete associations to the world of finance and implies concepts familiar to most dynamically oriented students of the human condition.

Yet, despite the theoretical attention to motivation, the notion that *simulation implies not only a patient who simulates but also an observer to appreciate the simulation* is rarely mentioned. Hall and Pritchard (1996) have obliquely referred to the observer when they stated, "There can be no deception without an *entity* to deceive. As a corollary, all falsehood is interactional and all interpersonal transactions are subject to deception" (p. 3; emphasis added). The patient and observer form a unit that is inescapably necessary if simulation is to have any effect and, therefore, Disorders of Simulation must involve *inter*psychic phenomena. The simulator's internal representations of the self and the object world are implicated, most particularly the impact of these internalized relations upon interpersonal relationships. Interpsychic systems involve the area of *object relations*. This crucial point is only rarely discussed in the literature on Disorders of Simulation although object relations capacity is central to the issue of motivation and must be fully explored in any attempt to understand why patients fabricate or exaggerate illness or injury.

The Issue of Personality Pathology

Various *personality types* may gravitate to different varieties of simulation. Current thinking considers primarily the Antisocial and Borderline Personality Disorders, a rather narrow focus that constitutes undue restriction of range. It is difficult to believe that, given the large number of combinations possible with at least 10 *DSM* personality disorders, only one or two are associated with simulation. Classification of personality pathology in ways that respect the full and complex range of behavioral orchestrations and motivational factors in Disorders of Simulation is necessary.

The *DSM* diagnostic criteria for personality disorders are primarily behavioral, descriptive, and largely derived from historical review. More theoretically and psychodynamically based concepts of personality pathology are not represented as a result of *DSM-III*'s introduction of a polythetic rather than monothetic approach. *DSM-IV* divides personality disorders into clusters based upon the degree to which the patients appear odd or eccentric (Cluster A), dramatic, emotional, or erratic (Cluster B), or anxious or fearful (Cluster C).

It is not clear that *DSM* clusters have heuristic value in describing Disorders of Simulation. For example, a patient with a Passive–Aggressive Personality Disorder (Cluster C) on Axis II may be expected to fabricate or exaggerate symptoms in a manner more akin to a Borderline (Cluster B) than to a Dependent (Cluster C). That is, motivational factors in Disorders of Simulation may cut across the *DSM* personality clusters rather than be confined by them. It may also be true that alternative personality diagnostic schemes may make rich contributions to understanding Disorders of Simulation.

Careful analysis of personality pathology must occur to fully understand Disorders of Simulation. When patients simulate, they assume an interpersonal stance that, by definition, is more *extroversive* than introversive. Tendencies toward social *nonconformity* or conformity are obviously important variables as is the degree of emotional stability or *instability* displayed by the patient. These are not new or revolutionary concepts in the psychopathology of personality but, for reasons that are hard to specify, they have received far less attention in the analysis of Disorders of Simulation than in more "legitimate" mental problems.

Rogers's (1988) caution that clinicians should not "attempt to go one step further and make statements regarding an individual's personality on the basis of his or her specific dissimulative style [Rogers appears to actually mean "simulative style"]" (p. 310) is important to heed. However, the converse statement requires less caution: *Knowledge of an individual's personality allows important statements to be made about the most probable types of simulation.* While is not true that simulation necessarily implies certain personality characteristics, it is reasonable to assume that personality styles may imply different ranges of simulative behavior.

SUMMARY AND CONCLUSIONS

Systematic classification—the arranging of phenomena into groups based upon their natural relationships—is one of the first undertakings of science. As is true for all other mental and physical disorders, an accurate taxonomy is critical to a full and complete understanding of Malingering, Factitious Disorder, and Compensation Neurosis.

Historically, simulation has escaped close taxonomic scrutiny since it was the stone from which true disorder was sculpted—the ground rather than the figure. Simulation lives in the backwaters of psychology because it involves the mundane world of sunlit consciousness rather than the exciting stygian depths of the psychodynamic unconscious. Psychologically, simulation is cast as a moral problem, more in the realm of ethics than science while, in general society, simulation is relegated to the courts as a fraudulent vexation to be forensically resolved by judge and jury. Consequently, critical thinking about Disorders of Simulation has not progressed apace with clarifications and revisions of the standard taxonomic systems used by practitioners, researchers, and theoreticians.

Any proposed taxonomy for Disorders of Simulation must do justice to the complexity of the classification problem. The need for a multiaxial system is evident since simulation is unlikely to be solely an uncomplex, willful, and unitary failure to respond truthfully. Neither is it simply motivated nor straightforwardly linked with only Antisocial or Borderline Personality Disorders. Rather, simulation involves multipolar behavioral orchestration, subtle shadings of intrapersonal motivation, and chameleon-like associations with Personality Disorders.

4

Axis I: Behavioral Orchestration Part A: Obtaining Reported Data

> ... [M]uch of the difficulty in the way of building a
> coherent theory of human behavior lies in our inabil-
> ity—or, sometimes unwillingness—to separate descrip-
> tion from prescription. (Szasz, 1961, p. 86)

The notion of multiaxial evaluation is part of the current diagnostic ethos and, because Disorders of Simulation are complex,
multiaxial evaluation is required in order to fully understand and
distinguish them from their "legitimate" brethren. The major
investigative axes required to fully discover, document, and diagnose Disorders of Simulation involve: (1) behavioral orchestration, (2) motivation, and (3) personality pathology.

Thus, a triaxial system is appropriate with each axis relatively
independent of the other two and capable of separate investigation. Disorders of Simulation are best characterized by the patterns displayed when all three axes are considered together. Each
axis is partitioned into several levels and displayed as a matrix or
continuum, to facilitate not only theoretically based discussion
but also practical patient assessment.

BEHAVIORAL ORCHESTRATION

Behavioral Orchestration refers to the nature and type of control
exerted by the patient over a variety of important behaviors associated with Disorders of Simulation. Traditionally, psychopathological behavior has been viewed as unconsciously determined but

it is a distinguishing requirement in Disorders of Simulation that some significant portion of the patient's presentation must be purposeful.

This requirement does not speak to the issue of motivation or necessitate that it be solely external; the patient may be as idiosyncratically motivated as he wishes without obvious desire for financial gain, avoiding combat or conscription, obtaining drugs, evading prosecution, shirking his work, or other such external incentive. It also does not speak to the issue of personality pathology since a moderate number of characterologic disorders may engage in simulation; the fabrication of illness, injury, or stress is not exclusively associated with any particular *DSM-IV* (APA, 1994) personality configuration. It is also true that the patient, unintentionally and involuntarily, may orchestrate some portions of his behavior while, simultaneously, engaging in other behaviors that are intentional and voluntary. Discovery of how a patent simulates mental and physical patterns is critical to differential diagnosis. Since fabricating patients seek to obscure their methods, evaluation of most cases requires appreciation of minimal cues and the application of subtle analyses.

During the course of evaluation and treatment, there are many opportunities for patients to simulate. The Axis of Behavioral Orchestration is extensive and easiest to understand when it is divided into two separate but related parts: part A—Obtaining Reported Data; and part B—Reporting Obtained Data.

Part A (chapter 4) involves collecting information from the patient or other sources while part B (chapter 5) involves appreciating the symptoms by actively evaluating or treating the patient. Both parts A and B are each subdivided into three sections, such that there are six individual "Windows of Opportunity" where simulation may occur.

WINDOWS OF OPPORTUNITY

The complex, two-part Axis of Behavioral Orchestration is easiest to evaluate when patient behaviors are systematically isolated and examined in Windows of Opportunity. These windows form a time continuum ranging from the first step of patient identification to the last step of patient response to treatment. The windows are not completely orthogonal and independent; overlap is unavoidable in complex areas. For example, it is impossible to discuss the problem of apparent causation without reference to the patient's claimed symptoms. Yet, the patient's specific symptoms are, in themselves, an important and separate Window of Opportunity that deserves separate treatment. The overlap, however, is only partial and it is important to examine the same phenomena through different windows such that each makes a significant contribution to understanding the whole problem of simulation. Part A of Behavioral Orchestration contains three windows, all of which involve basic determinations such as identification of the patient, collection of complaints, allegations of cause. In essence the windows of part A may be thought of as "obtaining reported data" whereas, in the following chapter, the windows of part B involve "reporting obtained data."

Window 1: Who Is The Patient?

Most commonly, individuals who simulate do so with reference to themselves and claim to be personally experiencing symptoms that prove exaggerated, misattributed, or false. Occasionally, however, other parties are intimately involved with the appearance of the presumed patient on the office doorstep so that, at times, the identified patient is not the true patient and the true patient is not the identified patient. This is a particularly important distinction in the frequent instance when one person accompanies another to evaluation or treatment sessions. As simple as establishing the "identified patient" sounds, it is not always easy to determine who the patient is, whether there is one patient or two, the degree to which "copatients" are involved, or what effect mental disorder in one has upon the other. Discovery of the identified patient is a crucial first step that must precede evaluation of the discovered patient.

Self-as-Patient

Usually, an adult—whether suffering from a Disorder of Simulation or not—designates himself as the identified patient, presents symptoms that are self-referenced, and thus specifies the self as symptom-carrier. If the apparent patient is a minor, very elderly, exceptionally infirm, or for some reason deemed incompetent, an accompanying parent, guardian, or other caretaker may identify the patient. Vigilance is important under such circumstances since a patient with induced symptoms may be a victim instead. Therefore, it is critical to determine whether the patient role is indigenous to the individual or the result of coercion or trickery. Even when the initial presentation seems to be solely self-motivated, there is some possibility of mistaking a falsely identified patient for a real patient.

Self-and-Other

When others, in a supportive role, accompany the self-identified patient, it is important to determine whether these other parties are involved in the patient's simulation of illness or injury. The presence of a "coconspirator" may result not only in retrenched symptoms and apparent confirmation of the patient's symptoms from an independent source but also in a unique broadening of the concept of "patient" from one person to two. Two individuals who willfully collude to falsely present one of them as patient sometimes occurs in Malingering but rarely, if ever, in Compensation Neurosis or Factitious Disorder. Coconspirators must be distinguished from *folie à deux* where the mutual pathological system is not willful on the part of either party, much less intentionally induced by one in the other.

Case Example 4.1—A Walk in the Woods

A male in his mid-30's arrived for a day-long examination in the company of his wife. During the office visit, he displayed dramatic gait disturbance reminiscent of astasia-abasia. His wife watched with concerned and anxious eyes whenever he traversed the short distance between the waiting and examination rooms. During the initial interview, she affirmed that he had had consistent problems with walking since his injury. However, a private investigator videotaped some of his activities during the day of evaluation. The tapes clearly showed the patient and his wife walking casually together up to the office door. Later in the day the patient and his wife left for lunch and, at the day's end, walked to their car for the drive home. On the next day, they were taped driving into the country and taking an extended walk in the woods. In no instance did the tapes reveal the marked gait anomaly that dramatically appeared as soon as the patient and his wife crossed the office threshold.

In the case example, the patient's wife played a central role in the simulation of gross gait disturbance and evidence of the wife's participation was important in differential diagnosis. Precisely the same set of observed patient behaviors but with the wife's un-awareness of her husband's simulated gait, would suggest some variety of Somatoform or hysterically based disorder versus a Dis-order of Simulation. In the present case, unambiguous documen-tation of the wife's coconspiratorial role through videotape and clinical observation suggested that the patient's simulation was a family affair. While the gait disturbance belonged to the identi-fied patient, the wife's validation obviously made a significant contribution. In a sense, her collusion broadened the definition of "patient" to include two persons.

Other-as-Patient

Under special circumstances, the identified patient is not the real patient. For years the reality of "scapegoating," "designated symptom carrier," and "identified patient" have been recog-nized in clinical settings. Falsely induced or mistaken identifica-tion of a second party as the patient is particularly evident when the family is involved in the assessment of problem childhood or adolescent behavior, when family evaluation or treatment is underway, and when family members allege mental illness or in-competence in an elderly relative. Illness is sometimes falsely re-ported or real illness actually induced in others by a caretaker. Reporting false symptoms in healthy individuals or inducing real illness in one person by another is unique to Factitious Disorder by Proxy where the purported patient is actually the victim of physical and/or psychological assault from a highly pathological true patient.

Case Example 4.2—Doctor, My Child is Sick

A young mother arrived at the hospital ER with her 4-year-old daughter and indicated, with great concern, that her child had a "fit" just before admission. In considerable detail, she described how the child had fallen to the floor, thrashed about, and become unresponsive. Upon examination, the child appeared perfectly healthy and neurological examination was within normal limits. Further discussion with the mother resulted in a profusion of reported symptoms that did not conform to typical seizure patterns. When the patient's chart arrived from medical records, it became evident that mother and daughter had presented at the ER several times previously with very similar complaints. Although prior comprehensive medical studies had always been unremarkable, the child carried a provisional diagnosis of atypical seizures based on the mother's reported history. On prior visits, the ER physician had scheduled appointments with a pediatric neurologist but the mother continued to present her daughter at the ER rather than follow through with the referral. A social worker confronted the mother and, following a rather emotional catharsis, the mother admitted to reporting nonexistent seizures.

In the case example, the child was the unwitting victim of the False Reporting subtype of Factitious Disorder by Proxy. Although the mother never physically injured the child, persistent hospital visits did expose the child to unnecessary medical testing and the emotional trauma associated with assuming the sick role. The "identified patient" and the "real patient" were two different individuals. Under slightly different circumstances, if the mother had actually induced seizures in her daughter by the surreptitious injection of insulin, for example, the differential diagnosis would include the more malignant and dangerous Active Symptom Induction form of Factitious Disorder by Proxy. Symptom induction is the most unhappily graphic illustration of the case where the true patient is not the person who presents but rather the one doing the presenting.

Table 4.1
Window 1: The Identified Patient

Pathology Level	Categories of Identified Patient	Malingering	Factitious Disorder	Compensation Neurosis
Minimum	Self-as-Patient	Yes	Yes	Yes
↓	Self-and-Other as Patient	Yes	No	No
Maximum	Other-as-Patient	No	Yes	No

Table 4.1 summarizes the Identified Patient window. When the patient begins to involve others in his simulating behavior, the level of attributed psychopathology obviously increases. This principle correlates with indications that Factitious Disorder and Factitious Disorder by Proxy generally involve more underlying

emotional disturbance than does Malingering which, in turn, involves more than does Compensation Neurosis. Whenever more than one person appears to be directly *involved* in symptom presentation or corroboration, the clinician should take particular care to examine for one of the more dramatic forms of illness or injury simulation. In contrast, bona fide cases, Factitious Disorder (excluding the Proxy variant), and Compensation Neurosis patients may be accompanied by others to the evaluation or treatment sessions but there is rarely evidence of active collusion and none whatever of victimization.

Some factitious individuals induce the role of patient in others, all the while remaining on the periphery of the clinician's evaluative sphere. That is, they intentionally engage in symptomatic engineering that identifies another individual as the sufferer and avoid placing themselves in the patient role. This problem does not occur in Malingering since patients present themselves by claiming to have experienced a trauma that never occurred or, if trauma did occur, they wrongfully use it to designate themselves as patient. Neither do Compensation Neurotics point the finger of illness at others. They become patients by unintentional design because they invariably have suffered some accident, illness, or stressor that automatically defines them as patient.

WINDOW 2: WHAT IS THE ALLEGED CAUSE?

The analysis of apparent symptom causation in Disorders of Simulation is fraught with difficulty. The alleged cause presented by the patient must be examined to determine if it is actually the cause and, if not, whether the presentation of causal misinformation was planned or involuntary, elaborated, or fabricated. It is important to examine the patient's history since, wittingly or unwittingly, the patient may have concealed a prior cause. While not directly related to cause, the symptoms presented by the patient also must be compared with the probable natural history of the problem since whether the symptoms are real, false, or amplified may help distinguish between varieties of causation. Thus, determination of cause is a formidable undertaking in Disorders of Simulation where causes may overlap, preexisting pathology may be concealed, overt symptoms fabricated, and genuine illness inadvertently obscured by the veneer of exaggeration and misstatement. Table 4.2 illustrates the varieties of causation.

Table 4.2
Categories of Apparent Causation

Varieties of Apparent Causation	Alleges a False Cause	Conceals a Past Cause	Presented Symptoms
True Causation	None	None	Typical
Functional Resurgence	None	Unplanned	Typical
Convenient Focus	Unplanned	Unplanned	Exaggerated
False Attribution	Unplanned	Planned	Exaggerated
False Imputation	Planned	Planned	Exaggerated
Event Fabrication	Planned	Planned	False
Illness Induction	Planned	None	Exaggerated

True Causation

Most patients do not suffer from Disorders of Simulation and, therefore, the vast majority will present with usual and customary causes followed by usual and customary symptoms, without any indication of false cause or reason to suspect that simulation has occurred.

Functional Resurgence

A variant of True Causation, Functional Resurgence occurs when seemingly healthy patients suffer gross disability following a minor precipitant, a fact pattern that initially raises the specter of a Disorder of Simulation. This pattern is frequent in cases of preexisting vulnerability where a recent trauma fans the embers of old injury and rekindles the flames of emotional distress. There is neither volitional concealment of the real cause nor report of a false cause.

Case Example 4.3—The Eggshell

An apparently premorbidly healthy patient experienced a minor fender-bender with no physical injury but developed a classic and severe Posttraumatic Stress Disorder (PTSD). He was 50 years old, had been employed for many years as an accounts manager, and was happily married with three children. The patient was grossly distressed but unable to account for the seriousness of his reaction given the minor nature of the accident. However, when the interviewer asked about similar problems, the patient revealed that, 10 years earlier, he had been involved in a very serious automobile accident that caused horrible injury and death to his young son. While the accident was not his fault, he had been driving and felt responsible for his son's death. After the original accident, he experienced many of the symptoms of PTSD. It became apparent that the recent accident opened an old wound so that he experienced a resurgence of prior symptoms, including a fear of driving or even riding in an automobile.

The patient's reaction to a minor stressor with full-blown PTSD seems excessive since *DSM-IV* (p. 424) indicates that the precipitating accident or trauma is invariably major and severe. PTSD rarely, if ever, results from a minimal stressor. However, in an obviously fragile and "psychosocial eggshell" patient such as in the case example above, even a minor accident may bring old memories to the fore, igniting a typical, full-scale, and genuine PTSD. The patient does not allege false cause or intentionally hide the prior trauma; he is often relieved to discover why he reacted so strongly to a seemingly minor precipitant.

Convenient Focus

Convenient Focus is a variety of causation where the alleged cause is false, a null factor, that neither causes the claimed condition nor influences its course but rather provides a stage or backdrop against which the preexisting pathology of the patient may be seen in full illumination. The patient does not plan to intentionally conceal the real causation since it is psychodynamically beneficial that it remain repressed, obscure, and hidden from the self. Although the symptoms are out of proportion to the claimed trauma, exaggeration is not an intentional act but rather a byproduct as the patient unwittingly attributes preexisting pathology to a recent accident, illness, or stressor.

Convenient Focus patients customarily present as emotionally disturbed or "neurotic" since the magnitude of the alleged cause and the degree of symptomatic complaint are out of synchrony and disproportionate to each other. Thus, a minor accident seemingly results in major emotional impairment, a paradox that may be resolved in most cases by adding the patient's enduring premorbid psychopathology into the equation. Because of the apparent "exaggeration" of cause, effect, or cause-and-effect, the patient appears neurotic but is nonetheless bona fide since willful distortion has not occurred. Convenient Focus patients may suffer from varieties of Somatoform Disorder, Psychological Factors Affecting Physical Condition, or similar entities.

The "neuroticism factor" which distinguishes Convenient Focus from simulation has important legal implications. As Lasky (1988) observes, Convenient Focus is nonindustrial in the worker's compensation system and occurs when:

> [T]here is reason to believe that the disability serves a psychological purpose; sometimes because the job events activated a pre-existing psychological conflict or where the paralysis or pain, as the case may be, allows the individual to avoid some undesired activity or get environmental support which cannot otherwise be obtained. We are referring here to conditions sometimes described as "functional overlay." (pp. 68–69)

The notion of Convenient Focus was reviewed in *Power v. I.A.C.* (1966) where the "applicant's demeanor may be sincere, yet his attributions of his problems to his work may constitute an after-the-fact rationalization." The phrase "after-the-fact rationalization" indicates that the mistaken attribution is involuntary and unconscious which serves to distinguish Convenient Focus from Disorders of Simulation. Even though the patient acts without volition and falsely attributes without intention, a disorder due to Convenient Focus is not compensable since its cause does not lie within the workplace and it therefore cannot be attributed to industrial accident, illness, or stress. Swezey (1968) discussed this issue much earlier noting that "an injury may provide an opportunity for latent symptoms to come out, but at the same time not be the cause of them" (p. 119) and cited *Hoskins v. I.A.C.* (1963) in support.

Although neither Convenient Focus nor Functional Resurgence are involved in Disorders of Simulation and both may display "neuroticism," further distinction between them is of considerable interest to the legal system where causation and liability are of great concern. True Causation sometimes occurs in the euphemistic "eggshell plaintiff," the tenuously integrated patient, who was premorbidly functional until the alleged cause led to actual injury (e.g., the PTSD patient noted above). The analogy of the "straw that broke the camel's back" also describes such individuals. Since the defendant must take the plaintiff as he finds him, even a minor accident may cause the emergence of significant and disabling symptoms when it adds to the patient's preexisting pathology. In such instances, both liability and dysfunction (damages) occur.

In Convenient Focus, however, there is no single preexisting or instant trauma that explains the patient's overreaction. Rather, the picture is of a long-standing "neuroticlike" adjustment that conveniently focuses upon the alleged cause and conceals from the patient the real cause: his enduring psychopathology and maladjustment. Thus, there is no cause and effect relationship and, even though there may be significant damages, there is no liability. The disabling symptoms and their putative relationship to an accident, illness, or stressor are no more than a retrospective psychological convenience, a peg upon which to hang the hat of preexisting pathology. Phrased another way, in Convenient Focus, preexisting disability is either "discovered" by the alleged cause or is the result of natural progression of long-standing psychopathology. In neither case does a causal relationship exist between the alleged cause and the symptoms presented.

Convenient Focus cases invariably fall within the "neurotic" spectrum and do not raise the specter of Disorders of Simulation. The patient's pathology is perfectly understandable by reference to traditional psychodynamic thought and diagnostic nomenclature. The patient invariably alleges a false cause but does so unintentionally and concealment of the real cause, the patient's enduring psychopathology, is similarly involuntary, often including involuntary symptom exaggeration.

Case Example 4.4—Lost Prior Life

A 23-year-old-female retail clerk was briefly dazed by a falling box but was never rendered unconscious and had full recall for the event. All medical studies were normal. She not only claimed enduring pain but also absolute memory loss for her entire prior life. However, she had perfect memory

for events occurring after the accident. Postinjury, she did not recognize
family or friends, her house was unfamiliar, she forgot how to drive, did
not know of "wifely duties," was mystified by household chores, and forgot how to cook. She did not recognize a vacuum cleaner, thinking it
might be a clothes rack. Her history revealed severe child abuse and an
extremely unstable, drug abusing, chronically disabled mother. As a child,
she was very isolated and preferred being alone in her room drawing
mythical animals. Before the injury, she began having serious marital
problems with a husband of different ethnicity. Preaccident she was passive around her husband but now became impulsive and assaultive. She
was formerly artistic but now could barely draw a circle or square. She
was right-handed before injury but now claimed ambidexterity (as near a
person can come to a shift in hand dominance). Before the injury she
was "crazy for sex" but now engaged only infrequently. Historically she
was poor in academics but now alleged not only superb skills in geometry
and trigonometry but also simultaneous fluency in Spanish, Hindi, Pun-
jabi, Urdu, and French. Most examiners felt her problems were functional
but the diagnoses ranged from Malingering to Psychogenic Amnesia to
Postconcussive Syndrome.

The dissociative and depersonalized quality of this patient's amnesia was impressive. It obviously served unconscious, ulterior
motives since amnesia held the promise of emotionally extracting
her from an unsatisfactory life situation. It was as if, at the time
of the accident, she threw an internal switch that discontinued
her prior existence and began a new one. She displayed obvious
disturbance in the normally integrative functions of identity and
memory, suggesting a Dissociative Disorder based in long-standing and enduring psychopathology. There were obvious psychodynamic motivations for massive, global amnesia as a "neurotic"
avenue that she could unconsciously travel in the hope of losing
the baggage of emotional distress she had carried for so long.
Despite the apparent loss of 23 years, the patient was not particularly distressed or depressed. She displayed the *la belle indifference*
sometimes seen in patients for whom the symptoms represent
more solution than problem and who are thus unconsciously satisfied.

Indeed, with surgical precision, she quite narrowly but involuntarily excised only the problem areas. She remained unimpaired in language, intellect, and short-term memory while
achieving intrapsychic relief through the dependency fulfillment
of somatic complaint, professions of helplessness as the result of

her lost prior life, and gratifying release of hostility though angry outbursts due to involuntary changes in personality. In this case, understanding her problems in terms of Convenient Focus and a Dissociative Disorder has greater explanatory power than a diagnosis of Malingering or some variety of bizarre Postconcussive Syndrome that was dramatically out of proportion to the injury sustained. The injury was not a substantial contributing cause but rather a passive condition and point of Convenient Focus for the emergence of preexisting pathology.

Her dense retrograde amnesia was actually "unconscious simulation" of mental disability so that the patient could deny and repress long-standing and enduring internal conflicts, anxieties, and life difficulties which would otherwise have been quite distressing to continue to endure. The accident simply allowed the patient to "resolve" ongoing intrapsychic conflict and thus did not lead to accident-induced psychopathology; the accident merely provided a stage for the dramatization of the patient's preexisting psychopathology.

Given the chronic emotional disturbance often associated with Convenient Focus, the emergence of dramatic, exaggerated symptoms is entirely likely. Any illness, injury, or stressor, no matter how minor, may be the point of Convenient Focus and dramatization. However, the causative force is not the accident itself but rather the need for some event, any event, that the patient unconsciously can press into service as an explanation for an unsatisfactory life situation.

False Attribution

The mildest form of spurious causation is the unintentional attribution of a genuine but lifelong pattern of illness or other preexisting problem to a current relatively minor accident, illness, or stressor with purposeful concealment of similar problems in the past and active exaggeration of symptoms. The patient does not present wholly false symptoms since the pathological picture is usually an enduring part of the patient's structure and functioning. However, in False Attribution the alleged cause may be involuntarily dramatized, excessively rationalized on an after-the-fact basis, unconsciously overvalued as an explanation for the patient's failures in life, and protracted and/or exaggerated beyond all reasonable limits set by the expected natural history of similar disorders.

Such patients have invariably experienced an accident, illness, or stressor but unintentionally view this specific, recent event as the cause of long-standing problems and, in the process of doing so, passively but volitionally conceal the real cause. The major difference between Convenient Focus and False Attribution is that, in the latter, hiding the real cause is *volitionally* mediated. Thus, False Attribution implies a Disorder of Simulation because it is associated with a volitional component.

It is typical for such patients to involuntarily underreport their lifelong pattern of pathology and prior symptomatic complaints. On evaluation it often appears that they have planned to take minor liberties with the truth, misrepresented their history, and engaged in petty, self-serving manipulations. That is, in False Attribution patients display a cumulative history where careful review demonstrates a building symptomatic picture such that numerous negative environmental or health traumas form a relatively unbroken chain. The alleged trauma is simply the last link in the chain rather than the chain itself.

Case Example 4.5—My Failures are Your Fault

A recently hired 56-year-old financial officer with ABC Corp. claimed to feel isolated by upper management. She felt humiliated by having to drive an inexpensive company car that she deemed incommensurate with her management status. After 3 years, ABC fired her, alleging poor performance. She subsequently sued for wrongful termination and infliction of emotional distress as well as age and sex discrimination, and being unfairly passed over for promotion. She alleged that her firing caused severe headache, multiple GI problems, sleep disturbance, and emotional devastation. Even 4 years postfiring, she was too distressed to work or attend vocational rehabilitation. Despite vigorous psychotherapy and psychopharmacy her symptoms had "quadrupled." She claimed her firing was a complete surprise but just before being fired, she induced a terminally ill former officer of ABC to sign an undated "letter of agreement" in her favor which she surreptitiously placed in her personnel file. Although she prepared the document on her boyfriend's typewriter, she denied that he, also a disgruntled ex-employee of ABC, helped her and stated that they had never once discussed her suit in 4 years of cohabitation! She also set up luncheon meetings with fellow employees who were slated for deposition although she had had no other contacts with them for the past 4 years. She claimed no prior work, medical, or emotional problems but records revealed serious performance difficulty on two previous jobs and her medical and emotional complaints had existed for at least a decade before employment at ABC. On clinical interview, the patient was melodramatic and angrily fixated on alleged injustices done to her by ABC. She was extraordinarily nervous, agitated, depressed, and tearful as well as very unsteady on her feet with a slow, shuffling gait. She talked slowly in a tremulous voice, intermittently covering her mouth with a handkerchief while engaging in a combination of hyperventilation and aerophagia. The symptoms rapidly abated when the examiner directed her attention elsewhere, when she was unaware of being observed, and when talking with office secretaries and patients in the waiting room. Although she claimed her concentration was grossly impaired, she sat for hours taking paper-and-pencil tests without a sign of difficulty.

This is a case of False Attribution. She unintentionally consigned years of prior vocational difficulties to ABC such that the institution and its executive personnel became the designated but falsely attributed cause of preexisting distress. She had an inflated self-image and unconsciously wished to hold her employers responsible for her own resistance to success. During her last three employments, her failure to ascend the management ladder beyond modest levels relentlessly confronted her with the discrepancy between her inflated sense of capacity and the actual evaluations of her employers. In addition, at age 56, she no longer had the energy to maintain the facade of unrecognized potential.

She unintentionally desired to both save face and obtain a pound of flesh in return for management's failure to recognize her narcissistically inflated sense of innate worth. The company must be at fault; her failures must be due to poor management, communication problems, discrimination, and other institutional difficulties. Thus, as is typical for False Attribution, she alleged that her symptoms increased, she resisted therapeutic treatment, she misrepresented herself on evaluation, she concealed significant prior problems, and she engaged in minor manipulation. She voluntarily exaggerated and displayed long-standing symptoms which she falsely attributed to the alleged cause and protracted her symptoms for over 4 years.

Her case reflects complex psychodynamics and the necessity for differential diagnosis from Convenient Focus. False Attribution occurs only in Disorders of Simulation, falling between bona fide *DSM-IV* (APA, 1994) disorders on one side and Malingering on the other. That is, in False Attribution, patients do not display the relatively full control over allegations of cause that is characteristic of Malingering yet they exert more volition through hiding the past than is associated with the fully unconscious processes of traditional mental disorders. Thus, a considerable amount of self-deception occurs over the alleged cause of the symptoms despite the fact that False Attribution patients are, at the very least, dimly aware that a cogent case can be made for preexisting pathology and causal factors other than those alleged. Nonetheless, the patient's self-view as nonpathological prior to the alleged cause is integral to the patient's psychodynamic structure. False Attribution cases make sense only under the assumption that while hiding the past may be volitional and denial of prior pathology rationalized as "not significant," false causal attribution is as much self-deceptive as other-deceptive.

False Attribution in quite frequent in Compensation Neurosis since ego salving is very important to such individuals. It is rare to nonexistent in Malingering because of the lack of full control over symptomatic complaints and the high "neuroticism" factor evident in the history. Factitious Disorders do not display False Attribution since their pattern is just the reverse with intentionally false allegations of cause.

False Imputation

When the patient *not only* obviously and intentionally alleges that preexisting pathology is the result of a current accident, illness, or stressor *but also* intentionally hides prior causation, False Imputation is suggested. The patient thus purposely encourages the examiner to attribute, fully or partially, a preexisting problem to the alleged precipitant. False Imputation differs from False Attribution since the allegation of cause is just as intentionally false and deceptive as is the concealment of prior pathology. In False Imputation, patients genuinely have symptoms but display great control over the magnitude and frequency of symptomatic complaint.

Thus, in False Imputation, patients engage in *intentional and active* as opposed to passive and unintentional strategies and do not engage in self-deception; the patient is *fully aware* that the presented symptoms cannot be attributed to the alleged cause but rather to some other, preexisting condition. In essence, False Imputation indicates wholesale misallocation of symptoms and differs from the next level, Event Fabrication, only because the patient truly has actual disorder and consequent symptoms. The patient sets about methodically and intentionally planning and devising ways to falsely pass off real symptoms (often volitionally exaggerated) as the result of the alleged cause. Although clear at conceptual levels, the distinction between False Attribution and False Imputation is not always easy in practice and borderline cases require considerable investigation.

Case Example 4.6—Hiding the Past

A 37-year-old male reported enormously negative life changes following a minor burn to his leg. In his suit against the manufacturer of the camping lantern that leaked, "exploded," and resulted in his injury, he claimed serious mental suffering, marital disharmony, loss of consortium, intractable pain, social invalidism, and vocational disability. He vigorously contended, of course, that he had been unimpaired in any of these areas previously. On clinical interview, he presented as having a substantial employment history and no prior mental problems. Yet, careful investigation produced records documenting chronic and serious marital problems, an unstable and erratic lifelong work history, and prior diagnosis of Paranoid Schizophrenia in the military which went into remission but which resulted in ultimate medical discharge. In effect, he had experienced virtually all his current mental symptoms in unchanging fashion for years before the accident.

In this case, the causal connection leaned more toward False Imputation than False Attribution. Although he did genuinely receive a burn to his leg and experienced some pain, it was minor. He also willfully alleged the burn trauma to be the cause of his chronic mental symptoms. The key is in the history. Without question, the patient was aware of his mental problems in the military since he had copies of his medical chart, knew of his prior Paranoid Schizophrenic diagnosis, yet actively withheld and hid this information when directly asked. Upon interview, he denied any outpatient treatment whatsoever but records indicated that, for many months before and after the accident, he and his wife had been active in marital counseling for problems virtually identical to those he claimed as accident-related. Since the patient was not actively schizophrenic and had good reality testing at the time of evaluation, it was impossible to sensibly assert that the residual of this serious but now latent mental disorder rendered him unable to appreciate the falsity of his own contentions. He clearly displayed planned, intentional control over his allegations of cause by contending that long-standing, preexisting problems, of which he was fully aware, were the result of a recent incident.

Perhaps the most telling difference between False Imputation and False Attribution is that no self-deception is either evident or required in order to understand the psychodynamics of a Falsely Imputing patient. In the case above, there was no evidence of psychodynamic necessity to hide prior pathology from the self or deceive the self by holding someone else responsible for his failures in life. Indeed, he was acutely aware of his prior problems and therefore could invoke no psychodynamic mechanism to hide them from himself. Such individuals display considerable planning in manipulating all aspects of their presentation, falsely imputing with full awareness and ascribing real but exaggerated symptoms to a false cause. Of course, most cases of False Imputation are less complicated by preexisting major mental disorder than in the above case but it is important to note that genuine disorder and simulation can coexist despite prohibitions codified in *DSM*.

False Imputation does not occur in Compensation Neurosis since planning to present a false cause is involved. In Factitious Disorder, False Imputation may occur but Event Fabrication and Illness Induction are far more prevalent. In Malingering, however, False Imputation is common where genuine but exaggerated symptoms due to a prior but concealed cause are intentionally attributed to a recent accident, illness, or stressor.

Event Fabrication

Considerably more rare than either False Attribution or False Imputation is Event Fabrication. The patient engages in outright faking of causation by either reporting events that never happened or staging events. For example, a man may make an insurance claim for objects stolen from his home or report a robbery while working at a convenience store. In fact, he pawned the "stolen" goods himself and pocketed the money during a "robbery" that never occurred. Patients may fabricate the symptoms of Posttraumatic Stress Disorder following an accident that never happened, or manufacture symptoms of psychosis presumably resulting from "hallucinogens put in their coffee by military scientists" in order to fake insanity and escape culpability for crime. In these examples, the patient presents with a fabricated cause, ranging from instances of simple false reporting to a staged event.

In Event Fabrication, the patient actively plans to report a false cause and does not engage in self-deception. Not only does the accident, illness, or stressor not occur but also the reported symptoms are patently false. The patient is actually a "healthy" person who presents false symptoms of false illness or trauma irrespective of the alleged cause. Full control over symptom presentation is characteristic. The patient does not have the symptoms, irrespective of how or why he came to claim them. In every way, the patient is fully aware that the presenting complaints are false and, even if they were real, they could not truly be attributed to the claimed cause since, in most cases, the alleged causative event never occurred. Patients who engage in Event Fabrication may present with a broad variety of falsely alleged causes. The nature of the fabricated event ranges from minor manipulation of convenient opportunities to the programmatic creation of an entire fictitious scenario.

Case Example 4.7—The Claim Without a History

A 32-year-old male was standing at a busy intersection in downtown Los Angeles waiting to cross the street. A vehicle driver slammed on the brakes as he realized he was about to run the stop sign. Just then, the patient stepped off the curb, bounced off the right front fender, rolled across the hood, and tumbled to the ground. Although not rendered unconscious, the patient complained of immediate neck and shoulder pain as well as low back and hip pain. He did not go the ER but, later that day, his lawyer arranged examination and treatment by a physician, and he immediately filed a lawsuit. The patient had two prior injuries under similar circumstances, both followed by lawsuits. Several months later, the patient appeared for psychological examination in a cervical collar, claiming severe emotional distress due to chronic and intractable pain that prevented him from working or doing much of anything. However, a surveillance video showed him functioning normally in daily activities without a cervical collar. Investigation revealed that the attorney and physician frequently worked together and had a history of litigating similar accidents where the injuries seemed slight and the claimed damages seemed enormous. Further, a witness said the patient had been standing at the corner for quite some time, saw the car coming too fast, and then darted into the intersection, placing himself in the path of the vehicle.

This patient was down on his luck and in financial trouble. He arranged a classic "medical-legal scam" with an unscrupulous attorney and physician, seeking to defraud the motorist's insurance company of a considerable amount of money. This is, perhaps, the prototypical event when the laity think of Malingering. Of importance is that presentation of symptoms, design of the event, and attribution of cause were fully volitional and orchestrated. Examination of the patient revealed no reason to believe that viewing himself as injured was in any way integral to his self-concept. Event Fabrication is distinguished from False Imputation because there is no prior history of physical or mental symptoms that could be opportunistically pressed into service as the result of the falsely alleged cause. Event Fabrication may obviously occur in Malingering. It is also common in Factitious Disorder where the patient stages or falsely reports events (e.g., seizures) but is rare to nonexistent in Compensation Neurosis. Factitious Disorder by Proxy (False Reporting Subtype) also involves Event Fabrication since the patient may report a fabricated cause of symptoms in another person.

Illness Induction

The rarest and most clinically fascinating form of causation is Illness Induction, the actual creation of physical or mental illness in the self or other. Irrespective of the target, Illness Induction obviously signals virulent levels of psychopathology. Although not invariably the case, many patients who engage in physical illness induction have considerable knowledge of medicine. Some are aware, for example, that the injection of milk subcutaneously leads to a retrenched form of cellulitis and that ingestion of Dicumarol is quite effective in producing gastrointestinal bleeding and hematemesis of unknown origin. With intelligence, imagination, and medical knowledge, Factitious patients may induce a broad range of physical disorders, often at considerable health risk.

It is less certain that the induction of mental disorder requires sophisticated psychological knowledge. Most recorded cases involve patients with very disordered personality organizations or, when they induce illness in others, patients often select very young children, gullible adults, or the defenseless elderly as victims. There is, of course, the rare event where mental illness is presumably falsely induced in the self but which, in the end, turns out to be true emotional disorder. Novels such as Andreyev's (1910) *The Dilemma* suggest that those who diligently work to simulate mental illness may well end up suffering from the disorder they sought to imitate. For example, a patient who is able to successfully fake Paranoid Schizophrenia may actually be displaying, during the phase of active simulation, the prodrome of this serious mental illness. By the time the patient realizes that he is no longer faking but rather genuinely developing the symptoms of the disease, it is too late to reverse course and the patient becomes irretrievably psychotic. Although some clinicians favor this view of pathology, the occurrence of this phenomenon remains a point of considerable dispute and is probably more valuable as a moral parable than as a clinical observation.

In Illness Induction, the patient does not pretend to cause illness but actually produces real pathology so that others will readily interpret it as the product of accident or natural process. Frequently, treating parties find themselves increasingly confounded and confused the more they study the patient's condition. This confusion occurs since patients are often able to invoke the disorder with comparative ease but find it difficult to arrange their activities so that the problem consistently appears to be the product of an identifiable event or disease process. That is, the closer the clinical examination, the more difficult it becomes for caregivers to link the presence of the patient's induced symptoms with naturally occurring and expected antecedent events. Further, patients often present with the same illness on a repetitive basis and the failure of the problem to go into remission with appropriate treatment or the tendency for the illness to recur unexpectedly is not only puzzling but also can be a distinguishing feature of Illness Induction.

In Illness Induction, the misattribution of causation is clearly planned action, just as is the case in Event Fabrication. However, symptoms are actively and purposefully induced in the self or others rather than resulting from naturally occurring pathology. Some researchers hypothesize that sadistic and masochistic elements are involved. However, given the tentative definitions in *DSM-III-R*, Appendix A, Sadistic and Masochistic Personality Disorders, it is probably best to consider these terms as descriptions of behavior rather than diagnoses. The differential diagnostic criteria for sadistic and masochistic personality disorder are in flux and ultimately may not conform to the traditional definitions. Further, the literature on Factitious Disorder, while sometimes referring to masochistic or sadistic *behavior*, does not clearly indicate the presence of underlying Masochistic (Self-Defeating) or Sadistic Personality *Disorder*. This is most particularly true since, in *DSM-IV*, Sadistic and Masochistic Personality Disorders have vanished from the taxonomy altogether.

Illness Induction falls within the province of Factitious Disorder, virtually to the complete exclusion of all other varieties of Disorders of Simulation. With this cautionary note, two subvarieties may be distinguished: Self-Induction and Other-Induction.

Self-Induction occurs when the patient actually induces illness or injury in the self. There is an almost limitless variety of problems that patients may self-induce as illustrated by the extensive listing of synonyms for Factitious Disorders (Glossary Tables 9.2, 9.3, and 9.4). Virtually all psychophysiologic systems are open to assault and patients can be quite ingenious in devising clever ways to inflict suffering upon themselves. Since actual damage and consequent pain result from self-injury—usually on an enduring or repetitive basis—patients who engage in such behavior undoubtedly suffer from a very disordered intrapsychic structure. At times, the patient appears to derive some masochistic enjoyment from suffering despite high levels of vigorous complaint but other psychodynamic factors have also been identified. In Self-Induction, the patient attributes his genuine illness to any cause other than the direct intervention by the patient himself. Thus, the patient presents as ill, damaged, or stressed as the result of extrinsic factors and the patient makes strong attempts to misdirect the examiner's attention toward external events.

Case Example 4.8—I Make Myself Sick

A 30-year-old LVN arrived at a hospital ER. Shortly after ingesting some sleeping pills, she reported seeing long black snakes coming out of faucets and laughing faces in a cup of coffee. Her pupils were dilated, she was disoriented, and wearing both a neck brace and left arm cast secondary to an auto accident. X-rays of her left arm were normal and there was no police record of a car wreck. Her hospital chart revealed six prior hospitalizations over a 5-year period, four for alleged seizure disorder. She was having marital problems and, although referred for psychiatric treatment, she made several ER visits for superficial lacerations and an alleged sexual attack. Further study demonstrated that she had been an outpatient and inpatient in most area hospitals with a litany of similar complaints. She had consulted numerous physicians including ophthalmologists, internists, endocrinologists, orthopedic surgeons, neurosurgeons, and psychiatrists. She was willing to either define herself as psychiatrically or medically sick, or both. (Jamieson, McKee, & Roback, 1979)

Other-Induction occurs when a patient induces real illness in another person who is then presented as the patient. This appears to be a relatively rare phenomenon typically orchestrated by a female parent with her very young child as the target. Since children have limited capacity to resist or independently judge parental directives, the patient with Factitious Disorder by Proxy preys upon this weakness. A few cases have been reported where the patient was elderly and senile, very debilitated, or otherwise lacked the emotional and intellectual skills needed to successfully challenge an abusive guardian.

Case Example 4.9—You Make Me Sick

The divorced mother of a slightly under 2-year-old male brought her son to the ER and reported he was having stomach cramps and continuous vomiting without obvious fever. At first, the mother reported, she felt her son had developed the flu but when he did not show signs of improvement after 2 days, she decided to seek help. Hospital records revealed three prior ER admissions for the same problem within one year and the child did appear dehydrated to ER personnel. He was hospitalized for nearly 2 weeks and received an extended battery of tests. All results were within normal limits but the child continued to suffer intermittently from cramps and vomiting during his hospitalization. A consulting pediatric gastroenterologist was unable to establish a cause. However, nursing personnel noted that the child usually had a relapse whenever he was alone with his mother in the hospital room for an extended time. The consultant suspected Factitious Disorder by Proxy but, when the mother was confronted, she denied any involvement in her child's illness and accused both the doctors and hospital staff of conspiring to protract her son's condition. Eventually, the natural father obtained custody of the child by court order. Within a matter of days, the child recovered without the relapses that were characteristic while under his mother's care.

Table 4.3
Summary of the Window of Alleged Cause

Pathology Level	Categories of Apparent Cause	Malingering	Factitious Disorder	Compensation Neurosis
Minimum	True Causation	No	No	No
⏐	Functional Resurgence	No	No	No
⏐	Convenient Focus	No	No	No
⏐	False Attribution	No	No	Yes
⏐	False Imputation	Yes	Yes	No
↓	Event Fabrication	Yes	Yes	No
Maximum	Illness Induction	No	Yes	No

As Table 4.3 makes clear, True Causation, Functional Resurgence, and Convenient Focus fall within the province of customary mental and physical disorders since none of these varieties involves active intent or volition. Compensation Neurosis patients engage only in False Attribution since the subsequent levels require more intentionality and volition that the psychodynamics of Compensation Neurosis will allow. Both Malingering and Factitious Disorder patients may engage in False Imputation and Event Fabrication but only the latter sinks to the depth of pathology implied by actual Illness Induction in the self or other.

WINDOW 3: REPORTING THE SYMPTOMS

Reported Symptoms refers to the accuracy of the catalog of complaints presented by the patient. Accurate assessment depends, in part, upon the availability of a reasonably accurate patient report of symptoms. Most mental diagnoses, according to *DSM-IV*, require that the patient's catalog of complaints be taxonomically compared with the symptomatic criteria and subcriteria associated with each disorder. Since patients rarely present their symptoms in technical terms, the evaluator must rely upon the art of clinical interviewing to exhaustively elicit and fully describe the symptoms without leading, prompting, or prejudicing the patient.

When a patient presents his case in terms that are technically correct, the examiner should be alert to possible simulation. A modestly intelligent nonprofessional is certainly capable of "self education" by reading the *DSM-IV* description of Posttraumatic Stress Disorder, for example, and thereafter describing his symptoms in ways that are suspiciously similar. In other cases, the patient may have been "therapeutically educated" by prior treatment or evaluative contact with mental health professionals, attorneys, or sophisticated friends.

The detection of invalid symptom reporting is a difficult task because, in clinical interview, there is no source of information other than the patient's statements. Of course, the claimed symptoms may be compared with those customarily expected following the type of injury, illness, or stressor alleged but there are always exceptions to the rule. The pattern of complaints may be examined for internal consistency although there are exceptions in this area as well, and no diagnostic system can fully account for all possible symptomatic variations. The patient's clinical presentation and behavior may be examined for conformity with or variation from expectations for nonsimulating patients, but serious questions may also be raised about the validity of this approach as well. Despite the drawbacks, all of these approaches are currently popular (Hall & Pritchard, 1996; Rogers, 1988).

The Spectrum of Distortion in Symptom Reporting

Sharpening versus Leveling

Minor sharpening and leveling of symptomatic complaint is natural and some inaccuracy invariably occurs when patient and doctor communicate about reported complaints. The process of symptomatic reporting is inherently unstable since complaints vary from day to day, different clinicians follow varying examination formats, and patients can never be truly objective when reporting their symptoms as the result of accident, illness, or stress. The reporting of some symptoms may be slightly *sharpened* because they represent areas of great personal concern and emotional investment while, in others areas, equally valid complaints may be *leveled* since they seem relatively unimportant to the patient. Different patients may also differentially weight some complaints based upon their experiential history and psychodynamic structure. The distinguishing features of sharpening and leveling is a catalog of symptomatic complaints generally proportionate to the trauma, the absence of obvious emotional weighting, frankness with regard to both positive and negative historical events, and a quality of nondefensive openness.

Minimization versus Maximization

Minimization is the failure to fully acknowledge and report current symptoms or complaints. Minimization occurs when the patient's report reduces the nature, scope, intensity, frequency, or magnitude of symptoms that either exist at present or truly existed in the past. To qualify as minimization, the attenuation of reported symptoms must be greater than the minor variations inherent in the natural sharpening and leveling (give and take) of the clinical interview in doctor–patient relationship. *Maximization* also refers to the reporting of current or past symptoms but in enhanced rather than attenuated form. Maximized reporting of symptoms leads the clinician to believe that the patient suffers from problems in significantly greater magnitude than may normatively be expected to result from the trauma in question. Maximization is identical to the *DSM-IV* notion of "complaints disproportionate to objective medical findings" or the observed ability of the patient to function psychologically. Therefore, with tongue only slightly in cheek, minimization should be known as "health disproportionate to known pathology." Both minimization and maximization are congruent with the defensive operations of many patients such as the Somatoform Disorders, some Anxiety Disorders, and other traditional diagnostic categories. Minimization and maximization may also occur in Factitious Disorders and Compensation Neurosis but are unlikely to occur in Malingering.

Concealment versus Creation

At the extreme, *concealment* occurs when the patient takes care to hide selected current or past symptoms. In order to qualify as concealment, it must be entirely clear that the patient could have answered the examiner's question faithfully but chose—through an act of intention—to avoid doing so. *Creation* is the opposite of concealment and occurs when the patient wholly fabricates past or current symptoms. In essence, not only are nearly all the reported complaints false but also the patient is aware of his wrongful presentation. Thus, while minimizing and maximizing may be the product of psychodynamic ambivalence and conflict, creation and concealment are solely the product of intent and deception.

Table 4.4

Summary of the Spectrum of Distortion in Reported Symptoms

Spectrum of Reported Symptoms	Range of Distortion		
	Positive .... Accurate .... Negative		
Candid Reporting		Sharpening...................... Leveling	
Defensive Reporting		Maximizing ....Minimizing	
False Reporting	Creating .... Concealing		

The Dimension of Reported Complaints

Deception versus Openness

The dimension of reported complaints requires a biaxial approach with deception versus openness on one axis and repression versus insight on the other (Figure 4.1). The axis of deception versus openness is an external variable, which refers to the manner in which the patient presents his catalog of symptomatic complaints to the clinician. That is, it is a measure of the degree to which the patient directly relates versus camouflages his truly perceived symptomatic complaints. In *deception*, the patient's presentation is intentionally disingenuous seeking to obscure, conceal, becloud, and confuse the clinician such that the patient's self-concerned feelings, simulatory thoughts, and ulterior motivations remain invisible and undetected. In contrast, *openness* indicates a forthright presentation with no intent to maximize or minimize symptomatic complaints although patients may unintentionally do so depending upon their level of repression. Obviously, deception versus openness is a continuous rather than a dichotomous variable with a range of intermediate positions where the patient reports normally, neither bent upon deception nor willing to be completely open.

Repression versus Insight

Repression versus insight is also on a continuum—approximately orthogonal to deception versus awareness—describing the degree to which the patient is aware of his own underlying psychodynamic machinations (Figure 4.1). When *repression* is in full force the patient "is unable to remember or be cognitively aware of disturbing wishes, feelings, thoughts, or experiences" (*DSM-III-R*, APA, 1987, p. 394). In extreme cases, this tendency may extend as far as the actual distortion of reality inherent in the mechanism of denial. When repression is less pervasive, the patient may have partial awareness and thus occupy the more normal central portion of the continuum, sometimes acknowledging his own motivations and sometimes hiding them from himself. *Insight*, of course,

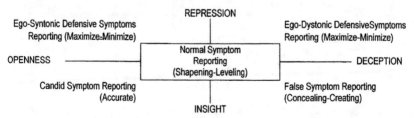

Figure 4.1. Reported Complaints Distributed Along the Axes of Repression-Insight and Deception-Openness

is the anchor point at the opposite end of the spectrum and indicates significant "knowledge of the factors operating to produce the symptoms" (Campbell, 1981, p. 324). Patients with insight know what they are doing and why, they are cognizant of their action, and can identify the forces that drive their behaviors. The four varieties of reported symptoms each represent a unique combination of repression-insight, deception-openness, and range of distortion. Interestingly, while "repression" was defined in the glossary of *DSM-III-R*, it has been removed—without definition—to "Criteria Sets and Axes Provided for Further Study" of *DSM-IV*. The definition of "insight" is nowhere stated in *DSM-III-R* or *DSM-IV*.

Five Varieties of Reported Symptoms

Normal Symptom Reporting

It is difficult for patients to be completely accurate and invariant in their recounting of problems on each occasion of evaluation. For a number of legitimate reasons, minor variation in the catalog of reported complaints is quite common as the result of sharpening or leveling. For example, patients may simply forget to mention minor symptoms or, depending upon the psychodynamics of their unconscious processes, temporarily level the importance of some symptoms unless queried in a direct and pointed fashion. The patient may involuntarily present other problems in slightly sharpened form in order to ensure that the doctor understands the seriousness of the problem. Patients may also use different descriptors for their pain, disability, or distress on different occasions depending upon the natural waxing or waning of their condition, on each occasion of interview, in combination with the examination procedures used by different clinicians.

Minor variations are entirely human and fall within the range of Normal Reporting. Slight variation does not suggest that patients have violated good faith in communication of their distress. Most patients report complaints with only minor sharpening or leveling. They tend to answer the clinician's queries directly, thoughtfully, and with reasonable accuracy, especially if an experienced examiner is interviewing the patient.

Candid Symptom Reporting

When the patient has insight into his complaints, states them faithfully when asked, and when there is no need to deceive the examiner, the patient is not only engaging in openness but also displaying lack of significant repression and self-deception. The patient may or may not prove to have significant emotional problems but, in either case, does not dramatically resist understanding his true state. The patient presents the residua of illness, injury, or stress with fidelity, clarity, and in a fashion that does not suggest an underlying need to shade self-perception or other-perception. Of course, few active mental patients fall into this category since most have not developed such exquisite awareness of their own intrapsychic mechanisms; it they did so, they probably would not be patients. However, effectively treated patients may be found in this quadrant as well as a few particularly psychologically minded and enlightened patients with a broad variety of medical, minor adjustment problems, or desires for personal growth.

Two Varieties of Defensive Symptom Reporting

In defensive reporting, there are clear indications that involuntary and unintentional elements play a considerable role in the presentation of an inaccurate catalog of complaints. This invariably occurs when the patient has true complaints but, for a combination of psychodynamic reasons, maximizes or minimizes them in scope, nature, magnitude, duration, or frequency.

Disorders of Simulation must be distinguished from the two defensive reporting quadrants that contain the usual and customary mental disorders. When the patient's complaints involve high levels of repression and are self-deceptive, the intrapsychic processes involved must be unintentional by definition since repression cannot occur if the patient has insight. Such patients are invariably "neurotic" and engage in either of two varieties of defensive reporting: (1) If others as well as the self must remain unaware of the patient's dynamics, the complaints are *ego dystonic*; (2) if only the self must remain unaware, the complaints are *ego syntonic*. Defensive patients of either variety differentially engage in minimization or maximization depending upon whether acknowledgment of psychological distress is ego syntonic or ego dystonic.

Ego-dystonic Defensive Symptom Reporting

When the notion of mental disorder must remain obscure to both the self and other for psychodynamic reasons, the patient is customarily very defensive and brittle, unable to tolerate the notion that he suffers from psychological disorder and, above all, needs to see himself and be seen by others as emotionally healthy. Therefore, the patient views his problems as palpably medical since the idea of mental distress—now or in the past—is ego dystonic. The patient strongly invokes repression in order to protect his fragile and vulnerable ego structure. These patients are likely to resist psychological or psychiatric evaluation, are largely nondisclosing, and uncooperative by default. Mental examinations are very threatening to such patients, they fear the revelations that may follow scrutiny of their intrapsychic organization, and they are therefore highly defended. Clinical interview, life history, and psychometric testing usually reveal features consistent with a strong need to minimize and conceal—from both the self and others—any possible mental weakness, flaw, or hint of psychopathology. Medical complaints mean medical problems—period; mental distress must be the result of faulty perception by someone else; psychogenesis does not exist.

Generally, ego-dystonic patients minimize the nature and extent of any enduring mental symptoms in favor of maximizing their current and past physical complaints, although a few patients may minimize the totality of their symptomatic presentation. This latter category is most likely to occur amongst populations where the patient finds it psychologically terrifying to acknowledge significant mental disorder. Only to the extent that such patients view psychological problems as the direct result of medical illness or injury can they be induced even to tentatively acknowledge emotional distress. Repression of such magnitude indicates that the patient is hiding his psychopathology from himself and is thus engaging in the defensive operation of minimizing. More commonly, however, ego-dystonic patients unintentionally recast and faithfully report their problems as solely medical—an acceptable form of injury or illness—while minimizing current or past psychological problems.

Case Example 4.10—What Mental Problem?

A 55-year-old male began having financial troubles following his dismissal from the mailroom of a private company. He filed a complaint with the state Labor Relations Board alleging improper personnel procedures on the part of his employer. He sought consultation with his general practitioner for his "medical problems" that included insomnia, weight loss, general malaise, and fatigue. He felt he simply needed medications and was strongly resistive and resentful when his physician suggested referral to mental health. He denied a historical pattern of recurrent depression and vigorously disavowed prior mental problems, although both appeared in frequent but veiled notes in his medical chart. In his view, his firing led to "medical symptoms" but he seemed unaware that his presenting symptoms were those of classic depression: sleep disturbance, weight loss, anhedonia, and reduced libido. Indeed, he was adamant in his view that he was not emotionally distressed and, but for his firing and subsequent financial problems, "I would be just fine."

This patient needed to deceive both himself and others with the statement: "I feel physically ill because I was unjustly treated" rather than the less satisfactory and more revealing: "I feel physically ill because I am mentally ill." While such ego-dystonic patients unintentionally minimize psychological problems, in the past or present, they may maximize their current physical symptoms in order to covertly express their emotional distress. That is, they engage in the self-deception (dissimulation) of emotional health. For the ego-dystonic individual, physical illness or injury is the only acceptable way of expressing mental symptoms or reporting emotional distress. Ego-dystonic patients are very unlikely to engage in Disorders of Simulation.

Ego-syntonic Defensive Symptom Reporting

Some patients engage repression in the quest to obscure their psychodynamics from themselves but have no resistance when others view them as emotionally distressed. Indeed, they may derive significant emotional comfort from the dependency fulfilling and nurturing aspect of medical and psychological attention. The patient's ego, although weakened, is nevertheless sufficient to allow others to see his psychopathology yet simultaneously protect himself from clear understanding of his own psychodynamics. He is not threatened when others view him as emotionally distressed, in fact he is quite open and may even welcome this perception. In such cases, defensive reporting is ego syntonic and the patient embraces mental evaluation with high levels of self-disclosure since the patient is dependent rather than brittle, compliant rather than defensive, and extraversive rather than introversive. Maintenance of psychosocial equilibrium does not require that the examiner be deceived; only that the patient's own psychodynamics remain obscure from himself.

Case Example 4.11—I Seek Only to Deceive Myself

A 49-year-old patient sustained a mild whiplash injury at worst but complained of "posttraumatic headache," a plethora of somatic problems, and emotional distress. She admitted mild headaches before the accident and had no hesitation in acknowledging prior psychotherapy for marital and familial distress as well as personal unhappiness. She and her husband had been having troubles for years and she discussed her emotional upset extensively. She also mentioned a long history of complaints about a broad spectrum of vague somatic ills. However, she claimed that her posttraumatic headaches were worse than ever, even "blinding," and rated them as 11 on a 10-point scale. They were so upsetting that her prior depression had returned, she could not work, and now required excessive amounts of antidepressant medication. Further, any movement could precipitate a headache and she would therefore neither rotate her head to the left or right nor would she tilt her head up or down. The patient produced pictures showing how she placed her telephone on a stack of boxes so she could dial at eye level without neck strain. She carried a special easel to doctor's appointments in the event she might be required to complete some paperwork, and walked very cautiously, turning her whole torso simultaneously as if her spine had been fused from top to bottom. Overall, she strongly identified with the role of the patient, both physically and mentally.

The patient slightly minimized her past problems with cephalgia but maximized her posttraumatic headache so that it was dramatically out of proportion to the objective medical findings and nature of the injury. She was not averse to admitting prior physical and mental health problems; she simply indicated that the recent accident had worsened her prior symptoms. Interestingly, many of her overly controlled and cautious physical behaviors evaporated when she was engrossed in a task or was otherwise distracted, a finding consistent with both her hysteroid–dependent personality dynamics on psychological testing and diagnosis of Somatoform Disorder. While the patient had no insight into the true cause of her reported symptoms, it was not difficult for the clinician to quickly penetrate the thin veneer of Somatoform complaint. Her lifelong physical and mental complaints resulted in significant emotional benefit; they provided an excuse to absolve her of adult responsibilities and solicited nurturance from her husband, repeating the early dependent relationship she enjoyed with her mother. The accident provided an avenue for the patient to justify her enduring ills by externalizing the cause to a recent event.

In general, ego-syntonic defensive reporting predisposes the patient to maximize current medical and psychological problems, often in melodramatic ways. Very dependent patients may also emphasize past problems—whether medical or psychological—in order to impress the examiner with the desperateness of their condition and their sorrowful plight. Ego-syntonic patients are often fragile, "egg-shell" cases where the patient finds it psychologically congruent to acknowledge preexisting deficits since the specter of mental and/or physical illness is compatible with the patient's self-percept. Their underlying psychodynamic structure requires fulfillment of enduring unmet dependency and the fact that others may see them as having significant mental problems is not threatening. Ego-syntonic reporting may occur in both Factitious Disorders and Compensation Neurosis.

False Symptom Reporting

Truly false reporting differs from defensive reporting because the patient creates symptoms that do not exist, or enormously exaggerates symptoms that do exist. They may also conceal chronic past problems in the interest of dramatizing their current complaints. Not only does the healthy patient create symptoms and pathology and the pathological patient conceal ill-health, but also the patient's psychodynamics do not require that these misrepresentations be unintentional or involuntary. The patient therefore willfully distorts significant aspects of their status, seeking to mislead the examiner but not the self.

It is crucial to diagnosis in Disorders of Simulation that candid reporting and the two types of defensive reporting be distinguished from false reporting. Unfortunately, only a process of elimination comes close to making such a distinction. That is, when candid, ego-dystonic and ego-syntonic defensive reporting can be ruled out or seem highly unlikely, all that remains is false reporting. However, exclusion is never as certain as inclusion. Demonstrating the absence of condition A is not the same as demonstrating the presence of condition B unless the entire universe consists only of conditions A and B and the differential diagnostic process for detecting condition A is infallible.

Detection of false symptom reporting is difficult because there are rarely any objective or visible signs on clinical interview. Concealment and creation are wholly internal operations and only the patient knows whether he is engaging in intentional misreporting. Thus, based upon the catalog of patient complaints during a single, relatively brief office visit, it is very hard to determine if false reporting has occurred. Across time, however, the patient's self-reported level of dysfunction may be erratic with dramatic presentation in the evaluator's office but far lesser levels of complaint under other environmental circumstances when there is no "official" medical inquiry. It is difficult to maintain consistency when false reporting requires contact with multiple evaluators and attendance at several evaluations sessions. By comparing the patient's current presentation with statements of complaint to other evaluators on prior occasions, sometimes it is possible to detect gross inconsistency. Patients may also present their complaints in markedly inconsistent fashion across multiple evaluations with the same examiner, concealing or creating more complaints on some occasions than on others. The structured interview techniques advocated by Rogers (1988), Hall and Pritchard (1996), and others are of immeasurable assistance in detecting false reporting.

While it is sometimes possible to independently demonstrate that the patient has been untruthful through review of records or reference to other outside sources, false reporting should not be assumed unless and until it can also be demonstrated that neither type of defensive reporting applies. If the psychodynamic factors of sharpening and leveling or minimizing and maximizing can be reasonably demonstrated to account for the patient's presentation, then it is improper to suggest that the patient is engaging in false reporting. This requirement exists because the critical feature that distinguishes false reporting from all other varieties of symptomatic complaint is overt, intentional, volitional concealment or creation of complaints in the absence of true illness, injury, or stress. In false reporting the patient never misleads himself but seeks only to mislead the examiner through concealment or creation. Concealment occurs when the patient clearly and deliberately hides evidence of past and concurrent symptoms, inducing the examiner to believe that the presented symptoms are the patient's only problem. Thus, a patient may allege serious neck problems as the result of a whiplash injury while concealing the fact that he has had serious cervical pathology for years.

Technically, pure concealment is a form of dissimulation but the motivations are likely to be quite different when dissimulation occurs in the context of Disorders of Simulation. For example, some psychotics may seek to conceal their mental disorder from others because they wish to view themselves and have others view them as nonpathological. Even under circumstances where it would obviously be a step in the direction of enlightened self-interest to acknowledge mental disorder, the patient may hide their mental state from the evaluator and, if in prison, their own attorney as well.

Concealment of psychopathology is not only more prevalent than creation (Diamond, 1956) but also the motivational structure, when symptom concealment occurs in isolation, is very much different from when it occurs as the handmaiden of creation. That is, in Disorders of Simulation, concealment of some symptoms allows fabricated symptoms to stand out in bold relief against a background allegedly free of prior or concurrent problems. When symptom creation is involved, a Disorder of Simulation is invariably present but the reverse in not equally true; concealment may occur in simulation or dissimulation.

In symptom creation, the patient clearly and deliberately reports nonexistent symptoms of an alleged illness, injury, or stressor. It is important to distinguish creation from sharpening and maximization since not only do these latter two varieties of reported complaint involve truly perceived illness, injury, or stress but also some degree of repression. That is, sharpening involves no more than normal symptom enlargement while maximization is unintentional exaggeration. Creation, however, requires full intent.

Case Example 4.12—The Illusion of Injury

A 31-year-old day laborer worked for a construction company, helping to lay carpet in a large office building nearing completion. After several hours on the job, he complained of headache, dizziness, joint pain, extreme fatigue, ringing in his ears, and vomiting. He stated that he had accidentally spilled carpet adhesive on himself and alleged the fumes were making him ill. However, none of his coworkers had similar complaints and some had worked with the adhesive for years. At the ER, his examination was within normal limits but his symptoms continued. He was referred to a toxicologist who saw him immediately and conducted a series of tests. All results were within normal limits. Although off work for several years, the records illustrated that he complained of an increasing number of symptoms, eventually culminating in alleged visual distortion, loss of balance, parasthesias in all four extremities, sexual impotence, and memory impairment. A variety of treatments, including chelation therapy, were tried without success and, after many failed consultations, notes regarding "psychogenesis" and "functional overlay" began to appear in his chart. He claimed to be totally and completely disabled in his suit for occupational injury. On neuropsychological testing, he obtained impossibly low scores and his MMPI reflected flagrant pathology that was incompatible with living independently and caring for himself. Yet, he attended his appointments, managed his own affairs, and was able to respond satisfactorily in a complex medicolegal deposition.

It is possible that the day laborer was mildly affected by toxic fumes initially but it seems likely that he took opportunistic advantage of an occupational situation and thereafter began to report false symptoms. Other workers, who had been on the job for years, were asymptomatic. His chronic complaints were not linked to any findings of medical pathology and rather than following a course of recovery, he worsened as the months passed. His remarkably preserved ability to experience "instant remission" when dealing with any aspect of his legal case was very suspicious. His inconsistent picture led to the request for mental examination where his deplorable performance on a variety of psychological tests was dramatically out of keeping with self-maintaining, outpatient, independent existence. False symptom reporting is frequently found in Malingering and Factitious Disorder while Compensation Neurotics are far more likely to engage in ego-syntonic reporting.

Table 4.5
Summary of the Window of Reported Complaint

Pathology Level	Categories of Reported Complaint	Malingering	Factitious Disorder	Compensation Neurosis
Minimum	Candid Reporting	No	No	No
⌶	Defensive Ego Dystonic	No	No	No
↓	Defensive Ego Syntonic	No	Yes	Yes
Maximum	False Reporting	Yes	Yes	No

As Table 4.5 illustrates, fully candid reporting is not associated with simulation although, in some cases, only minor misrepresentations of reported complaints may occur if the patient focuses upon distorting his presentation in another Window of Opportunity. Only Malingering and Factitious Disorders readily engage in False Reporting which is fully under patient control although these Disorders of Simulation may also occur without flagrant creation or concealment. For example, Malingering may occur not because the patient has falsely *reported* symptoms but rather because he falsely *attributes* genuine symptoms to an unrelated cause. Ego-dystonic reporting is very unlikely to occur in any Disorder of Simulation. Ego-syntonic reporting may be associated with Compensation Neurosis and Factitious Disorder because both of these diagnoses characteristically require that at least some portion of the patient's psychodynamics remain hidden from himself.

BEHAVIORAL ORCHESTRATION: THE FIRST OF THREE AXES

The three Windows of Opportunity outlined in this chapter are summarized in Table 4.6.

One immediate question is, of course: "How many of the above factors make the diagnosis of Simulation?" The short answer is "none" because Simulation should never be diagnosed

Table 4.6

Behavioral Orchestration Associated with Axis 1: Part A—Windows of Opportunity

Windows of Opportunity	Behavioral Orchestration Associated with		
	Malingering	Factitious Disorders	Compensation Neurosis
The Identified Patient is	Self or Self-and-Other	Self or Other	Self
The Alleged Cause is	False Imputation Event Fabrication	False Imputation Event Fabrication Injury to Self Injury to Others	False Attribution
The Reported Symptoms are	False Reporting	False Reporting Ego syntonic	Ego syntonic

based solely upon simple patient interview. While assessment of symptom presentation in various Windows of Opportunity is critical, as can be seen from Table 4.6, there is sufficient overlap between the types of Simulation that even careful analysis is not adequate to differentially separate one disorder from another.

The long answer is "it depends" because other variables must be assessed in order to accurately distinguish Disorders of Simulation. It is therefore important to investigate not only the three remaining "windows" under Behavioral Orchestration but also the two remaining axes (motivation and personality pathology) in order to fully understand the dynamics of simulation, the varieties of pathology involved, and the differential diagnostic issues. As is usually the case, diagnosis does not hinge upon one index but upon several. It is important to resist the temptation to make immediate diagnoses based upon a simplified view of a complex topic.

In short, because of the ease with which patients may exaggerate their report of symptoms, the clinician must make additional observations. In order to validate the patient's reported symptoms, other sources of information are critical such as performance on formal testing, response to treatment, life history, review of records, and statements from other informants.

5

Axis I: Behavioral Orchestration Part B: Reporting Obtained Data

> The more we learn about mind and brain, the less we
> blame the patient for pain.

Patient behavior during active evaluation and treatment is the second half of the axis of Behavioral Orchestration. It is difficult to detect simulation in the typical free-form interview but much more likely in a highly structured clinical interview or with specialized psychometric techniques. Rogers (1988) and the various contributors to his edited work rely strongly upon the structured clinical interview for the detection of Malingering and deception. The interview is certainly essential in the evaluation of any patient and is important in uncovering Simulation. However, the clinician should also direct strong attention toward process psychological testing, interview with collateral informants, careful review of accumulated records, and interdisciplinary consultation as well as motivation and personality pathology. Like part A, Reporting Obtained Data involves assessment in three sections, each constituting an individual Window of Opportunity where Simulation may occur.

WINDOW 4: DEMONSTRATING THE SYMPTOMS

Symptom Control

Symptom control is conceptually similar to the issue of Reporting the Complaints addressed in the prior chapter (Window 3). However, symptom control is behaviorally distinct since it involves the actual *demonstration* of symptoms rather than *reporting* of symptomatic complaint. For example, when the patient states "I have short-term memory loss since the accident," he is reporting a symptom. In contrast, when the same patient functions poorly on instruments designed to assess his memory, he demonstrates actual memory impairment. The *demonstration* of a memory deficit upon clinical assessment—whether organic or functional—is a different matter from the simple *claim* of dysfunction. Further, when deficits are functional, they invariably require orchestration in their design and display through conscious or unconscious processes.

Conscious versus unconscious processes are concepts that have been part of psychology since the early 20th century, but they are too vague at operational levels to be of much use in evaluating the subtleties of Behavioral Orchestration. It is somewhat easier to conceptualize and assess the processes involved in Simulation as being the product of planning and action. In words borrowed from the legal profession, planning may be either intentional or unintentional while action may be either volitional or involuntary.

Intentional refers to the ideational process in planning behavior, much as an author writes the lines for a play. The playwright has an idea to convey and intentionally sets about mentally creating literary circumstances or situations that illustrate his point. The play does not have to be performed for the author to have engaged in the intentional, willful process of creation.

Unintentional processes occur in everyday life where the individual experiences unplanned feelings and impulses of the moment. While an individual's psychodynamic structure sets broad limits upon his perceptions, his perceptions are for the most part spontaneous and unplanned. Away from his writing desk, the playwright experiences emotions of the moment without forethought or intending to do so even though, at a later date, he may draw upon these experiences to craft intentional illusion in one of his plays.

Volitional refers to action itself as opposed to simply thinking about or planning action. Actors do not plan scripts but rather interpret them through the ability to simulate feelings and actions that the actor may not, at the moment, truly experience.

When they are successful, they seduce us into viewing their expressions as spontaneous, unplanned expressions of human action. Thus, they act but do not plan and therefore only express volitional behavior; intent belongs to the playwright.

Involuntary action is analogous to an actor off stage where his behaviors and reactions are not constrained by carefully crafted words of the playwright's art. He is likely to act—by timing and expression—automatically, reflexively, spontaneously, and genuinely. As Figure 5.1 illustrates, if the notions of intention and volition are crossed, each quadrant illustrates a different arrangement of planning and action that, taken together, compose human interaction.

Figure 5.1. Traditional Concept of Consciousness Distributed Along the Axes of Intention and Volition

The Intentional–Volitional quadrant is associated with consciously derived activity, customarily described as rational and logical, where the individual is aware of his plans and responsible for his actions. The diagonally opposite quadrant, Unintentional-Involuntary, is the familiar province of the psychological unconscious where the patient does not willfully plan and produces behavior that is spontaneously generated. All this is quite clear and conventional. However, the remaining two quadrants defy simple categorization into conscious and unconscious processes. Mental health disciplines have only hinted at the nature of the Intentional–Involuntary quadrant, assigning to it solely the peculiar diagnosis of Factitious Disorder where the behaviors are intentionally planned but the plans are acted upon in a driven and compulsively involuntary manner. The last quadrant, Unintentional–Voluntary, is largely ignored by mental health professionals although some authors have hinted at the existence of intermediate states between full conscious Simulation on the one hand and fully unconscious processes on the other. For example, Travin and Protter (1984) proposed a "Mixed-Deceptive" category where the patient's symptoms are partly intentional-volitional and partially unintentional-involuntary.

The legal profession, however, has long recognized the need to address the two quadrants that seem to be of so little concern to psychology. In the area of insanity two landmark decisions—M'Naughten (1843) and *People vs. Drew* (1978)—demonstrated that not all behavior can be readily categorized as either fully conscious or fully unconscious (Figure 5.2).

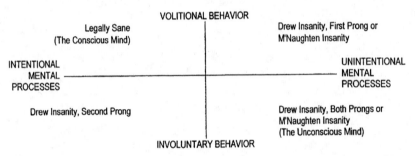

Figure 5.2. Legal Sanity Distributed Along the Axes of Intention and Volition

Under M'Naughten insanity, a defendant may act volitionally but without intent and thus could be found insane if: "at the time of the act, the party accused was laboring under such a defect of reason, from disease of the mind, as *not to know* the nature and quality of the act he was doing, or, if he did know it, that the *did not know* he was doing what was wrong" (emphasis added).

The M'Naughten decision acknowledged that an individual may act wrongly and volitionally, *without intent*. That is, under the M'Naughten rule, insanity is a cognitive matter where individuals may act in ways that are dangerous or illegal without intending to do wrong.

The Drew decision accepted M'Naughten as the first prong of a two-part, disjunctive test of insanity and added a second prong—involuntary behavior. Under Drew, the defendant could also be insane if "as a result of mental disease or defect, he *lacks substantial capacity . . . to conform his conduct* to the requirements of the law'' (emphasis added). Drew was an important decision since it addressed the notion of wrongful, *involuntary action* despite awareness on the part of the defendant that what he was doing was wrong. Although Drew is not now part of the insanity test in most states, the decision is important because it acknowledged the distinction between intention and volition as a basic factor involved in human action. This distinction is quite relevant to Disorders of Simulation. Just as intention is distinct from volition in examples from the theater and courtroom, this same distinction applies to symptom control in Disorders of Simulation.

THE DIMENSIONS OF SYMPTOM CONTROL

Symptom design indicates the degree of awareness of *intent* displayed by the patient in symptom engineering (type, elaboration, intricacy, knowledge required), ranging from unplanned to premeditated. An important consideration in symptom control is the sophistication of deception, which involves the patient's knowledge base regarding the simulated disorder and, indirectly, his or her cognitive level. Intellectual capacity can be influential in symptom design; patients with low intellectual capacity are limited to relatively unsophisticated fabrication strategies while brighter individuals may simulate symptoms ranging from simple and unelaborated to highly complex.

When symptom design is simplistic, the patient presents with a disorganized symptom collection that is not consistent and often makes little medical or psychological sense. Symptom design is little more than extreme exaggeration of an existing or past condition filled with vagaries and simple failures to respond in a timely or appropriate fashion. It may also reflect simulation of conditions overheard in discussions from other patients but not experienced first hand. At somewhat more sophisticated levels, patients may learn from various doctor visits to produce symptom patterns that emulate complex and legitimate medical conditions with increasing consistency. Rarely, some patients engage in independent research while others are relatively well educated or experienced in health care fields and therefore able to very

believably simulate disease or disorder. A few patients have sufficient cognitive capacity and knowledge to fabricate a consistent,
technically correct symptom pattern with great fidelity but, for
most, high verisimilitude is an arduous task unless they are well
educated in medical–psychiatric–psychologic areas.

For example, patients with Factitious Disorder are amongst
the most crafty and sophisticated of symptom fabricators. Quite
commonly, Factitious patients have detailed medical knowledge,
present with textbook histories of disease onset and course, and
alter their physiology by injection, ingestion, or trauma with as
much misdirection as a magician. Such exquisite symptom engineering requires substantial knowledge and planning, procure-
ment of necessary materials, forethought in methods of secreting
contraband, systematic development of skill in the use of some
instruments, and the like. When the patient actually performs
according to his deceptive plan, the element of intentionality
is clearly evident in well-blueprinted, refined symptom design.
Obviously, clever symptom engineering is highly planned and
must be partly intentional.

The sophisticated symptom design of the patient with Factitious Disorder stands in sharp contrast to the naive and outrage-
ously simple fabrications of the Ganser Syndrome sufferer, for
example. It does not take much engineering or premeditated wit
to reply that dogs have five legs or that it is dark out when it is
light. An artless, naive mental set to reply in opposite or near-
miss fashion reflects little in the way of significant design effort
and is likely to be marginally intentional or unintentional in
nature.

Simulating patients display a broad range of symptom design
capacity ranging from the depths of naive blundering to the
heights of sublime calculation and premeditation. While patients
of normal to superior intellectual capacity and knowledge may
present with great sophistication, they do not necessarily do so;
it is not true that intelligence correlates with the level of planfulness. Rather, it is simply true that the variance in symptom sophistication is broader for intelligent and knowledgeable patients
than for the dull and uninformed.

Symptom display refers to the degree of *volition* in actual behavioral presentation (timing, intensity, frequency, and duration)

independent of planfulness, and ranging from complete lack of control to fully volitional symptom production. For example, the Factitious Disorder patient is, by definition, compulsively unable to refrain from symptom display and often simulates under circumstances that a prudent Malingerer would avoid. The Factitious patient does not simply desire to be caught but rather cannot not simulate. Thus, although symptom design may be intentional, symptom display is automatic, compulsively driven, and involuntary. Malingerers, however, retain the ability to produce symptoms volitionally, choosing to simulate at times that, in their judgment, seem most opportune and prudent.

Choosing when to display symptoms is always risky and the patient may or may not choose wisely. If the patient's timing is off, others may discover his Simulation but, if he calculates accurately, the symptoms may pass muster as genuine. Patients with complex, volitional symptom display demonstrate considerable sophistication in precisely organizing a pattern tailored to meet the circumstances. However, voluntariness of symptom display does not require that the patient accurately forecast the proper moment, intensity, frequency, or duration of Simulation; it requires only that he attempt to do so in ways that demonstrate voluntary symptom display.

Symptom display is independent of symptom design and it is the task of the clinician to discriminate between four types of combined symptom design and display. The task is made somewhat easier by placing intentional and unintentional symptom design (the mental processes) on one axis approximately orthogonal to volitional and involuntary symptom display (the actual behaviors) on the other axis (Figure 5.3).

Varieties of Symptom Control

Reflexive Control

When design is unintentional and display is involuntary, the patient exerts no direct symptom control. This level involves the traditional diagnoses such as Somatoform, Posttraumatic, Dissociative Disorders, Psychological Factors Affecting Physical Condition, and other customary psychodynamic conditions. Disorders

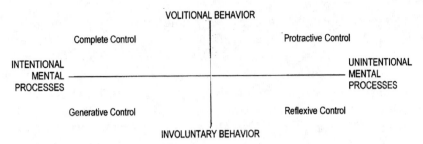

Figure 5.3. Symptom Control Distributed Along the Axes of Design and Display

of Simulation do not fall within the Unintentional–Involuntary quadrant since neither design nor display is under direct control. Rather, this quadrant involves the familiar psychodynamic forces that generate most mental disorders. Reflexive Control is the anchor point for Disorders of Simulation that reside in the remaining quadrants.

Detection of the Unintentional–Involuntary type of symptom control is a familiar task for mental health professionals. Historical information, review of records, clinical interview, and psychometric assessment all point to a well-known, coherent diagnostic entity. There is evidence of unconscious conflict resolution, tendencies toward psychopathologic repetition or perpetuation, customary defense mechanisms, symptoms with symbolic value, and a patient history that supports the presence of familiar mental disorder. Indeed, since Disorders of Simulation are relatively rare, it is wise to assume each patient unintentionally designs and involuntarily displays symptoms until proven to the contrary.

Some observers have suggested that, in cases where the legal system is involved, just the opposite assumption should be made (Meloy, 1989). That is, the clinician should assume Simulation is present until the patient proves his genuineness. The problem with this approach is threefold. First, it requires proof of the null hypothesis and it is obviously much more difficult to demonstrate that a patient is not doing something than to prove that he is doing something. Second, it requires the unsettling assumption that the patient is "guilty until proven innocent," a philosophy that runs contrary to Western notions of justice and fair play.

Third, even in forensic circumstances, the rate of simulation is low, no more than 10 to 20% (Mills & Lipian, 1995). To automatically assume the presence of Simulation flies in the face of base-rate statistics.

Generative Control

When Generative Control occurs symptom design is intentional and the patient displays planning and intention in design but no volition in symptom display. Factitious patients fall into this category, displaying exquisite intentional control over symptom design with symptom display compulsively driven, involuntary, and automatically actuated. While the patient intentionally plans his symptoms, his symptoms are not necessarily free of symbolic value and true illness may coexist. It is the artisanship and complexity involved in engineering patently false symptoms or elaborating true symptoms that indicates thoughtful design processes. The patient must develop symptoms so that they either cleverly simulate genuine illness or seem fascinatingly bizarre in sufficient measure to repetitively engage the concern of health professionals.

While the patient may plan and blueprint his symptoms, actual symptom display waxes and wanes according to fluctuating motivational levels and environmental need/press, but not in a fashion that suggests controlled, prudent selection of the circumstances or timing. The clinician confronts the paradox of calculated symptom design yet impulsive, compulsive, driven, automatic, and inveterate symptom display that seems wholly unconsidered, unplanned, and outside volitional control. The Generative patient feels obliged to act upon his plans and thus displays symptoms under circumstances and conditions that a prudent Malingerer would avoid.

Case Example 5.1—I Can't Help It

A 45-year-old female ambulance driver was hospitalized for complaints of generalized bleeding and menorrhagia. The problem had been present for several years and, during that time, she required several transfusions and had even undergone laparotomy when no etiology was detected by less invasive tests and procedures. Her physician wondered about possible ingestion of coumadinlike compounds but her plasma analysis was negative. During the course of several weeks of hospitalization, the nursing staff witnessed several bleeding episodes and, on one occasion, anticoagulants were present in her blood analysis. When confronted, she denied taking any medications other than those prescribed but the medical staff was convinced that she was surreptitiously ingesting anticoagulants. The staff arranged to send her to the lab for X-rays the next time she had a bleeding episode so that they could search her room. Dicumarol was discovered in the back of one drawer and the patient, when asked, insisted that she thought the medication was simply a mild antianxiety drug. She could not explain how Dicumarol had gotten into a bottle labeled as Xanax. After the staff confronted the patient, the frequency of bleeding episodes decreased but continued intermittently, further reinforcing the presumption of willful ingestion. The staff assumed that she had another "stash" in her room that they had simply failed to discover.

In this case, the patient continued to create symptoms even when it threatened discovery. A prudent simulator would have avoided detection by ceasing self-administration, at least while under scrutiny in the hospital, attempting to divert attention and suspicion elsewhere. However, this Factitious patient was compulsively unable to refrain from inducing bleeding, demonstrating that she did not have voluntary control over symptom display.

Protractive Control

When a patient voluntarily displays symptoms that he has not intentionally designed, Protractive Control has occurred. At first glance, this appears impossible since design seems to be a prerequisite for display. However, the unintentional–volitional type of symptom control occurs quite frequently in patients who exaggerate or prolong genuine injury. That is, rather than being manufactured, the nature of the patient's current symptomatic presentation is defined by the original trauma, injury, or illness. Thus, little to no intentional symptom design occurs since the symptoms are congruent with the original cause. After the trauma has healed or resolved to low levels, however, the patient continues to display his symptoms—perhaps with some unintentional exaggeration. That is, the patient perpetuates his symptoms beyond reasonable limits and the overall effect is of genuine symptoms that fail to go into remission.

In some retrenched cases, the symptoms actually seem to become worse as time passes. Actually, as the true symptoms decline, the patient "makes up the difference" through unintentional replacement, which leads to two curious phenomena: dramatization and instant remission. *Dramatization* is prevalent because it is much easier for the patient to remember the type of original symptoms experienced than their actual intensity. This is particularly relevant when, beneath the facade of voluntary display, the true symptoms have either remitted or reached a stable, low level. In order to be sure that observers understand the seriousness of his condition, the patient involuntarily overplays symptom intensity and maintains consistently high levels of complaint. Consequently, the patient often presents with the paradox of increasingly more intense and dramatic symptom presentation when, according to customary expectations, his condition should be improving. To paraphrase *DSM-IV* (APA, 1994), the patient's symptomatic display leads to apparent physical, social, or occupational impairment that is grossly in excess of what would be expected given the original trauma, the current physical findings, and the natural history of such conditions.

The second phenomenon of *instant remission* occurs when the patient is alone, unaware of being observed or evaluated by others, or is unwittingly distracted. Under these circumstances symptom production falls off to low levels or becomes nonexistent. The curiosity of instant remission results because the patient who volitionally displays symptoms only does so when it is advantageous, and it is almost never advantageous when no one is watching. It is also quite difficult to continuously maintain false symptoms in the presence of distracting factors such as anxiety, competition, or engrossing tasks. A brief lapse of attention to symptom display in the doctor's consulting room reproduces, for a few moments, the same "instant remission" that such patients display in their own living room. Thus, symptom production waxes and wanes according to the patient's perception of environmental need/press as well as the natural difficulty in maintaining symptom consistency.

Compensation Neurosis fits into the unintentional–volitional category where the factors of heightened secondary gain influence symptom display in a more obvious manner than in traditional diagnoses but less malignantly than in Malingering. *DSM-IV* (APA, 1994) defined Compensation Neurosis out of existence, designating it as either Malingering or genuine disorder but not a disorder itself (Hyler, Williams, & Spitzer, 1988). However, without Compensation Neurosis, there is no "middle ground" where the patient is not quite Malingering but neither is he quite classically psychodynamic. The gulf between Malingering and true disorder as defined in *DSM-IV* is excessively broad. It can be bridged by careful examination of a unique feature found in this Disorders of Simulation: unintentional design but volitional display.

Case Example 5.2—The Illness That Keeps On Giving

A psychiatrist (Liddon, 1970), in his "personal confession," described his experience working in a military emergency room where the duty is generally unpleasant, onerous, and arduous. Dr. Liddon developed knee trouble but persisted in taking his rotation, although being on his feet for many hours at a stretch led to painful swelling and ultimately the need for crutches. "After much discussion, it was then arranged that I would be relieved of the emergency room roster until the knee condition subsided. This eventually occurred and crutches were no longer needed, but it was apparent that prolonged standing would aggravate the trouble. It was at this point that the 'malingering' set in. The situation which existed was that I could walk in a natural manner, and only with lengthy standing or walking was pain or swelling encountered. My gait appeared normal, and to all appearances I looked as fit as anyone. I noticed, however, that on several occasions I limped slightly when approaching one of my fellow physicians in the long corridors of the hospital. This occurred in spite of the fact that there was no pain, muscle strength had improved, and I had no limp while walking alone. At first I took little notice, but after it happened repetitively I gradually took cognizance of the situation. It slowly dawned on me that my limp was fabricated! It was a reflex I had developed on encountering one of my confreres, and it was designed to testify to the fact that I had, indeed, an ailment which would justify my removal from the emergency room duty roster. (p. 278)

In this self-confessed example, Liddon was often in a twilight state of awareness, limping with vague awareness that his presentation was disingenuous. That is, he knew but did not want to acknowledge, acted with volition, and displayed symptoms but did not design them. Initially, he repressed his insights but, due to his training in psychiatry, ultimately developed insight into his repression.

According to the current formulation, Liddon's self-diagnosis of "Malingering" is unduly harsh yet a fully psychodynamic (neurotic) explanation is also inadequate to explain the phenomenon. His behavior falls into the category of Compensation Neurosis with symptoms involuntarily designed by actual injury but protracted symptom display on a volitional basis. As is often true in Compensation Neurosis, the "compensation" is not monetary just as the disorder is not a "neurosis." Unfortunately, *Compensation Neurosis* is the only modestly descriptive term widely available in the literature.

Liddon's case clearly illustrates the unintentional–voluntary type of symptom control. As is typical in cases of Compensation Neurosis, the patient was genuinely injured and subsequently protracted the symptoms of injury as the process of natural healing progressed. As time passed, Liddon began to limp only when confronting one of his fellow physicians (dramatization) in the hospital corridors but walked normally under other conditions (instant remission). Most Compensation Neurotics are not trained in psychiatry and would not have developed his level of insight or been able to follow Liddon's example by ceasing symptom display. Characteristically, they volitionally display their original, unintentionally designed symptoms—sometimes in exaggerated form—far beyond the point of actual recovery.

Complete Control

Patients who fall in this quadrant simulate with full control over their symptoms. Patients design and display symptoms at will according to their perception of what is necessary and may vary their presentation on a moment-to-moment basis. Either no injury has occurred and the patient wholly fabricates symptoms or the patient intentionally elaborates, redesigns, or expands upon minor symptoms that result from true injury. That is, symptom production appears and disappears according to the patient's perception of who is watching and how important it is for the intended observer to be aware of the patient's "disability." Symptom display is opportunistic and, in particularly retrenched cases, relatively protracted and continuous.

The essential symptom control difference between Complete Control and Protractive Control is intention. In symptom design, the Complete Control patient intentionally fabricates complaints

from whole cloth or dramatically expands upon minimal symptoms, while the Protractive Control patient customarily continues
with symptoms quite similar in type, if not identical with, those
experienced during initial injury or illness. That is, a Compensation Neurotic is much more likely to have actually experienced
injury or illness with subsequent active "symptom replacement"
while the fully simulating patient often engages in "symptom
invention." Thus, the Complete Control patient is concerted,
aggressive, and likely to be involved in intentional acts such as
data tampering, staged events, or similarly egregious behaviors.

Case Example 5.3—Alphabet Soup

> A 55-year-old male filed a workers' compensation case following an indus-
> trial accident where a large crescent wrench fell from a scaffold, striking
> his hard hat. He was not rendered unconscious but was somewhat dazed.
> Thereafter, he claimed grave mental deterioration and inability to func-
> tion. Neurological examination was within normal limits and all medical
> studies were negative. When seen for neuropsychological testing, the ex-
> aminer repeated random letters of the alphabet. The patient's task was
> to pick out the alphabet in sequence by tapping on the table as he heard
> the next letter. Thus, in the series D, R, Y, *A*, H, *B*, E, P, *C*, W, H, *D*, O,
> S, F, etc., the patient should have tapped when he heard the italicized
> letters. However, the patient tapped to A, B, and C but failed to tap to D
> or E, then picked up the series with F, G, H, and I. He ignored J, K, and
> L but then again began tapping with M, N, etc. The examiner noted:
> "You seem to be having trouble with concentration and attention. Let's
> try it again." The test was repeated with the same response from the pa-
> tient.

This patient believed that he was demonstrating loss of attention and concentration but paradoxically demonstrated excellent
tracking ability since he never lost his place. He simply chose to
tap to some letters of the alphabet and not others, demonstrating
full control over his claimed "symptom" of concentration and
attention deficit. A truly organically impaired individual with difficulty on this task would have become lost early in the sequence,
confused, and simply stopped functioning. Like all "tests of Malingering," however, the ABC test is obviously not sufficient to
designate the patient as Malingering since a hysteroid individual
could have produced a similar result.

Table 5.1
Summary of the Window of Symptom Control

Pathology Level	Categories of Symptom Control	Malingering	Factitious Disorder	Compensation Neurosis
Minimum	Reflexive Control	No	No	No
↑	Protractive Control	No	No	Yes
↓	Generative Control	No	Yes	No
Maximum	Complete Control	Yes	No	No

As Table 5.1 summarizes, analysis of symptom control is effective in separating one Disorder of Simulation from another. However, Symptom Control is not a reliable index by itself since it is linked to the other five Windows of Opportunity and cannot be wholly separated from them. It is also important to resist the temptation to focus upon one Window in Axis I when the two additional axes await evaluation.

WINDOW 5: RESPONSE AFFECTIVITY

The affect employed by the patient when responding to clinical interview and evaluation is different from simply claiming to have specific symptoms (Window 3) or demonstration of the symptoms on formal or informal testing (Window 4). Response Affectivity involves the interpersonally based emotional behavior displayed by the patient. Affect is subject to observation and description, but is more qualitative than quantitative and more emotive than cognitive. Patients usually demonstrate more than one variety of emotion or affect during the same evaluation session. Some of the affects that the patient displays may suggest, but cannot prove, simulation since patients emote and react differently, depending upon the circumstances. Even grossly simulating patients simulate on some occasions but not on others.

Obviously, most patients do not simulate and therefore present with relatively straightforward affect and a direct interpersonal manner. The patient is anxious to be understood and works cooperatively with the clinician to develop an accurate picture of his symptoms. Although invariably well motivated, bona fide patients sometimes display defensiveness, resistance, or dramatization as a function of self-perpetuating and self-defeating neurotic tendencies. These mechanisms, although sometimes affectively tinged with hostility, constitute the classic defensive array that, in some degree, all patients marshal against anxiety. Most examiners are aware of the basic mechanisms of defense and their emotional correlates, identify them quickly, and have developed effective strategies for their attenuation or mitigation.

In Disorders of Simulation, however, the standard rules do not apply and the patient attempts to deceive, misdirect, or otherwise mislead the examiner through hostile affectivity, displayed either actively or passively. Thus, analysis of the patient's Response Affectivity is important since, when simulation occurs, the patient's reaction to the evaluation process is accompanied by hostile affect that is much stronger and often far more dramatic than is found in the classic mechanisms of psychic defense.

The distinction between the hostile affect of simulation and the hostile affect of defense is easier to make than to describe. When patients engage in simulation, the usual and customary therapeutic maneuvers used by clinicians to overcome a patient's defense mechanisms are substantially ineffective. Failure to respond is characteristic of simulation under many evaluative circumstances; reassurance, support, interpretation, confrontation, and similar tactics fail to lead the patient to greater levels of openness and cooperation. The patient, bent upon his selected strategy, continues to display evasion, withholding, invention, or overt anger irrespective of the clinician's best efforts. Episodes of Response Affectivity suggesting simulation may occur many times per session, in response to specific tasks or procedures. Two dimensions are important to consider in evaluating the axis of Response Affectivity: the type of distortion and the type of aggression.

The Dimensions of Response Affectivity

Positive versus Negative Distortion

The patient's attempts to add or subtract behaviors during the clinical examination are referred to as positive versus negative distortion. In *positive distortion,* the patient adds factors to the assessment situation and produces behavioral excess. Thus, he may deceive by displaying a surfeit of activity, acting and reacting in ways that confront the clinician with a surplus of behaviors and emotions. Just the opposite occurs in *negative distortion* where the patient subtracts factors from the clinical examination and deceives through displaying behavioral deficit. His actions and emotions are scanty and seem to disclaim emotion, imply a paucity of internal life, and a dearth of behavior. Thus, he attempts to interfere with the procedures of clinical assessment by withholding or delaying.

Passive versus Active Aggressive Behavior

Simulation is an interpersonal phenomenon and, in order to be effective, the patient must deceive the clinician. With deception, anger and hostile affectivity are implied. Therefore, it is important that one axis of Response Affectivity reflects the type of aggressive behavior used by the patient in his attempts to deceive. When *active-aggressive*, the patient's hostility is direct and overt, ranging from combative and bellicose—possibly even physically intimidating—to belligerent and contentious, down to thinly veiled rancor at the least.

At other times, however, patients are interpersonally *passive-aggressive*, seeking to shelter themselves from direct, conflictual contact with the examiner. The patient refuses to own his anger, asking the therapist to own it instead. Consequently, the patient's behavior is guilt-inducing and he seeks to make the therapist deal with the patient's covert passive–aggressive anger. Thus, the patient's hostile affect, while substantial, is covert. Passive–aggressive patients manage to be unbelievably dilatory, frustratingly evasive, and stubbornly obstructionistic, often in a polite, cooperative, and deferential way—all with syrupy sweetness. Their inactivity and inertness prevent them from actively participating in evaluation.

As Figure 5.4 illustrates, crossing the axis of positive versus negative distortion with the axis of passive versus active aggressive behavior yields four basic response strategies with a "normal" field in the center. Patients who suffer from Disorders of Simulation tend to respond to assessment or evaluation by invoking behaviors typical of one or more of the four quadrants.

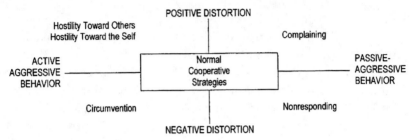

Figure 5.4. Response Affectivity During Evaluation Distributed Along the Axes of Distortion and Type of Aggression

Varieties of Response Affectivity

Normal cooperative strategies are the hallmark of patients who do not attempt to deceive. They display no more than brief flurries of distorted Response Affectivity and fall within the central field. Normal patient emotions include a cooperative attitude and a veridical quality such that the clinician is strongly impressed with a "what you see is what I've got" response honesty. The patient gives the examiner no reason to suspect willful attempts to distort the response process by altering response affect. Within the cooperative field, patients display normal flashes of anger or dramatization of response as well as some degree of defensive or resistive behavior. However, these affective patterns remain within the range of customary variation during clinical assessment. The direct, normal response style contrasts with the emotional behaviors falling into one of the quadrants where patients actively engage in distortion of Response Affectivity. Further, with normal patients, the usual strategies employed by clinicians to counter the mechanisms of psychic defense and their associated emotions are customarily effective or, at the least, lead the patient to somewhat greater levels of disclosure and cooperation.

Nonresponding is similar to defensiveness but, unlike the latter, implies willful effort. When patients are simply defensive, they engage unconscious mechanisms to guard against and repress dangerous impulses or affects, usually involving anxiety, guilt, disgust, or shame. When patients limit their responses, however, they impede the examination process, negatively distorting through behavioral reluctance to function adequately despite the best efforts of the clinician. Affectively, nonresponding individuals are interpersonally passive and withholding but overtly submissive, apparently cooperative, unassertive, and saccharine. They can be covertly but powerfully obstructionistic. The patient's failure to truly cooperate with the examination involves nonresponsiveness with, more often than not, passively hostile affect despite an aura of superficial conformity.

Nonresponding patients may engage in oppositional behaviors and fail to perform adequately, often using the simple behavioral deficit strategy of withholding, delay, and procrastination. Some patients, while apparently earnestly trying to answer, manage to avoid responding in a timely manner—often with an overly polite and honeyed quality. At the expenditure of somewhat greater effort, patients fail to perform by engaging in self-defeating behaviors, seem bemused by explicit instructions, interpret directions in unconventionally concrete ways, and have great difficulty understanding simple questions. At the extreme, patients in this category simply fail to participate, becoming mute and inactive, passively refusing to answer or function. Although their refusal to perform is accompanied by a polite demur and indication that they are incapable of even relatively simple tasks, the underlying affect is nonetheless covertly angry.

Case Example 5.4—Apologetically Erecting Roadblocks

A 28-year-old male suffered a minor whiplash without objective medical injury. Since the accident he claimed inability to remember his own birth date, names of family members, and was confused about the month, day, and year. He reported virtually no memories before age 15 and even thereafter gave only the most sparse and terse of historical answers. He required over 40 seconds to count from one to 20, an overlearned task that most seriously injured patients perform easily. He sometimes "apologized" for his failures in an obsequious manner, claiming that the "enormous effort" involved in answering such difficult questions made his head hurt terribly. More often, he simply failed to respond without explanation. He grievously "misunderstood" simple instructions but had no difficulty with similar tasks when he was unaware of being directly assessed (e.g., completing clinic registration forms). When given a MMPI, he performed so slowly that he failed to complete enough questions to allow proper scoring or interpretation, despite two office visits of several hours each. When given the Rorschach inkblots, he responded minimally and often claimed to see nothing at all. Despite rapport-building, encouragement,

empathy, support, and compassion from the examiner, the patient was
dilatory, obstructionistic, and nonresponsive, maintained a low rate of
self-disclosure, subtly but overtly refused to answer, and failed to conform
to reasonable expectations.

This patient's responses illustrate the withholding–nonresponsive type of Response Affectivity. Most clinicians would classify him as displaying strongly passive–aggressive behaviors, especially since the techniques customarily helpful in dealing with resistant patients were of no avail. Nonresponding strategies may occur in any Disorder of Simulation although the strongly passive–aggressive affect is most congenial to Compensation Neurosis and Factitious Disorders. Nonresponding is least congenial to the Malingering patient who often is interested in exerting active control of the examination situation.

Circumvention, like nonresponding, involves behavioral deficit but active aggression in hiding information despite direct, pointed requests from the examiner. Although the patient answers or responds, perhaps with considerable energy and in a seemingly direct fashion, the emotional distortion is nonetheless negative. In most cases, the patient has something to hide or fears the outcome of the evaluative or therapeutic process. Since the patient actively conceals information, the associated affect is considerably more active-aggressive than the passive-aggressivity associated with being dilatory and nonresponsive. Thus, the patient evades the question or task with a quality of hostile affectivity, often presenting with an edgy, brittle quality, and taking umbrage when the examiner questions areas the patient wishes to keep hidden. Other types of passive opposition with behavioral deficit include attempts to distract the examiner with tangential responses and near-miss answers (*Vorbiereden*). Thus, the withholding patient politely demurs while the distracting patient aggressively circumvents; the withholding patient dallies while the distracting patient actively misleads; the withholding patient fails to answer adequately while the distracting patient answers in order to misdirect the examiner. In essence, a patient who circumvents is like the killdeer who makes a great fuss and feigns a broken wing, limping and dragging itself in the opposite direction from its nest, in the hope of drawing a predator off the scent.

Case Example 5.5—Circumventing the Truth

When a 44-year-old male was asked whether he had an alcohol problem, he replied, "There is alcoholism in my family and in my wife's family and I vowed I would never be like her father or mine so I rarely use it these days." Asked if he had ever used alcohol excessively, he stated, "No, not really. I'm against using pills and alcohol and drugs because I saw what it did to people when I was in the Navy." Upon more pointed inquiry about alcohol or drug treatment programs, he noted, "Once my wife was concerned because I would drink a little wine with dinner so I just stopped. I handled it myself." Extensive additional probing elicited no admission of alcohol problems. When records became available for review, they indicated that the patient was a self-acknowledged alcoholic, had been self-admitted to inpatient alcohol programs at least twice, and had returned to drinking heavily thereafter. His statement that, "I handled it myself" was an active refusal to provide sufficient information to the examiner. Upon subsequent interview, when confronted, he indicated, with hostile affect, "Well, I did tell you that 'I handled it myself!' I went voluntarily, so one forced me to do it!"

Initially, he evaded disclosure of his problem yet gave himself an "out" in case the examiner discovered his actively misleading responses. Thus, patients in the active aggressive–negative distortion quadrant may begin responding with apparently direct answers but, when pressed further, rapidly move to angry evasion, indignation, and active avoidance. That is, rather than just fail to report accurately, the patient works to conceal and deny through actively asserting misleading responses. Sometimes, patients seek to completely bury information from the outset without any attempt at initial evasion, blatantly and aggressively misdirecting the examiner in the hope that their bluff will pass muster as genuine. All varieties of simulating patients may engage in evasion but its hostile, active quality is more attractive to Malingering and Factitious patients than to the more passive Compensation Neurotic.

Complaining patients whine endlessly, positively distorting in passive–aggressive ways that range from significant exaggeration of existing distress to persistent bemoaning and bewailing. When asked to perform, they indicate they are incapable and may become tearfully emotional, seeking to entangle the examiner in a morass of dramatized complaints, plaintive symptoms, and helplessness. They present as invalids and apologize for their "disabilities" that, in fact, are a lachrymose expression of passive hostility rather than true incapacity. The patient uses his complaints and apparent disability to frustrate the evaluation process, complaining that he is incapable of performing due to pain, stress, exhaustion, or some other grievous problem.

Case Example 5.6—Gilding the Lily

A 32-year-old railroad brakeman was knocked to the ground and sustained apparent injury to his right side when two boxcars unexpectedly moved. Consistently negative findings resulted from orthopedic and neurological examinations but he carried a diagnosis of lumbar sprain-strain and soft tissue injury by history. On psychological examination, the patient walked with great difficulty, apparently suffered enormously, and could not ambulate without a cane. His professions of pain seemed quite convincing and he appeared to be in agony whether sitting, standing, or lying down. The examination required far more time than normal, he failed to complete some tests, could not concentrate effectively, and demanded to go home and lie down. When pressed to continue, he became tearful—nearly hysterical—and pleaded for the examiner to stop torturing him with questions. After the examination, he was observed through an office window and noted to hook the cane over his left arm while walking briskly toward his car without difficulty or signs of discomfort.

At the time of examination, the patient's response pattern suggested fabrication of his claimed pathology although he may have been injured originally. The patient displayed positive distortion of the passive–aggressive variety. That is, the pitiful, agonized behaviors he displayed in the clinical examination were the invented residual of his alleged injury, a deceptive ploy designed to inhibit adequate examination and impress the clinician with the "seriousness" of his case. His jaunty gait when believing himself to be unobserved, however, indicated the patient's cane was more a stage prop and his pain more an act than residuals of true injury. Whining and complaining is a response category that is equally attractive to all Disorders of Simulation but more congenial to Factitious Disorder and Compensation Neurosis than Malingering.

Hostility is evident when patients are actively aggressive and distort in a positive direction. The target of the hostility, however, may be others or the self. The degree of hostility may range from overtly aggressive behavior, to confrontation, to threatened hostile acts.

Hostility toward others results when the patient attempts to control the examination and coerce, force, or intimidate the clinician into accepting the claimed disabilities as genuine. Paradoxically, the mildest form of hostile coercion is excessive familiarity where the patient hails the examiner in an overly friendly manner, immediately assumes a first-name relationship, winks a sly wink, and otherwise tries to coopt the direction of the examination. While this strategy may seem friendly, underlying hostility is nonetheless present, as the clinician will discover if he fails to "string along." The most common variety of hostility, however, is fractious, impatient, irritable, angry behavior that implies the patient is barely containing himself. The patient seeks to intimidate the examiner by subtly threatening loss of control or negative consequences if the clinician fails to conform. When familiarity and veiled hostility fail, the patient may escalate to overt threats involving suits for malpractice, reports to licensing agencies or, at interprofessional levels, complaints to other treating or evaluating parties. The ultimate level of interpersonal aggressive acceleration is, of course, a direct personal threat or actual physical assault.

Case Example 5.7—Intimidating the Doctor

A 29-year-old male was in a motorcycle accident and was seen for neuropsychological assessment with a lawsuit for brain injury in the balance. The outcome, while demonstrating some residual impairment, did not reflect dramatic problems. Understandably, the patient's attorney was mildly disappointed by the results and noted, during a telephone conversation with the examiner, that the deficits did not seem to be as severe as either he or the patient had anticipated. Some days later, the patient arrived at the examiner's office for a personal conference about the testing results. He was overtly friendly and cordial but inquired in a hypermoralistic manner whether the examiner was a Christian, preferably "born again." Not receiving a satisfactory answer, he stated: "You know, I am a Christian. I could have gone to one of our own doctors and gotten any results I wanted. We Christians stick together and help each other out. Of course, all I want from you is the truth but I'm really not doing well at all and I expected your results to prove it. I already know how bad it is. I just need a doctor to testify to it in court because my future depends on it. I know I really got badly hurt and my attorney says it would be malpractice for anyone to say I am not seriously injured."

Hostility directed toward others is a response style often seen in Malingering but is too direct and interpersonal for Compensation Neurotics since it requires taking an active, aggressive posture. Patients with Factitious Disorders may engage in open hostility but usually only upon confrontation, and then only briefly. They may become angry and hostile if the clinician suggests that their pathology is self-induced or that they have induced pathology in others but, most commonly, those with Factitious Disorders simply fail to return for treatment or discharge themselves against medical advice.

Hostility toward the self occurs when individuals turn their anger inward upon themselves—attempting suicide, scarifying, or self-inducing illness—although these latter behaviors generally precede the clinical examination by a considerable period. However, the presence of self-destructive actions in the past should alert the clinician to the possibility that the patient may use threats of self-injury in the present to manipulate and control the inquiry or examination. For example, some patients may overmedicate themselves during the clinical process or arrive in an intoxicated state, failing to respond adequately as the result of chemical ingestion. Conversely, other patients fail to take their medications, thus suffering deterioration and a resurgence of symptoms that had been chemically controlled which, in turn, interferes with the examination or treatment process. A minority threaten self-injury, obliquely hinting that they have a gun at home, or a stash of pills, that they will use if the examination presses them beyond their preset limits.

Case Example 5.7—Pill Power

A 48-year-old male with a history of Borderline personality, including episodic decompensation to near psychotic levels, was involved in a minor automobile accident with no objective signs of injury. His functional level declined postaccident and he was referred for psychological testing at the request of his treating psychiatrist. The patient was quite resistive and did not want to be tested, but did agree to participate. In a telephone call on the day of his appointment, he stated that he was ill. When questioned, his speech was slurred and he had trouble communicating coherently. He acknowledged having taken "some pills" but was very vague about the type and number, indicating that he had amassed a considerable stash of psychotropic medications over his years of treatment. He would not reveal his location, stating only that he was "somewhere safe" and would not stay on the telephone. When the treating psychiatrist was notified, he revealed that such manipulations were customary for this patient.

Compensation Neurotics and Factitious Disorders are most likely to threaten hostility against the self although only the latter is likely to inflict self-damage. Actual self-injury is anathema to Malingerers but they may falsely threaten to do so in the interest of manipulating the examination.

Table 5.2
Summary of the Window of Response Affectivity During Evaluation

Pathology Level	Categories of Response Strategy	Malingering	Factitious Disorder	Compensation Neurosis
Minimum	Nonresponding	Rare	Yes	Yes
⏐	Circumvention	Yes	Yes	Moderate
⏐	Complaining	Moderate	Yes	Yes
↓	Hostility Toward Others	Yes	Rare	No
Maximum	Hostility Toward Self	No	Yes	Yes

Identification of the specific strategies employed in symptom production as outlined in Table 5.2, in itself, is helpful because the particular strategy displayed by patients is of great importance in documenting their behavior on examination.

WINDOW 6: RESPONSE TO TREATMENT

When patients are in treatment or extended evaluation, they customarily attend regular sessions over time. While Response Affectivity (Window 5) deals with molecular behaviors that are evident on brief evaluation, Response to Treatment involves molar, global behaviors that often require several sessions to identify.

Simulating patients do not simulate inveterately—many initially appear cooperative, tractable, friendly, and even charming—even as they resist, obstruct, and oppose treatment success. It is also true that different varieties of simulating patients respond differently to treatment interventions. Malingerers may remain in treatment for a while, at least as long as they continue to see a way to manipulate the system to their advantage. Patients with Factitious Disorder occasionally enter psychotherapy but usually will not tolerate confrontation and tend to flee when challenged. In contrast, Compensation Neurotics are very dependent and clinging, often remaining in therapy for a long time.

Because the presentation of simulating patients during treatment varies widely, several sessions are customarily required before the clinician is able to fully discover and document distorted transference and countertransference. It is not always easy to penetrate the simulating patient's superficial presentation and discover how he manages to be uncooperative and fails to make the expected psychotherapeutic progress given a working diagnosis selected from the "genuine" taxonomy. This, of course, is frustrating to the clinician who is working for cure or remission and subtly gratifying to the patient who is bent upon maintaining his disability. In a few rare but flagrant cases, the clinician may be able to predict failure in treatment from verbal or nonverbal behavior in advance of the first session, simply by observing the patient's behavior in the waiting room. More commonly, however, when patients simulate accident, illness, or stress, observation over time leads to more accurate description of Response to Treatment.

The Dimensions of Response to Treatment

Interpersonal versus Intrapersonal

The simulating patient's response in treatment may effect external, *inter*personal events during the course of treatment. Of course, the primary other in treatment is the therapist and thus the patient may direct his attention outwardly, seeking to distort the doctor–patient relationship through manipulation of countertransference. Other patients react in the opposite manner, focusing upon primarily internal, *intra*personal events. That is, the patient may internalize his reactions and direct his attention away from others and toward the self. Thus, one of the dimensions involved in treatment response involves noticing whether patients move toward the self or toward others.

Active versus Passive Opposition

As in active versus passive aggression, active versus passive opposition is an important dimension of Response Affectivity. In Response to Treatment it is critical to note the degree to which the patent's response reflects active as opposed to passive opposition. In *active opposition*, simulating patents resist strongly, countering the therapist's maneuvers with behaviors designed to thwart effective intervention. In *passive opposition*, despite the therapist's best efforts, the patient fails by involution and collapse. Simulation does not necessarily occur in all four quadrants illustrated in Figure 5.5 although the failure of a simulating patient to respond to treatment is likely to invoke at least one of the quadrants.

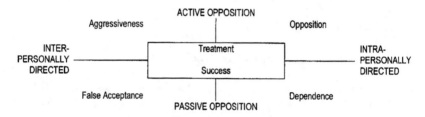

Figure 5.5. Response to Treatment Distributed Along the Axes of Personal Direction and Active versus Passive Opposition

Varieties of Response to Treatment

Treatment success occurs when a Simulating patient is well and truly treated. If treatment is successful, the patient is, by definition, no longer simulating. The literature on the treatment of Simulation is minimal since most individuals do not receive treatment. They are simply dismissed at the point of diagnosis so that treatment is never initiated. In the rarely reported instances of treatment success with a simulator, the patient accepts the notion that his problems are intentionally or volitionally mediated, at least in some degree. An effectively treated simulator is unlikely to display an excess of any of the problems identified in the four quadrants of Figure 5.5.

False acceptance is a variety of apparent success in which a simulating patient seems to openly accept full responsibility for his behavior. Nevertheless, the patient engages in passive treatment sabotage by False Acceptance. Individuals who fall in this quadrant customarily make the same statements as do those for whom treatment is successful: "I understand. I accept. I can see how what I did was wrong. I regret my actions and take full responsibility," etc. They reflect upon intrapsychic motives and feelings, ostensibly complying with the treatment regimen. The difference between real treatment success and false acceptance is difficult to specify, although experienced therapists would say: "He walks the walk and talks the talk but he doesn't believe a word of it." Thus, the patient gives the appearance of treatment success without making significant changes within himself or, in therapeutic parlance, without integrating his insights.

Case Example 5.8—Mea Culpa

A 22-year-old male was convicted of a rape that had taken place in a department store women's restroom. He claimed that he had no intent to molest, was violently ill and had entered the wrong restroom by mistake, and that the victim "came on to me." Throughout the trial and for the first months of incarceration he was resistant, petulant, and claimed his innocence at every opportunity. He would not give institutional psychotherapists the time of day. Gradually, he softened and began to respond, albeit with many instances of backsliding and recidivism. Overall, however, he made progress. Finally, he admitted he was wrong, started fully participating in group therapy, and held nothing back, freely confessing a litany of past sins. As his release date neared, he was certified as no longer a threat because he had insight, was compliant rather than defensive or defiant, had given up his massive denial, and had developed a sound plan for independent living outside prison. In group and individual therapy, the patient had examined his attitudes toward women in great detail. He realized that rape is aggressive rather than sexual and openly discussed his fears of sexual inadequacy. He was able to accurately empathize with the plight of the victim in role-playing exercises. In every way, he seemed to be a model rehabilitated offender. With very favorable ratings from all treating and evaluating parties, he was recommended for parole. Three days after release, the patient was arrested for another rape.

False Acceptance is unlikely to occur as a variety of treatment failure in all Disorders of Simulation. It is most likely in Malingering because it requires considerable orchestration. In turn, the strategy is too consciously orchestrated to be attractive to Compensation Neurotics and admission of culpability, even for manipulative purposes, is anathema to Factitious Disorder.

Dependence involves passively invoking failure through affecting an overly compliant, sticky, and dependent quality. Patients take great pains to submit, but nonetheless manage to violate the spirit of treatment by either rigid adherence to the rules or failure to "remember" to comply. Such persons may arrive late for treatment or not at all. Others "forget" to take their medications, leave their glasses at home when they know they have insurance paperwork to complete, invalidate forms with misstatements or omissions, and show up on the wrong day for treatment. All the while, these patients profess a genuine desire to comply and apologize that they were unable to do so due to no fault of their own. Sometimes, dependent behaviors are as dramatic as they are passive-aggressive; one patient, who proclaimed back pain, assumed a prone position sprawled on the waiting-room floor with papers and other materials spread out, occupying virtually all the available space for himself and forcing others to step over him. Other failure-prone patients display enormous dependency and seem virtually unable to make an independent decision, requiring assistance with every aspect of even preliminary contact with the office. They have problems taking simple directions over the telephone, absorb most of the secretary's time with minor problems, need help completing the simplest of office forms, and request endless protective letters and certifications of incapacity. Any involvement in therapeutic activity requires inordinate amounts of instruction, support, clarification, and definition. When confronted about their passive–aggressive failure to perform, their response is to display even more helpless and inappropriate behaviors, punctuated by tears and protestations of gross incapacity.

Case Example 5.9—Please Don't Hurt Me

A 57-year-old male claimed intense and disabling back pain following a minor injury. Upon extensive orthopedic and neurological examination, his complaints appeared to be grossly in excess of objective medical findings and he displayed "instant remission" when he was unaware that others were watching him. He pleaded helplessness and incapacity when asked to take psychological tests, and he was markedly viscous and "sticky" in interpersonal relations. He started treatment with the goal of reducing his intractable pain-related behaviors and excessive dependence upon frequent medical visits. In the waiting room, before his first therapeutic visit, he rearranged the furniture by commandeering several chairs and moving them together near the center of the room. Having made a bed, he assumed a prone position and then asked the secretary for a blanket! When the secretary called for him to enter the office, he complained that he could not arise and tearfully begged that he not be forced to do so since the pain would be intolerable. Despite the presence of several other patients, he pleaded for the doctor to conduct treatment in the waiting room. He did not appear to be embarrassed or realize that he was acting inappropriately.

The Factitious patient is likely to display dependency but generally, only if not confronted. With confrontation, Factitious patients move into one of the more oppositional quadrants. Compensation Neurotics are almost uniformly dependent, only briefly flirting with the more oppositional and aggressive quadrants before collapsing into dependency once more. Malingerers are rarely so clinging and dependent because their interpersonal style is more usurious and aggressive.

Opposition, the willful denial of underlying problems, projection of problems onto others, and refusal to accept the notion of psychological causation, is a strategy that allows some patients to actively resist treatment. They find reasons to cease or not fully comply with recommended treatment, fail to show for appointments, decline to take prescribed medicines, and attend therapy erratically. They are often aggressive and demanding, arguing with office procedures, badgering the secretary, or persistently using the telephone to call family, friends, or attorneys. Confrontation and interpretation usually invokes fight or flight.

Case Example 5.10—Fractious Failure

A 43-year-old female with complaints of attention, memory, and concentration deficits following minor exposure to an industrial adhesive, appeared for neuropsychological rehabilitation on referral through her attorney from her primary care physician. She was angry about her alleged condition, snappish in response to benign questions, and irritable due to what she claimed were fully disabling mental symptoms. From the outset, she complained that she should not have to undergo "mental" treatment because "no good could come of it" and she demanded an exception in her case. She indicated she would not comply unless her attorney or an observer was present at the sessions, an obviously impossible request that the therapist denied. She called her attorney only to have the denial affirmed. Subsequently, she became even more fractious and refused to continue unless the sessions were tape-recorded. Therapy had to be delayed until she could obtain the necessary recording equipment and even then, she constantly attended to the tape recorder, changed tapes, asked the examiner to repeat phrases for the benefit of recording, etc. Further, she invariably sidetracked therapy by taking every opportunity to indicate that the present treatment, although recommended by her physician, was not only unnecessary but also an unfair and improper imposition. Treatment progress was impossible.

Compensation Neurosis patients are too interpersonally passive to engage in actively oppositional strategies but Factitious Disorders may be quite oppositional as it true for Malingering.

Aggressiveness occurs when patients actively attempt to destroy or frustrate treatment in interpersonal ways. They seek out conflicting opinions from other doctors, play one doctor against another, threaten suit, accuse the treating party of duplicity, or are antagonistic toward the clinician. In some instances, the simulating patient may blatantly threaten the clinician, usually in a crudely hostile manner. Rarely, the patient may go so far as physical assault. Far more likely, however, are hostile attempts to intimidate the evaluator into accepting false disability by threatening suit, making negative reports to other caregivers, or reporting alleged objectionable actions to licensing boards and professional societies.

Case Example 5.11—My Doctor Was Dead Right

A patient with an alleged back injury was seen by several medical examiners. Each independently agreed that there was no physical basis for his complaint and, in essence, labeled him a Malingerer. After brooding for months, he shot and killed two physicians before committing suicide. Upon autopsy of the patient, there was no evidence of the alleged back pathology. Thus, the diagnosis of Simulation was vindicated, proving his physicians to be "dead right." As Parker (1979) wisely noted in his report of several such cases, "There is more to emotional disturbance after injury than a mere quest for compensation."

The high level of interpersonal hostility required by the aggressive response to treatment is not congenial to Compensation Neurotics who are more passive and dependent. It is apparently rare but not unheard of in Factitious Disorder and common in Malingering.

Table 5.3
Summary of the Window of Response to Treatment

Pathology Level	Response to Treatment	Malingering	Factitious Disorder	Compensation Neurosis
Minimum	Treatment Success	Rare	Rare	Moderate
│	False Acceptance	Yes	no	Rare
│	Dependence	No	Rare	Yes
↓	Opposition	Yes	Yes	No
Maximum	Aggressiveness	Yes	Rare	No

BEHAVIORAL ORCHESTRATION: THE FIRST OF THREE AXES

Table 5.4 summarizes the three Windows of Opportunity outlined in this chapter.

As is true for the three Windows of Opportunity under Observing Reported Data (chapter 4), a diagnosis of Simulation should never occur solely as the result of patient behaviors on examination or treatment. While it may seem possible to be certain that a Disorder of Simulation is present after the patient has

Table 5.4
Reporting Obtained Data Associated with Windows of Opportunity

Windows of Opportunity	Reporting Observations Associated with		
	Malingering	Factitious Disorders	Compensation Neurosis
Symptoms Control is	Complete	Generative	Protractive
Response Affectivity During evaluation is	Nonresponding Circumvention Complaining Hostility to Others	Nonresponding Circumvention Complaining Hostility to Others Hostility to Self	Nonresponding Circumvention Complaining
Response to Treatment Involves	False Acceptance Opposition Aggressiveness	Dependence Opposition Aggressiveness	False Acceptance Dependence

been rated in all six Windows of Opportunity (three in Part A and three in Part B), it is important to resist the temptation to shortcut the diagnostic procedure by skipping over the axes of motivation and personality pathology. Without examination of these latter two axes, it is insupportable to jump to a diagnostic conclusion based upon analysis of behaviors alone. Windows of Opportunity are, in fact, no more than the "critical feature" or "list" approach taken to a logical, systematic, organized extreme. While important to and necessary for ultimate diagnostic certainty, qualification in one or more Windows of Opportunity is not sufficient to detect Simulation. A "hit" in one or more Windows of Opportunity does not affirm Simulation any more than does a "hit" in one or more criteria from the numerous available lists chronicled in chapter 3. However, the contrary position is valid. That is, if it is impossible to qualify a patient as hitting in one or more of the six Windows of Opportunity, the clinician should not render a diagnosis of Simulation.

6

Axis II: Motivation

> It is inescapably true that Simulation requires both a Simulator and an observer; Simulation is pointless unless someone else is present to appreciate the Simulation.

In Disorders of Simulation, it is simplistic to think that motivation refers solely to internal versus external incentives, the bipolar, behavioral dichotomy of *DSM-IV* (APA, 1994). Complex human motivation is certainly not limited to such simple goal-seeking as financial compensation, exculpation from criminal penalty, or evasion of unpleasant duty, the traditional views of secondary gain. Simple focus upon intrinsic or extrinsic factors does injustice to the diversity of human motivation. Worse, such focus mistakes the finger pointing at the moon for the moon itself. That is, it reads the signpost as arrival at the destination and mislabels the vehicle in which the patient travels as the act of traveling. Money, escape, and exculpation are but a few of the means simulating patients use to fulfill the destiny of their characterologic distortions.

Motivation is a complex amalgam of drives, needs, satisfactions, and frustration tolerances that cannot easily be reduced to simple rubrics and one-sentence summaries. *Simulation has many motivations; all of them based in defective object relations.* True analysis of motivation in Disorders of Simulation lies in understanding

---

This chapter was coauthored by Karen Hutchinson, Ph.D., as adapted from her 1992 dissertation, *An Integrated Theory of Developmental Object Relations* (San Francisco: California School of Professional Psychology).

the patient's distortion of object relations, given the patient's level of developmental fixation, and the implications of their fixation for the range of possible motivating factors. The notion of extrinsic versus intrinsic motivation is not helpful in analyzing Disorders of Simulation because these motivations are superficial, not psychodynamically robust, and may be present at nearly any level of object relations capacity.

Patients may be motivated to simulate because, at a particular level of object relations, they seek egocentric control over the object, confirmation by it, or magical reunion with it. They simulate to assuage abandonment-depression and avoid direct contact with underlying fears of engulfment or separation, escape from annihilation anxiety, prevent loss of control, or death of the self. Some simulate to survive, maintain the fantasy of infantile omnipotence, or to experience the clinging satisfaction of dependency fulfillment. Conversely, some simulate to redress the anger they feel for the humiliation of having to cling so desperately to others. A few simulate to express psychopathic rage over unmet dependency needs and insufficient mirroring by an unappreciative world. Others simulate as self-punishment, finding distorted gratification in suffering a disability because the counterfeit of disease is as good as disease itself. Some simulate for the thrill of inherent risk; quite simply, their object relations capacity is nil and they will therefore use any method to obtain whatever instant gratification seems likely to fulfill them at the moment.

DEVELOPMENTAL OBJECT RELATIONS CAPACITY

Drives and needs are fundamental motivational variables and a broad range have been identified in the psychological literature. *Drive* is usually defined as an internally generated organismic force, quite narcissistic in nature, present in the neonate, persistent, and unchanging. Some authors opine that new drives may emerge throughout the person's life while other theorists, noting the linkage between drive and inherited behavior, limit drives to those identified as instincts. In either case, drives impel psychopathology as well as normal behavior and are central in the understanding of all mental disorders.

Need reflects an internal, dynamic relationship between imbalanced emotional equilibrium or psychodynamic tension and a perceived external source of satisfaction. Some needs are basic, physiological, and perpetual: food, water, shelter, sleep, and the like. Other needs are less basically physiological, more interpersonal, and developmentally generated as the result of interaction between the person and environment, usually during the formative years. This latter area involves the critical concept of object relations capacity.

The Interpersonal Nature of Simulation

Drives and needs, of course, help shape the object relations capacity of the individual that, in turn, leads to character structure and, ultimately, interpersonal relations. While some mental aberrations are wholly intrapsychic and would exist in a patient whether he lived on a desert island or in the midst of New York City, *Disorders of Simulation are, in all cases, interpersonal phenomena.* That is, an Obsessive–Compulsive person may engage in ritualistic calculation when others surround him as well as when he is entirely alone. He can tally passengers on crowded subway trains while being jostled to-and-fro by dozens of fellow New Yorkers and, just as readily, neurotically count and recount periwinkles along a deserted stretch of beach in the Outer Hebrides. A patient who simulates, however, must have an external observer present to effectively simulate because *simulation can only be appreciated in an interpersonal context.* No benefit accrues to the patient who falsely and intentionally maintains that he cannot count either people or periwinkles unless someone else is present to appreciate his "disability." While the neurotic is driven to count compulsively in order to contain and manage his anxiety and either does not understand or rationalizes his ritualistic behavior, the simulator is at some level aware that his complaint is counterfeit, engages in no self-deception, and seeks to deceive *others.*

In a more traditional example than periwinkles, some patients complain of intractable and severe low back pain that effectively leads to invalid status despite minimal to nonexistent objective medical findings. This group of low-back pain patients may be subdivided into three general categories: (1) true back pain sufferers; (2) those who experience psychogenic pain in greater or lesser degree; and (3) back pain simulators who either have no pain or grossly exaggerate pain that does exist.

The True Sufferers

Those with an authentic organic generator for the pain that simply defies detection by current medical diagnostic techniques are the true sufferers. Although the patient's genuine pain customarily has inter- and intrapersonal aspects as the result of the impact of the disability upon the self, friends, and family, the patient does not generate the pain and has no intent to deceive the self or others.

The Psychogenic Patient

Unintentionally and involuntarily, the psychogenic patient generates, maintains, or exaggerates the experience of low back pain as the result of primary and secondary gain. Both the true back pain sufferer and the psychogenic patient experience pain and display pain-related behaviors whether others are present or not. For example, unbeknownst to the psychogenic patient, powerful dependency fulfillment desires often serve to prolong the pain in order to sustain the flow of attention and nurturance from family, friends, attorneys, and doctors. According to Freud, this is *neurotic regression in the service of the ego* and the patient genuinely feels the pain; he does not seek to deceive others with it. Neither does the patient willfully deceive himself but rather fails to see his own true motivations as the result of intrapersonal defense mechanisms invoked by "unconscious" processes.

The Simulator

At some level the simulator is aware that his back pain is not real, grossly exaggerated, excessively protracted or falsely attributed, and does not deceive himself by invoking intrapsychic defense mechanisms; rather, he seeks to deceive others. Motivation is an interpersonal phenomenon and must therefore involve the issue of object relations—invariably distorted—with roots in early development. To paraphrase Freud, the simulator engages in *characterologic deception in the service of defective object relations*.

Developmental Object Relations

When the early development of object relations is disturbed—often to the point of fixation—pathological distortion of basic needs occurs and ultimately finds expression in some variety of dysfunctional interpersonal relations. Since Simulation is an interpersonal phenomenon, assessment of the patient's level of object relations capacity or incapacity is fundamental to an understanding of the patient's motivation to simulate accident, disease, or mental disorder.

A major problem in discussing object relations is the matter of surplus meaning in terminology. In the developmental object relations literature, labels such as *Psychopathic, Narcissistic,* and *Borderline* have specific definitions and imply specific ranges of interpersonal relations capacity that are theoretically based, developmentally complex, and psychodynamically robust. Object relations theory refers to a spectrum of developmentally based object relations, ranging from nonexistent at one end through rapprochement at the other. Therefore, the term *borderline* (small case initial) personality disorder as used by Kernberg (1975), Kohut (1977), or Masterson (1981), for example, is not fully synonymous with the *DSM-IV* diagnosis of *Borderline* (capital initial) Personality Disorder. Indeed, the latter is not only a subset of the former but also lacking in psychodynamic formulation and developmental object relations theory. Therefore, the atheoretical, behavioral, checklist format of *DSM-IV* for diagnosis of Personality Disorder frequently ascribes somewhat different meanings to the traditional terms used in object relations theory.

Faulty communications are quite likely to occur when, in the same discussion, one clinician uses the term *borderline* in the developmental object relations sense while a second clinician refers to *Borderline* as a variety of *DSM-IV* (APA, 1994) Personality Disorder. Developmental object relations labels such as *Psychopathic, Narcissistic,* and *Borderline,* as used in this chapter, are not the same as *DSM* labels of the same or similar name with capital initial letters, as used in chapter 7, "Personality Pathology." Table 6.1 summarizes traditional object relations terms.

Table 6.1

The Terminology of Traditional Object Relations Theory

Traditional Terms	Description of Object Relations Level
Symbiotic	No object relations capacity, a fused self-as-object, and largely chaotic functioning.
Psychopathic	Paranoid, antisocial, and sadistic disorders with angry and empty self-object relations.
Narcissistic	High-functioning types may initially appear "phallic neurotic" while low-functioning varieties seemingly present as no more than psychopathic. However, both types have fused self-object representations that are angry and grandiose.
Borderline	A split self-object representation is characteristic of a large cluster of Borderline Disorders, including both the high-functioning varieties that mimic neuroses and the low-functioning types that may transiently display psychoticlike symptoms. Also included are emotionally convoluted patients who present with a narcissistic, dependent, histrionic, compulsive, passive-aggressive, or "neurotic" defense engrafted upon a borderline core and thus seem to be neurotic, at least initially.
Mature	Resolution of rapprochement and completion of separation individuation leads to mature object relations and the capacity for either healthy adjustment or true neurotic disorder. A critical difference between mature types and the levels that precede them is that mature patients have the object relations capacity to experience *intra*psychic conflict while the lower levels invariably suffer from *inter*personal difficulties.

Mirror, Mirror on the Wall

Symbolically or in reality, every person looks in the mirror as part of the process of growth and development. The identity established by an accurate reflection helps each individual to differentiate themselves from the other. By analogy, if the other party in prerapprochement relationships is a mirror, then the mirror will reflect the nature of the patient's object relationships, depending upon his developmental level. In all the prerapprochement stages, the mirror reflects a distorted, transitive image. The *symbiotic* is like a young child playing in front of a mirror. He recognizes his reflection but if he moves to one side, his reflection instantly vanishes, as does his sense of self. The *psychopath* practices his confidence tricks in the mirror, employing it as an expedient means to a usurious end rather than as an object of value. When it no longer serves its purpose or is used up, he angrily breaks the mirror. The *narcissist* expects to see a Nobel laureate in the mirror, commanding it to reflect his overblown sense of self. If the mirror fails to do so, he angrily abandons it and looks for another mirror that better reflects his grandiose image. The *borderline* looks in the mirror and sees a reflection of the bad-self with no more than fleeting glimpses of the good-self. His vacillating good–bad perception is intensely abhorrent and he desperately asks the mirror to love him. When it fails to do so, he angrily breaks the mirror and uses a sliver of the glass to wound the bad-self, injuring the good-self in the process.

Of all the personality disorders that suffer from prerapprochement object relations problems, all but one have difficulty reciting the egocentric question posed by the evil queen in the tale of *Snow White.* The symbiotic utters in confusion: "Mirror? Mirror? On the wall?" The psychopath pronounces: "Mirror, mirror on the wall, I can con and deceive you all!" The borderline declares: "Mirror, mirror on the wall, I love you, I hate you, I want it all." Only the narcissist recites it exactly: "Mirror, mirror on the wall, who's the fairest of them all?" and then, only because the evil queen was a supreme narcissist.

LEVELS OF OBJECT RELATIONS CAPACITY

With cautionary notes about labels in mind, Table 6.2 illustrates that varying levels of object relations capacity result from the interaction of basic drives and environmental need-press, molded and formed by the relationship with early or original love objects. The *drive to satisfy needs* based upon distorted developmental object relations is one of two primary sources of motivation in Disorders of Simulation. The other major source of motivation is the avenue for satisfaction: the *discharge of anger*—directed either at the self or at the other.

Drive Origins—Original Love Object

Considerable differences result in the person's capacity to manage object relations depending upon drive origins and whether

Table 6.2
Developmental Object Relations Divided into Levels Reflecting Object Relations Capacity

Theoretic Variable	Developmental Object Relations Levels				
	Symbiotic	Psychopathic	Narcissistic	Borderline	Mature
Drive-Original Love Object	Nonexistent	Hostile-rejecting	Exploitative-unavailable	Unstable-ambivalent	Nurturing-whole
Need State	Undifferentiated	Survival	Infantile omnipotence	Dependency fulfillment	Separation-individuation
Objective or Goal	Reduction of panic	Egocentric power over the object	Egocentric confirmation with object	Magical reunion with the object	Whole object relations
Major Area of Developmental Conflict	Reality	Annihilation Anxiety: loss of control	Abandonment-depression: loss of self (death)	Abandonment-depression: (separation-engulfment)	Competence versus neurosis
Object Constancy	None	No trust	Minimal to no trust	Moderate trust	Substantial trust
Self-Object Representations	Fused: very primitive	Fused: anger	Fused: empty or aggressive	Split: very intense	Whole
Reality Testing Capacity	Very low to nonexistent	High except for object investments	High except for egocentrism	Moderate but episodically low	High: Observing ego
Strength of Ego Functions	Weak to nonexistent	Firm but aggressive self-image	Firm but grandiose self-image	Moderate but ambivalent self-image	Firm with realistic self-concept
Interpersonal Conflict Resolution	None	Sacrifice others: active	Sacrifice others: active or passive	Sacrifice self: active or passive	Good conflict resolution
Object Relations Capacity	None: objects as people	Usury: people as objects	Mirroring: self as object	Unstable: self and other as one object	Self-assertion and object mastery

the original object was absent; present but hostile or rejecting; intrusively smothering, controlling or unavailable; available but unstable or ambivalent; or present, whole, and nurturing. The variations in object relations capacity interact with basic, physiologic drives and lead to developmentally determined need states.

Need States

At the lowest (symbiotic) level, the need state is simply undifferentiated and diffuse. Somewhat greater, though still defective, levels of object relations capacity lead to more defined need states such as survival, infantile omnipotence, or dependency fulfillment (avoidance of separation-individuation). At the highest level, of course, the individual has achieved separation-individuation through tolerably effective differentiation, practicing, and rapprochement. When the individual experiences frustration of need states, lack of satisfaction negatively affects the development of frustration tolerance. That is, frustration tolerance and the observing ego both develop partly through the experience of grief over many "mini" narcissistic disappointments that, in the mature individual, summate to forbearance in the face of defeats, setbacks, and mistakes. The psychopath, however, has never learned to grieve. The narcissist can grieve but it may produce depression. The borderline grieves constantly.

Objective or Goal of the Drive

The objective or goal of drives combined with needs is satisfaction. That is, the person is internally driven to rebalance (increase or decrease) internal tension and thus restore psychodynamic equilibrium. The return of equilibrium, however, does not mean that the individual sustains no change in the process; it means only that the individual has managed to reduce his psychodynamic imbalance to bearable levels. Indeed, the individual often identifies new needs in the process of attaining satisfaction, a process that results in the rich diversity of human behavior. For example, the evolution of the ability to traverse developmental stages is based upon the presence of satisfaction in a sustaining

object relationship. There must be a "good enough" object relationship to provide safety and trust so that the individual can
resolve stage-related conflicts. The reduction of panic is the symbiotic goal. At psychopathic levels, the individual attempts to attain satisfaction from exercising power over the object. Higher
level goal distortions include egocentric confirmation by the object or magical reunion with it while the mature objective is age-
appropriate whole object relations.

Major Areas of Developmental Conflict

However, satisfaction does not always occur as the result of the
interaction between needs and drives; major areas of conflict may
be pathologically persistent. Specifically, infantile and childhood
fixations create needs that perpetually demand satisfaction from
the growing organism leading to failure to develop psychodynamically, regression under stress, or other pathology. For those with
object relations fixated at symbiotic levels, reality is a major conflict. Psychopathic individuals have little to no conflict and only
dread loss of control over the other which translates into fear of
annihilation (loss of the self). The narcissistic and borderline
individuals have in common a major conflict over abandonment-
depression, but the variety of fear that remains unconscious differs. Fixation at the narcissistic level results in fear of loss of the
self (death). Borderline patients fear loss of the other (separation) or incorporation by the other (engulfment) with the more
functional types experiencing primarily the former and the less
functional variety, the latter. When conflict is within manageable
limits, of course, the individual strives for and develops competence, usually with substantial success. In summary, for the psychopath, there is no other; for the narcissist there is a self but no
other; and for the borderline there is a self but they fear loss of
or engulfment by the other.

Object Constancy

Object constancy increases as a function of the complexity and
growth of object relations and thus rises in direct proportion
to maturity of motivation. Individuals at both the symbiotic and

psychopathic levels have virtually no trust in interpersonal object constancy. For the symbiotic patient, this observation naturally follows since there is no adequate reality perception to trust. Psychopaths perceive reality but persistently expect that others will thwart their desires and thus the psychopath must not only always be on guard and anticipate control attempts by others but also must attempt to control and manipulate others as well. Narcissistic individuals do have some capacity for object relations and therefore may display minimal but brittle trust. Such trust is fragile and easily fractured when others fail to provide the perfect mirror for their projections of superiority, uniqueness, and special ability. For patients fixated at the borderline level, their object constancy is very unstable, variable, and self-defeating. They are perpetually torn between the good-self and the bad-self but are capable of accepting therapeutic confrontation about the destructive effects of their behavior. Instead of rejecting or feeling attacked by this therapeutic intervention (as do psychopathic and narcissistic patients), borderline individuals react to confrontation by integration which, in turn, leads to the experience of depression.

Self-Object Representations

The intrapsychic structure of symbiotic individuals is essentially schizophrenic. That is, the self-object representations are fused and very primitive. Such patients are often fixated at chaotic levels and experience psychotic episodes based in primary process thought, direct impulse discharge, and organismic distress. At first glance, psychopathic individuals often seem to have adapted well and exist relatively free of anxiety and depression. Nevertheless, underlying fears of loss of control signal an angry and empty self-object representation in which the individual has no emotional investment in the object. Narcissistic individuals have a fused self-object representation that is grandiose and empty. Although ego boundaries are paradoxically firm, the grandiose self is a fragile facade; empty, envious, devoid of meaning, and prone to directed, rageful aggression toward objects that are insufficiently mirroring. Borderline individuals experience an intense, profound split in self-object representations where the patient's split ego allies with either the rewarding or withdrawing aspect of a relationship. The capacity of such patients to experience depression is much greater than the other levels and they often attempt to avoid depression by distancing, clinging, or displaying irrational behaviors.

Capacity for Reality Testing

The capacity for reality testing, of course, strongly differentiates between symbiotic level patients at one end who are overtly psychotic, and normal or neurotic individuals at the other who have good reality testing. Between these two poles lie three characterologic types characterized by partially defective reality testing. Psychopathic patients, like narcissistic individuals, display levels of reality testing that seem paradoxically high given fixation at pre-rapprochement developmental stages. Psychopathic individuals treat people as objects and their attachment is fleeting, based upon their needs at the moment. They are active takers whose lack of emotional investment in objects signals deficient reality testing, although not in the psychotic ways that characterize the prior level. They aggressively manipulate others as objects for self-satisfaction or, more rarely, engage in gross paranoid projections that violate reality.

Narcissistic types also display flaws in seemingly high levels of reality testing since, when it comes to their projections of grandiosity, they do not recognize imperfections in the self any more than they tolerate lack of perfect mirroring by others. Borderline individuals have low to moderate levels of reality testing and are particularly sensitive. They frequently misread the environment as threatening to abandon them one moment and engulf them the next. As Masterson (1981) acutely states, they behave "as if all life were one long, unresolvable rapprochement crisis" (p. 29). Such patients may deteriorate into brief psychotic episodes under stress, with temporary compromise of the capacity for accurate reality testing. In sum, the psychopath does not care how he affects others because he is invested in taking and conning; the narcissist cares but does not realize how he affects others because of his deficient observing ego; the borderline simply cares too much.

Strength of Ego Functions

The strength of ego functions correlates with reality testing but speaks directly to the capacity of the individual to function independently and effectively in the world, particularly in the use of coping skills when faced with emotional difficulty. Of course, symbiotic patients are unable to survive outside a protected and contained environment. Psychopathic types have firm ego strength as well as a large reservoir of relatively conflict-free aggression and are thus able to manage rather well until caught violating the rules. At such times, they may display anxiety and depression when their manipulations fail to extricate them from their present predicament. Narcissistic individuals also have firm ego strength but their defect lies in an extraordinarily self-centered image and need for the perfect mirror. Under stress, they may deteriorate into unbridled arrogance, infantile rage, or stunningly oblivious denial that, in turn, blinds the patient such that he may fail to avoid some remarkably desperate plights. The ego strength of borderline individuals is low to moderate at best and based in a defective self-image. Such patients are highly dependent and frequently cannot cope with reality in adaptive ways, resorting instead to self-defeating and sometimes self-destructive behaviors, particularly during periods of intense stress.

Interpersonal Conflict Resolution

The ability to resolve interpersonal conflict is directly correlated with the individual's level of object relations. For the symbiotic patient, conflict is intolerable and they take refuge in avoidance or separation of affect from cognition. Psychopathic individuals see conflict but they tend to resolve interpersonal differences in an extreme and self-serving way. Due to the distance between themselves and others, their first impulse is toward aggressive action, "taking no prisoners," and view interpersonal relations in a cold-blooded, "any means justifies the end" fashion. The narcissist, like the psychopath, "wants what they want when they want it" but their means to this end is less interpersonally usurious because conflict resolution is constrained by guilt. That is,

guilt signals the budding of superego development and an observing ego. For the borderline, object representations are internal
concepts and not at all externalized. The object and self are split
but entirely within the intrapsychic structure of the patient rather
than partially externalized as is true for the psychopath and narcissist. Consequently, borderlines resolve interpersonal conflicts
by aggressing against the self, often with the good-self harshly
judging and punishing the bad-self. Mature individuals, however,
resolve interpersonal conflicts by externalizing and internalizing,
negotiating and resolving conflict without being usurious, aggressive, or experiencing crippling assaults against the self.

Objects Relations Capacity

In summary, individuals at the symbiotic level have no object
relations capacity, no observing ego, and thus can develop no
effective frustration tolerance, object constancy (trust), capacity
for guilt, or healthy defense mechanisms, and their response to
therapeutic confrontation is customarily irrelevant. At the psychopathic level, patients establish usury object relations where others
are seen only as a means for personal gratification. Narcissistic
level patients are more sophisticated and engage in mirroring
where the object is recognized and needed, although it only
serves to reflect the self. The borderline types remain conflicted
but develop a hostile–dependent relationship with the object.
Individuals who are on the road to maturity function at the highest level and strive toward developing self-assertion and object
relations mastery.

While interesting, theoretical distinctions between various
levels of object relations capacity are difficult to observe first-
hand because they are theoretical constructs. A clinician cannot
"see" the drive origins, need states, ego strength, or object relations capacity directly in brief clinical examination. Historical
material may make an important contribution to accurate assessment of object relations capacity. However, history is often unavailable to the patient's conscious recollection, misremembered
if available, and sometimes willfully suppressed or distorted if
remembered. Obviously, rapid determination of object relations
capacity in the context of brief evaluation, rather than in the

more traditional context of extended psychotherapy, is essential in Disorders of Simulation.

MOTIVATIONAL STRUCTURE AS DERIVED FROM OBJECT RELATIONS THEORY

Developmentally based object relations theory is helpful in understanding and roughly categorizing the motivations involved in Disorders of Simulation. Since Simulation reflects disturbance in the interpersonal sphere, Simulation must be an interpersonal phenomenon and, since defective object relations are the sine qua non of interpersonal pathology, they must reflect upon interpersonal motivation. In essence, *motivation in Disorders of Simulation is interpersonal and directly relates to the patient's ability to form object relationships*; specifically, the observable, behavioral, or affective expression of underlying conflictual psychodynamic tension involved in object relationships. As illustrated in Table 6.3, observation of the patient's behavior in clinical interview, evaluation, or treatment provides motivational information, roughly compiled into five levels depending upon the patient's capacity for object relationships.

Capacity for Therapeutic Alliance

A very telling difference between those individuals who have successfully completed separation-individuation and those who have not is the capacity for therapeutic alliance. Patients with poor object relations capacity communicate an attitude of alliance with deficiencies in the self to form a working relationship against the clinician. The mature individual communicates a feeling of alliance with the clinician to form a working relationship against deficiencies in the self. Masterson (1981) has discussed the phenomenon, its linkage to whole self and object representations, and capacity for object constancy. Acute evaluators and therapists often sense this crucial distinction as early as first meeting the patient in the waiting room. Those who have the unique perceptual ability to sense the degree of therapeutic alliance—and those who aspire to learn it—informally describe it as a kind of "therapeutic sixth sense" that is difficult to teach since it usually develops from broad experience over a period of years. Limited

Table 6.3

The Axis of Motivation in Disorders of Simulation as Derived from Developmental Object Relations Theory

Observed Variables	Developmental Object Relations Levels				
	Symbiotic	Psychopathic	Narcissistic	Borderline	Mature
Capacity for Therapeutic Alliance	None	None	Minimal	Moderate	Substantial
Frustration Tolerance	None	None to minimal	Minimal to moderate	Moderate	Moderate to substantial
Capacity for Development of Guilt	Irrelevant	None	Minimal to none	Substantial	Mild to moderate
Response to Therapeutic Confrontation	Irrelevant: paralogical	Rejection: fight	Rejection: fight or flight	Acceptance: emergence of depression	Acceptance: internalization
Response to Therapeutic Interpretation	Irrelevant: paralogical	Rejection: manipulation	Acceptance: emergence of depression	Resistance: transference acting out	Acceptance: internalization
Interpersonal Conflict Resolution	Irrelevant	Aggress against others	Aggress against or abandon others	Aggress against themselves	Resolution without aggression or abandonment
Typical Defense Mechanisms that Are Used to Deal with or Avoid Abandonment-Depression, Fears of Engulfment, or Death	Parasitism & Psychotic-like symptoms such as Derealization, Depersonalization, Dissociation, Detachment	Avoidance, Projection, Denial, Antisocial acting out, Sadism, Rationalizing, Paranoia	Omnipotence, Grandiosity, Devaluation, Introjection, Withdrawal, Mirroring, Avoidance, Denial, Egocentric acting out, Exhibitionism	Splitting, Clinging, Projective-identification, Primitive idealization, Devaluation, Externalization, Rationalization, Irrational acting out, Distancing, Self-depreciation	Repression and higher neurotic defenses suggesting primarily intrapsychic conflict

capacity for therapeutic alliance often manifests as resistance, defensiveness, passive-aggressivity, and low levels of self-disclosure in psychometric evaluation and clinical interview.

Frustration Tolerance

Customarily, defense mechanisms emerge in the attempt to deal with developmental fixations, irresolvable conflicts, and lack of satisfaction. Depending upon the individual's current state, early experiences, and perhaps heredofamilial factors as well, some persons can tolerate more or less frustration than others. Frustration tolerance is the degree of delay of gratification, abstinence, or deprivation that the individual can endure without the emergence of typical defense mechanisms. Again, this factor may be readily observed in clinical situations as, for example, in noticing how the patient deals with some delay in the appointment time, the news that he will have to return for an additional evaluative session, compliance with filling out forms on initial contact, or the arduous task of completing lengthy psychological paper-and-pencil tests.

Capacity for Development of Guilt

The capacity for the experience of guilt does not correlate directly with the level of object relations maturity. While guilt is irrelevant at the symbiotic level, it is wholly deficient at the psychopathic level since such individuals have defective object relations, are usurious, or otherwise treat people as objects. Narcissistic individuals also have limited capacity for guilt since they view the self as object and engage in mirroring. While usually not experiencing guilt over his actions, the narcissistic patient may at least learn from experience and acknowledge that some of his behaviors are less likely to be tolerated than others. In contrast, borderline individuals have substantial capacity for guilt since they are closer than psychopaths or narcissists to resolution of the rapprochement crisis. They are burdened with a harsh and punitive superego that leads them to learn from experience all too readily. With maturity, and resolution of separation-individuation, guilt is transformed into the observing ego. Consequently, patients at the mature level are less driven, display object mastery, and competence such that self-assertion coexists with trust and low levels of guilt. Capacity for guilt is an inverted "U-shaped" function, absent in the symbiotic and increasing in degree to maximum in the borderline individual then declining to modest levels in mature persons. Of course, the clinician cannot observe guilt directly but may infer the capacity for it from patient statements, particularly in the context of a thorough case history.

Response to Therapeutic Confrontation

Response to therapeutic confrontation as suggested by Masterson (1981) is a litmus test for defensive structure. Confrontation requires that the therapist challenge the patient's active denial by pointing to the maladaptive defenses in a direct but nonjudgmental manner. Since therapeutic confrontation requires at least some preliminary capacity to separate self from other, it is irrelevant in the symbiotic individual who is likely to respond paralogically at best. Psychopathic and narcissistic patients are quite likely to reject confrontation since they are too vulnerable to tolerate it, although the former is likely to become aggressive (fight) while the latter is disposed to leave treatment (flight). For both, confrontation is a noxious roadblock to the satisfaction of their needs. Borderline individuals accept confrontation but, when they do so, they experience the onset of abandonment-depression. Only mature individuals tolerate therapeutic confrontation and internalize the results at emotionally meaningful levels without risking the onset of abandonment-depression.

Response to Therapeutic Interpretation

A similar test in clinical evaluation or treatment involves the patient's response to therapeutic interpretation (Masterson, 1981). A traditional, interpretative response to the patient's verbalization is, of course, irrelevant to the symbiotic and quite likely to be misinterpreted by the psychopathic patient with paranoid trends or manipulated by those with antisocial tendencies. Narcissistic patients often respond to interpretation of their egocentric vulnerability and the fact that their grandiose self-image is not always fulfilled although such patients are ever-alert to any sign that even carefully rendered interpretation may contain a hint of subtle, implied criticism. The use of interpretation with border-line individuals, however, often leads to transference acting out because the patient may use the clinician's insight as a supporting force for the pathologic portion of the ego. Mature patients are quite likely to benefit from either type of therapeutic technique and neither is likely to negatively affect the therapeutic or evaluative alliance.

Interpersonal Conflict Resolution

The manner in which the individual customarily resolves conflicts with others tells a great deal about their object relations level. Symbiotic patients, of course, have no object relations and there is therefore no interpersonal conflict to resolve. The psychopath qualifies all interpersonal relations in terms of anger and is most likely to resolve conflicts by aggressing against others. That is, "if it's me or thee, I choose me and to hell with thee." In dealing with conflict in a person at the psychopathic level, the clinician may expect that he inevitably will be manipulated, assaulted, or betrayed and his treatment subverted or co-opted in hostile, angry ways. When the narcissist and the clinician have conflict, the narcissist, like the psychopath, may become aggressive but a more typical tactic is simply to angrily abandon the relationship and search elsewhere for a more suitably reflective mirror. Border-lines are as angry as psychopaths and narcissists but tend to turn the anger inward and aggress against themselves. They resolve conflict by scarifying, disfiguring, overmedicating, threatening suicide, or otherwise damaging the bad-self. Mature individuals adopt appropriate interpersonal styles when attempting to resolve conflict and are more likely to talk things through (i.e., real psychotherapy) than display the angry aggression associated with prerapprochement patients.

Typical Defense Mechanisms

Finally, Table 6.3 lists readily observable and customary but mal-adaptive defense mechanisms that are associated with and help discriminate one level of motivational structure from another. The cataloging of the patient's defensive structures is a familiar task for most mental health professionals and little need be said about how this task should be undertaken.

Variants and Veneers

It is important to understand how subvarieties and variants are different from each other within—and sometimes between—levels of object relations. For example, patients with a borderline level of object relations capacity may initially present as narcissistic. In such cases, the narcissistic presentation is a veneer and defense against a borderline problem; in essence, the appearance of being narcissistic is a "defense" against the borderline level. While the distinction between pure narcissism and the narcissistic defense against a borderline core is never simple, careful observation and case history make the task easier.

Another differential diagnostic problem involves the distinctions between high- and low-functioning patients at narcissistic, borderline, and occasionally even symbiotic levels. Individuals who function at high borderline levels may look remarkably like neurotics but often betray themselves by demonstrating a clinging defense while low-functioning borderline patients tend to gravitate to distancing defenses. Indeed, low-level borderline types may distance to such an extent that they episodically look symbiotic and may suffer temporary psychotic episodes under stress. Narcissistic patients may also function at high and low levels. Higher functioning individuals may present with apparently neurotic symptoms often with a "phallic" quality. Lower functioning narcissistic types are, in the view of some authors, virtually identical with psychopaths although the acting out is usually quite egocentric as opposed to the antisocial psychopathic variety.

FIVE TYPES OF MOTIVATIONAL STRUCTURE

There are five types of motivational structure based on object relations capacity and these levels hold substantial implication for the diagnosis of Disorders of Simulation. While there is clearly some relationship between these levels and the psychodynamics of personality disorders, the standard *DSM-IV* descriptions do not refer to motivation or object relations directly. Since motivation is a critical variable, it must be considered in greater detail than the internal–external incentives dichotomy offered in *DSM-IV* for Factitious Disorders and Malingering.

Symbiotic Motivation

At the symbiotic level, the original object was nonexistent or unavailable and the child received no help in organizing or making sense of the "booming, buzzing, confusing" external world. Needs are undifferentiated and diffuse with the only goal being a state of object stability and reduction in the infant's sense of panic. Obviously, in the absence of attachment, emotional nourishment, and sensory stimulation, the infant experiences impoverishment and gross stunting of emotional development. The experience of reality is a major conflict for persons whose growth stopped at the symbiotic level. Object constancy is nil, self-object relations are fused, and reality testing is very low to absent. In essence, the patient has weak to nonexistent ego strength and the capacity for object relations is virtually zero. In an attempt to bring stability to a puzzling and overwhelming stimulus environment, the patient often uses predictable, inanimate objects as a substitute for the panic-inducing uncertainty of human relationships.

Symbiotic individuals have no real capacity for therapeutic alliance and their frustration tolerance is wholly deficient. The patient lives in a highly personal world where the wish and the deed remain indistinguishable and the experience of guilt is not relevant. The individual does not relate to others in any effective way since there is no sense of object constancy and the response to therapeutic confrontation or interpretation is therefore irrelevant or paralogical. Therefore, the symbiotic has no effective strategies for interpersonal conflict resolution. They also do not have the capacity for development of complex defense mechanisms and their symptoms remain at the low level of chaotic thinking, emotional parasitism, detachment, and psychotic-like behaviors.

Patients who simulate are usually more complex than symbiotics since simulation is an interpersonal phenomenon and threshold levels of object relations are required at a minimum. However, even very dysfunctional individuals usually have periods of remission with temporarily elevated levels of ego strength and object relations. While institutionalized or appropriately maintained on an outpatient basis with therapy and antipsychotic medications, patients may episodically experience some elevation in ego functioning, allowing them to imitate a higher level. That is, the structure involved in inpatient programs or well-tracked outpatient treatment may result in some clearing of gross symptoms.

Case Example 6.1—Chaos Reigns Supreme

A chronic paranoid schizophrenic was sent to a correctional medical facility for inpatient evaluation and treatment following his arrest on charges of first degree murder. Although still moderately symptomatic, treatment allowed temporary elevation to the psychopathic level of object relations capacity. He was able to recognize that evidence of gross organic disturbance on psychiatric and psychological evaluation would be of assistance to his legal defense. Under conditions of institutionally and psychotropically imposed structure he was able to erratically simulate brain injury on neuropsychological testing in primitive, unsophisticated, and wholly transparent ways. Although his simulatory activity was uncomplex and relatively easy to identify, his case illustrates that even patients with grossly deficient object relations capacity can, under some circumstances, at least attempt simulation. Clearly, simulatory attempts by symbiotic patients require elevation—however temporary and by whatever means—to a higher motivational (object relations) level.

Psychopathic Motivation

The psychopathic level often results from hostile or rejecting early objects with the result that the individual interprets the world as a dangerous place where survival is the paramount concern. They look to the self as the primary source of satisfaction and are most secure when negotiating for or reveling in a state of egocentric power and control over others. Such individuals have few conflict areas other than the establishment of their own identity but experience underlying primitive concern over loss of control. Psychopathic individuals do not trust others (minimal object constancy), view the world with suspicion, and fail to develop customary social and interpersonal values. Their self-object representations are empty and angry but reality testing is good in all areas except, of course, their object investments. Ego strength is firm but aggressive. That is, others exist solely to gratify and satisfy the self and such gratification, in turn, provides a sense of identity. In daily life, maintaining control over others holds annihilation anxiety at bay. Thus, the object relations capacity of psychopaths is quite usurious and people are simply objects to be manipulated.

Psychopathic individuals have essentially no capacity for establishment of a therapeutic or evaluative alliance just as they have no frustration tolerance or capacity for delay of gratification. No guilt is evident when they control or manipulate others for their own self-centered ends, even when others are emotionally or physically injured by their actions. Therapeutic techniques such as confrontation and interpretation are pointless. Psychopaths strongly resist and fight confrontation through projection, denial, rationalization, and paranoid or antisocial acting out. When the therapist attempts interpretation, rejection occurs through avoidance and attempts to fool the clinician by faking a dyadic relationship. Any interaction is a conflict for psychopaths unless they are in complete control and the usual method of conflict resolution is therefore interpersonal aggression.

The early reinforced fears of annihilation and loss of control generate such an arid basis for interpersonal development that the seeds of object relations fall on barren soil. The patient's motivational structure involves nothing more than egocentric satisfaction at the primitive level of detached object control. Concern over control occurs because external objects represent either a threat or potential gratification. In effect, fulfillment of impulse or fantasy, whether negative or positive, is experienced as being at least as important as reality; external objects are a ready and convenient means to this end.

Such patients attempt to influence objects by force, ingratiation, or manipulation in order to gain immediate gratification and a sense of control. The capacity for delay of gratification is marginal at best and, consequently, there is little of the self-discipline needed to attain satisfaction through protracted effort. Psychopathic individuals violate customary social standards with demonstrated lack of concern for the welfare of others and without a sense of guilt over their transgressions. Moreover, because psychopathic individuals fail to profit from experience, they frequently fail to profit as much from their illegal activities as would be the case if they directed equal effort toward more socialized activities. This is true, of course, because the patient's motivation is for control over objects rather than relationship with them. To achieve control, psychopathically motivated patients justify, rationalize, claim special privilege, or otherwise manipulate in a limitless variety of ways but always with a sense of detachment from the object rather than attachment to it.

Because control is the objective and because satisfaction is hedonistic, psychopathic patients are quite unlikely to develop Factitious Disorders where self-injury or self-degradation is usually part of the clinical picture. It is also true that Factitious patients require greater levels of object relations than psychopaths can muster, involving rapprochement difficulties with self-object splitting, conflicts between good-self and bad-self, guilt, and related object relations issues. Compensation Neurosis in psychopaths is possible but unlikely since the course of the disorder is usually protracted and the control exerted over others is more passive than active. In essence, Compensation Neurosis requires that the psychopath give up more control to others over a longer time than he can tolerate. When psychopathic patients appear to be extending, elaborating, or exaggerating the effects of injury, a close clinical examination generally reveals that they do so with a sense of active aggression yet emotional detachment rather than the passive dependency usually associated with Compensation Neurosis. Malingering is the most likely Disorder of Simulation since the patient is actively in control of both symptom design and display, a feature that is certainly congruent with the usurious view psychopaths take of people-as-objects to be manipulated for self-satisfaction on an immediately gratifying basis. Indeed, some may covertly challenge the clinician to discover their Simulation since the clinician's anticipated failure to do so is interpreted as enormously satisfying proof of the patient's ability to exert control.

Case Example 6.2—Visual Gratification

A 42-year-old construction worker sustained a light, glancing blow to the head without loss of consciousness. Medical records suggested a mild postconcussive syndrome and possible diplopia that rapidly cleared. Months later, however, he began to experience worsening of his "diplopia" which was now noted to be present even when one eye was occluded. Upon psychological evaluation two years postinjury, he wore dark glasses and persistently collided with walls and furniture during the walk to the examination room. He maintained that his vision was so bad he could not read even very large print. Yet, when asked to recite words starting with the letter "C," he mentioned words such as *cerebral*, *clinical*, and *cortical*, obviously reading titles from an office bookshelf. He had a normal visual angle as measured by the letter sizes and the distance from the patient's eye to the bookshelf. Moreover, he read the tiles from books standing vertically, in subdued lighting, through dark glasses, and with a casual expression rather than the intensely furrowed brow and squinty eyes he displayed earlier when failing to read very large type. The patient's wry smile suggested he took considerable perverse pleasure in "defeating" the examiner and exerting control by "cheating" on the test despite the fact that, in doing so, he betrayed normal visual functioning. Sometimes, gratifying the self takes precedence over prudent Simulation.

Narcissistic Motivation

Patients in this motivational category frequently experienced either exploitative, unavailable original objects or original objects that were the perfect mirror. Often there is a considerable component of perfectionism in the original object's idealizing projections. Consequently, the child often fails to move beyond the need for infantile omnipotence and they perpetually expect egocentric confirmation of their grandiose but empty self-image. Despite their overt expectations, narcissistic individuals greatly fear loss of the self (emotional and/or physical death) as the result of abandonment-depression induced by the original object. Such patients have minimal to no object constancy and do not trust in others. They have a fused self-object representation as is true for the symbiotic individual but it is empty or aggressive rather than psychopathic. The major factor distinguishing the fused self-object representation of the symbiotic from the narcissistic patient is the capacity for reality testing; the narcissistic individual's capacity for reality testing is excellent except in the area of their grandiose and egocentric projections. Ego strength is firm but revolves around mirroring relationships and the individual is therefore concerned with external representations such as power, beauty, status, prestige, and wealth. That is, the patient's motivational structure involves egocentric satisfaction and the external object is simply an extension of the self.

Narcissistic patients have minimal to no capacity for forging a therapeutic or evaluative alliance and frustration tolerance is equally low. Object relations are sufficiently disturbed that mirroring is paramount and there is little room for empathy, guilt, or concern for the welfare of others. To the extent that the patient displays apparent compassion, the presentation is often false and results from the expectation that seeming to attend to the welfare of others will result in self-satisfaction. Acting out, however, is more likely to be egocentric than antisocial. When faced with therapeutic confrontation, narcissistic patients immediately reject this approach through fight or flight. That is, they either argue about the confrontation in order to avoid the assault to the grandiose self-image or seek to deny and escape the therapeutic situation altogether. Narcissistic patients are more amenable to traditional therapeutic interpretation—they require the distance that interpretation provides—and may often become depressed over the realization that the world has failed to perfectly mirror their projections.

Therapeutic interpretation versus confrontation also helps to distinguish between high- and low-functioning narcissistic patients. Lower level individuals often appear brittle and rigid, constantly on guard against any real or perceived threat to their grandiose self-image. Like the psychopathic patient, they are often more ready to fight than flee, bristle with anger and paranoid vigilance, and thus seem quite insecure and vulnerable despite their projections of omnipotence and power. The patient often displays a quality of righteous indignation, rationalization, or justification of symptom elaboration with appeal to an initial real injury. Like the psychopath, they externalize and project. These feelings may be transmuted into desires that a personal wrong be righted, a wish to punish others for base or revengeful motives, or indication that the patient desires to hold others responsible for his own long-standing failure and lack of success. Higher functioning narcissistic patients, while equally grandiose, seem less hostile and are more likely to simply leave the field upon confrontation rather than fight with the therapist. They project a quality of invulnerability, self-assurance, and imperviousness that allows them to readily discount real or imagined criticisms. Both high- and low-functioning narcissistic patients view others as inferior, expect special status or privilege, and hold themselves above the rules of social custom. However, the high-functioning variety seems quite comfortable with this view while the low-functioning patient rigidly defends his view with a quality of desperate aggressivity. Customarily, narcissists encounter conflict with the clinician if therapy or evaluation lasts for sufficient time. Their most likely avenue for resolution of the conflict is to leave the field and seek someone who will more perfectly mirror their grandiose sense of self.

Because narcissistic patients are concerned with completely egocentric needs and satisfaction, the frequency of self-abnegation and self-inflicted injury such as in Factitious Disorder is low. Compensation Neurosis is possible in narcissistic patients although it is more likely to emerge when dependency needs are stronger, such as amongst those patients who have a dependent or histrionic and thus "neurotic-appearing" overlay. Compensation Neurosis may emerge in low-functioning narcissistic individuals whose grandiose projections are more tenuously held than they would have themselves or others believe and who, through their hostile affectivity, betray strong unacknowledged dependency needs. Malingering is quite likely to occur amongst narcissistic patients since highly self-centered individuals do not view themselves as doing wrong when they fabricate or grossly exaggerate symptoms; they only seek that which they desire, need, and feel they deserve. Their sense of superiority and omnipotence is so pervasive that they may fabricate gross symptoms on a very thin base, ignore the capacity of others to detect even the most obvious of manipulations. They may assume that their deception will pass muster because they cannot imagine that others would doubt their word. As Millon (1981) states, "since they reflect minimally on what others think, their defensive maneuvers are transparent, a poor camouflage to a discerning eye. This failure to bother dissembling more thoroughly also contributes to their being seen as cocksure and arrogant" (p. 168). In this instance, Millon probably intends "dissembling" to mean the same as "simulating" although an argument can also be made that such patients dissimulate as well.

Case Example 6.3—Filial Duty

> The patient was a 62-year-old, obviously bright, intact, CEO of a family corporation. He disliked having to deal with the corporate president who was his younger brother and an incapable bumbler. The patient, who had invested heavily in the corporation, desperately wished to retire but was trapped in his role of CEO to protect his financial investment as well as to fulfill his promise to his mother to protect his inadequate sibling. During a fishing trip, the patient stood behind their rented RV to help guide his brother out of a parking lot. The patient was lightly grazed by the slow-moving vehicle and suffered no apparent damage but, in a suit against his brother's insurer, he claimed emotional distress and physical injury with consequent inability to work. On evaluation, the patient's claims were excessive and undocumented. Because of his grandiosity, his strategy for simulation was very obvious and transparent: he simply described emotional and physical injury without displaying any customary clinical or psychometric features. He believed that others would accept his self-reported symptoms and could not imagine otherwise, self-confidently assuming he would succeed because he could not conceive that anyone would question his word.

Motivationally, this patient's simulation of injury satisfied his need to express disdain for his brother and anger over a promise exacted by a demanding mother. It was also an expression of his belief in his own superiority and a fortuitous solution to his dilemma. If his lawsuit were successful, the financial recovery would amortize his investment; it would void his promise to protect his inept brother; it would provide an excuse for resignation as CEO without suffering humiliation or financial loss. Like most narcissists, the patient was intensely interested in protecting his own grandiosity and omnipotence and it was easy to demonstrate his direct, volitional symptom control. His claim of injury was thus an act of narcissistic motivation rather than an unconscious, neurotic solution.

Borderline Motivation

Patients at the borderline motivational level frequently experience a highly unstable and ambivalent early love object. Chaotic and inconstant original life experiences have led to deficits in nurturance and left the child with grossly unmet dependency needs. Therefore, the patient experiences constant longing for the goal of magical reunion with the original object. Fear of loss of the object, in the form of abandonment-depression, is the major conflict area for borderline patients. Borderlines experience twin fears and are perpetually storm-tossed between two dangers. On one side, borderline individuals experience fear of the Scylla of separation from the object while, on the other side, they worry about the Charybdis of engulfment by the object.

By definition borderline individuals do not develop full object constancy and therefore have no more than moderate levels of interpersonal trust. Their self-object representations are split into separate but intense conceptions of the good-self and the bad-self. On one side the patient experiences rewarding and libidinal affect associated with feeling good but, on the other side, the patient experiences withdrawing and aggressive affect associated with hopelessness, helplessness, as well as rage fostered by underlying abandonment-depression. Reality testing is no more than moderate and may decline precipitously under severe stress such that the patient may experience brief psychotic episodes. The patient's ego strength is very shaky due to a defective self-image and the capacity for object relations is poor. The patient attempts to avoid separation-individuation at all costs so that the self and other remain as one.

Despite the borderline patient's poor object relations, there is moderate capacity for the development of a therapeutic or evaluative alliance. The alliance is, of course, fragile and vulnerable to distortions through attempts by the patient to maneuver the clinician into the role of either a positively or negatively rewarding object. Frustration tolerance for borderline patients is moderate at best but, in contrast, their capacity for guilt is substantial. This is, of course, consistent with patients whose motivational structure reflects deep underlying ambivalence toward objects. Such patients are resistant to therapeutic interpretation and often display their distress through transference acting out. Frequently, they do respond to therapeutic confrontation of the variety suggested by Masterson (1981) and their acceptance allows underlying depression due to abandonment-depression to emerge.

As with other motivational levels based in developmental object relations, different characteristic defenses are employed by patients at the extremes of borderline functioning. Low-functioning patients tend to distance whereas those at the high end of the spectrum are more inclined to cling. All levels engage in splitting, although those who display a narcissistic defense against a borderline disorder may appear to display merging or fusing on initial evaluation. Lower level patients use rather simplistic defense mechanisms and may decompensate to near psychotic levels, often preceded by depersonalization, loss of reality, and irrational acting out. High level borderline individuals, however, often present with classically "neurotic" defense mechanisms.

On clinical evaluation, borderline patients display interpersonal ambivalence, a conflict between dependency and independency. They are either good or bad and fail to appreciate intermediate positions. At this level, patients experience or anticipate some measure of emotional satisfaction from externalization of the bad-self, projecting and blaming problems on others. In such cases a minor injury at the hands of another may be held responsible for the patient's current dysfunctional state and a variety of other problems that, with investigation, prove to have been part of the patient's life for many years. Rarely, the patient may have had no injury at all but, through the indirect expression of interpersonal ambivalence and disturbed object relations, produces symptoms in the form of self-inflicted injury, self-abnegation, or self-castigation. This occurs, of course, because the borderline patient tends to resolve interpersonal conflict by turning his rage inward and aggressing against the self.

In either case, these patients focus upon dependency fulfillment or anxiety resolution. Although the patient may erroneously blame others for their predicament, at a deeper level, the patient obtains gratification of underlying needs for emotional support, sympathy, pity, or caretaking. These needs are probably based in early deprivation and lack of nurturance. For example, a patient experiences partial alleviation of a dependency crisis through the attention and support forthcoming from others. Another patient is depressed and gains substantial support and relief from his somatoform complaints and the medical attention they elicit. In such cases, the patient relieves anxiety, saves face, or hides failure in life from the self, all the while displaying overt distress or consternation over the symptoms. In the case of some very dependent and passive individuals, the patient may find it easy to conform to the expectation that he is seriously defective since his dependency makes him an easy target for manipulative relatives.

While high-functioning borderline patients may engage in Malingering under particularly fortuitous circumstances, the degree of planfulness and consistency usually implied is difficult for low-functioning individuals who are already quite occupied managing their chaotic object relations. Factitious Disorders are most likely to occur within the borderline population and, in fact, may be limited to it. Since there is an enormous capacity for underlying guilt and since it is common for such patients to mutilate, injure, or brutalize themselves, the ground is fertile for growth of a Factitious Disorder. However, Compensation Neurosis is probably the most common Disorder of Simulation since the dependency-inducing aspect can be strongly tempting and there is usually some real accident, illness, or injury to be extended, exaggerated, or otherwise amplified.

Case Example 6.4—A Pain in the Department

A recently promoted Black male in his early 40's, a 17-year veteran laborer, sued a City department alleging harassment, racial discrimination, unfair duties, and inequitable treatment. He felt excessively disciplined, not credited for overtime, thwarted in career advancement, and treated without respect. He claimed significant emotional and physical difficulties due to job stress. Evaluating physicians described the patient as having many more complaints than could be medically verified and the record was replete with suggestions of "functional overlay." There seemed to be virtually no coworkers with whom he did not have a history of angry "flare-ups." A comprehensive Department of Fair Employment and Housing investigation revealed constant personality clashes between the patient and most of his multiracial coworkers, supervisees, and supervisors, but no evidence of discrimination. The patient had long been a burr

under the department's saddle but was nonetheless promoted in the for-
lorn hope that, if the department met his incessant demands for advancement, perhaps his eternal passive-aggressivity and contentiousness
would diminish.

Although he sued, financial compensation was secondary. He had
very retrenched object relations problems manifested as projection, blaming, and conflict between dependency and independency. He needed dependency fulfillment, anxiety resolution, a
way to direct blame to others and, at a deeper level, gratification
of his long unmet and highly conflictual underlying needs for
emotional support, sympathy, pity, and caretaking. Simultaneously, he felt intense anger and resentment over his inability to
function independently. His pattern was one of manipulating others in an attempt to resolve his lifelong separation–individua-
tion issues.

Mature Motivation

Mature individuals, of course, have completed rapprochement
on the way to separation-individuation and whole object relations.
In their formative years, the original love object was present,
whole, and nurturing. Rather than resisting the establishment of
a separate identity and positive self-image, mature individuals
strive for these goals. Their conflicts are less interpersonal and
more intrapsychic such that they tend to develop normally or, if
conflicted, display dysfunctional traits, neurotic styles, or actual
disorder that, prior to *DSM-III* (APA, 1980), would have been
characterized as neurosis. The mature individual has substantial
trust since object constancy is high and their self-object representations are whole. Reality testing is excellent with the firm ego
strength that their self-assertive object relations capacity requires.
They strive for and attain very acceptable levels of object mastery.
Mature individuals have a well-developed observing ego, are capable of effective conflict resolution, and are better able to consider
a variety of options in interpersonal relations.

When mature patients enter evaluation or undertake psychotherapy, they quickly display substantial capacity for a helping
alliance. In contrast to psychopathic, narcissistic, and borderline

patients, the mature patient accepts the clinician's offer of help with the desire to form an alliance against the defective part of the self. Although mature patients may experience high levels of emotional discomfort and moderate levels of guilt, they neverthe-less display substantial frustration tolerance. They respond to therapeutic confrontation or interpretation with acceptance and internalization. Patients use repression and higher level neurotic maneuvers to defend against anxiety and depression, and the defensive strategy often has clear psychodynamic implications.

Individuals at the mature level also display a motivational structure based upon intact object relations capacity and an ob-serving ego. Since simulation is an interpersonal phenomenon, and since mature patients are intrapsychically rather than inter-personally conflicted, their frequency of simulation is very low. Of course, from time to time all mature individuals tell "little white lies," or stay home from work a day longer than needed for recovery from the flu, or fail to tell the IRS about gambling winnings from Las Vegas. While some authors (Yudofsky, 1985) have gone so far as to identify such events as Malingering, these instances suggest neither a Disorder of Simulation nor evidence of deficient object relations. Focus upon such normal behaviors trivializes the notion of simulation (Weintraub, 1989). To indicate that false excuses such as "Not tonight dear, I have a headache" fall within the same category as Malingering, Factitious Disorder, and Compensation Neurosis is to confuse the symptom with the disease. All mature people make false excuses or otherwise en-gage in mild forms of deceit but they do so with *intact* object relations capacity while those with Disorders of Simulation do so with incomplete object representations and subsequently defi-cient object relations capacity.

SUMMARY

Intact versus disturbed object relations capacity and, specifically, the level of object relations when disturbed (Table 6.4), consti-tutes the second major axis in evaluation of Disorders of Simu-lation.

As is true for Axes I and III, no one score or level of function-ing on any Axis is sufficient to warrant the conclusion that the

Table 6.4

Varieties of Motivation Frequently Associated with Developmental
Object Relations Levels

Level of Object Relations Capacity	Motivational Structure Associated with		
	Malingering	Factitious Disorders	Compensation Neurosis
Symbiotic	Rare	No	No
Psychopathic	Yes	No	No
Narcissistic Low-Functioning	Yes	No	No
Narcissistic	Yes	No	Rare
Narcissistic High-Functioning	Yes	No	Yes
Borderline Low-Functioning	Yes	Yes	Yes
Borderline	Yes	Rare	Yes
Borderline High-Functioning	Yes	Rare	Yes
Mature	No	No	No

patient suffers from a Disorder of Simulation. However, it might
be fair to state that one of the main techniques for making the
eternally troublesome discrimination between the hysteria-like
disorders and simulation is evaluation of the patient's developmental object relations level. If an individual's level of object
relations is sufficiently mature to allow him to climb above the
rung of rapprochement on the developmental ladder, he is unlikely to descend. He will probably continue to climb to hysteria
or beyond.

7

Axis III: Personality Pathology

> Malingering cannot be considered independent of the personality types who employ it or of the pressures which occasion its manifestations, any more than a physician can treat a fever independent of the disease or infections that cause it. (Flicker, 1956)

In Disorders of Simulation, the patient's presentation occurs in the context of his personality type. Since deficient object relations are involved in simulating disorders, it is entirely likely that patients who fabricate have documentable personality pathology or, at the very least, strongly dysfunctional personality traits that nearly rise to the magnitude of formal disorder. Of course, formal Personality Disorder, as well as important but subclinical personality trait disturbances, are customarily diagnosed on Axis II of *DSM-IV* (APA, 1994). As discussed in chapter 6, a significant problem of terminology quickly emerges when differential diagnosis is attempted according to *DSM-IV* (APA, 1994) standards by a clinician who must also consider the patient's object relations capacity.

THE *DSM* PERSONALITY DISORDER DIAGNOSTIC SYSTEM

With the advent of *DSM-III* (APA, 1980), traditional concepts of character disorder, personality pathology, and neurosis were substantially revised. There is, for example, a less than perfect correlation between the developmental object relations notions of narcissistic and borderline personality conditions and the Narcissistic and Borderline Disorders according to the diagnostic criteria of *DSM*. Indeed, the revised taxonomic system basically allows for diagnosis of the lowest functioning borderline and the average narcissist. It does not address the complex psychodynamic formulation required to detect high functioning borderline patients or low functioning narcissists, for example. Patients may slip through the wide mesh of the *DSM-IV* (APA, 1994) differential diagnostic sieve because they are more finely grained than the gross and widely spaced criteria set to capture only enduring "clinically significant distress or impairment in social, occupational, or other important areas of functioning" (*DSM-IV*, APA, 1994, p. 633).

Consequently, high-functioning borderlines escape diagnosis altogether while high-functioning narcissists may be mistaken for "neurotics" and low-functioning narcissists for Antisocial Personality Disorder. Additionally, diagnosis of narcissistic defense against a Borderline Personality Disorder is difficult. Some patients who present with this defensive structure may thus be erroneously diagnosed as Narcissistic Personality Disorder. Although a less frequent phenomenon, borderlines may also present with a broad range of veneers in sufficient degree to qualify for Histrionic, Dependent, Obsessive-Compulsive, Passive-Aggressive, or other less severe variety of *DSM-IV* Personality Disorder. Another unaddressed and particularly difficult discrimination occurs when the clinician attempts to distinguish psychoneurotic conflict manifested by regression to narcissistic or borderline defenses from true Borderline or Narcissistic Disorder.

THREE *DSM* OPTIONS FOR DIAGNOSING DIFFICULT PERSONALITY CONFIGURATIONS

In part, *DSM-IV* (APA, 1994) attempts to address the problem of complex formulations in Personality Disorder by offering the clinician three options. First, combinations of several types are allowed under Personality Disorder Not Otherwise Specified (NOS). This diagnostic category is relevant when the patient displays: "features of more than one specific Personality Disorder that do not meet the full criteria for any one Personality Disorder ('mixed personality'), but that together cause clinically significant distress or impairment in one or more important areas of functioning (i.e., social or occupational)" (p. 673). Thus, it is possible to diagnose patients who partially display both Borderline and Narcissistic elements, for example.

The second option is the diagnosis of two or more separate Personality Disorders on Axis II when the patient simultaneously fulfills all the criteria for each. The third option is to note nondiagnostic but significant personality *traits* which, by definition, neither constitute formal disorder nor rise to the level of significant impairment or subjective distress. While not constituting a diagnosis, the description of personality traits may be helpful in further evaluation or treatment. The problem with the threefold *DSM-IV* (APA, 1994) approach is, in itself, threefold.

Problems with the Threefold Approach

First, diagnosis of Personality Disorder requires significant impairment in social or occupational functioning, or subjective distress, a criterion that neglects highly pathological individuals with defective developmental object relations who nevertheless manage to remain married, hold a job, and acknowledge no complaints of subjective distress. In essence, *DSM-IV* requires that the patient first be found behaviorally disordered with the psychodiagnostic formulation a secondary matter, rather than first evaluating the patient's psychodynamics and level of developmental object relations in order to next determine whether and what kind of diagnosis is applicable. The nondiagnostic notation of significant personality traits on Axis II only partly ameliorates this problem.

Second, since the Axis II criteria for diagnoses are largely if not wholly descriptive and behavioral, they cannot reflect the subtle shadings of defensive structure unconsciously erected by developmentally crippled patients to deal with abandonment-depression and other object relations issues. Such shadings are often only evident in dynamic psychotherapy or upon depthful evaluation in response to tests of insight and psychological mindedness, frustration tolerance, capacity for guilt, response to confrontation

or interpretation, as well as the careful cataloging of specific defense mechanisms. Thus, in many cases, evaluation of object relations is needed to affirm the presence of psychopathology,
particularly when the patient cannot be qualified for more than
"traits" on Axis II.

Third, although the most important disorder should be listed
first when Personality Disorder, NOS is diagnosed or when more
than one Personality Disorder is noted on Axis II, it is difficult
to sensibly designate which personality is primary and which is
secondary. In neither case are issues of defense against pathology
versus actual pathology, primary versus secondary pathology, or
generic versus variant pathology addressed. That is, without psychodynamic and developmental knowledge and with only a list
of personality descriptions and behaviors as reference, subtle dis-
criminations are difficult. For example, no *DSM-IV* (APA, 1994)
criteria exist for distinguishing between low-functioning Narcissists and high-functioning Antisocials; between Narcissism and
Narcissistic defense against a Borderline Disorder; between Histrionic Personality Disorder and Histrionic defense against Borderline or Narcissistic Disorders; or between high- and low-
functioning Borderlines.

This problem is further compounded when attempts are
made to group or cluster Personality Disorders according to specified criteria. In part, this difficulty results from the *polythetic DSM*
Axis II format where a certain number of features must be present
to diagnose Personality Disorder but where less frequently is a
single symptom or group of symptoms absolutely required. This
approach is essentially atheoretical and has probably served the
intended purpose of increasing diagnostic reliability, although
many fear at the cost of richness, diversity, and, ultimately, validity. Nevertheless, *DSM-IV* is the only widely accepted differential
diagnostic taxonomy and most mental health professionals refer
to it frequently when a formal report of findings is required. It is
the text most often cited in depositions and court testimony and
variation from it in a forensic setting can have significant negative
consequences.

With all its benefits and failings, the *DSM-IV*'s polythetic,
multiaxial approach is part of the current reality of mental health
research, diagnosis, and treatment. In Disorders of Simulation,

patients invariably display personality disturbance in the form of either significant traits or formal disorder, encouraging the clinician to attempt qualification on Axis II of *DSM-IV*. It is because the description of Personality Disorders in *DSM-IV* does not accurately describe patients with subtle shadings of object relations problems that it is necessary to consider both the Axis of Motivation (object relations), discussed in the prior chapter, and the Axis of Personality Pathology in the present chapter. These two axes are not in perfect alignment and some loss of meaning will occur if Disorders of Simulation are considered solely on either the Motivational or Personality Pathology Axis alone.

DSM-IV lists 10 official Personality Disorders and two additional under Criteria Sets and Axes Provided for Further Study. The 10 basic Personality Disorders are subdivided into three clusters: Cluster A disorders are odd or eccentric (Schizoid, Schizotypal, Paranoid); Cluster B disorders are dramatic, emotional, or erratic (Histrionic, Borderline, Antisocial, Narcissistic); and Cluster C disorders are anxious or fearful (Dependent, Obsessive-Compulsive, Avoidant). Two Personality Disorders listed in *DSM-IV* for further study are Passive-Aggressive and Depressive (unstated but probably in Cluster C). The *DSM-III-R* (APA, 1987) listed two other disorders, Sadistic (probably Cluster B) and Self-Defeating (probably Cluster C), bringing the grand total to 14. The rationale for *DSM* clusters is not explicit but appears to reflect phenotypic similarity rather than genotypic analysis or theoretical principles. A particularly cogent criticism has been formulated by Millon (1981, pp. 62–64).

MILLON'S ALTERNATIVE CLASSIFICATION SYSTEM

Millon's (1981) alternative conceptualization of personality types is more relevant to Disorders of Simulation since he emphasizes the external social context, interpersonal dynamics, and the patient's intrapsychic organization in equal measure. The patient's relational manner in interpersonal and social contexts elicits feedback that tends to amplify, stabilize, or diminish the patient's Axis I problems and, to some extent, modify the presentation of

their Axis II Personality Disorder as well. While Millon acknowl-
edges the central importance of psychodynamic organization, he
also incorporates significant elements from social learning theory. "It is not only structural ego capacity, therefore, but also the
particular features of social and familial behavior that will dispose
the patient to relate to others in a manner that will prove increasingly adaptive or maladaptive" (p. 65).

Millon subdivides the 11 Personality Disorders into three
groups. The first group includes Disorders that are interpersonally either dependent or independent (Dependent, Histrionic,
Narcissistic, Antisocial). The second group involves a midlevel of
personality pathology where the patient is ambivalent, isolated,
or estranged (Compulsive, Passive-Aggressive, Schizoid, Avoidant)
while the third group involves the lowest level of personality functioning where the patient is socially incompetent, difficult to relate to, and often confused (Borderline, Paranoid, Schizotypal).
Millon cogently formulated groups on both social and intrapsychic dimensions and they require only minor, further refinement
in order to categorize Personality Disorders in ways that are particularly relevant to Disorders of Simulation.

PERSONALITY CLASSIFICATION IN DISORDERS OF SIMULATION

The combined 14 Personality Disorders of *DSM-III-R* and *DSM-IV*
may be arranged along various dimensions and partitioned in
different ways depending upon the particular theoretical framework or practical requirements of the problem under study. Obviously, *DSM* Personality Disorders cannot easily be cataloged
according to developmental object relations theory. If there was
perfect overlap between the meaning of "narcissistic" as used by
developmental object relations theorists and "Narcissistic" as
used in *DSM-IV*, there would be no need for separate axes devoted
to motivation and personality pathology in Disorders of Simulation. At present, however, diagnosing patients who simulate illness or injury requires the use of a *DSM* axis to calibrate a
patient's standing as well as the axes of Behavioral Orchestration
and Motivation. A theoretical basis for organizing Personality Disorders is needed in order to accomplish this goal efficiently.

While there are endless permutations for categorizing the 14 disorders, the relevant dimensions for Disorders of Simulation are social conformity versus nonconformity, extroversion versus introversion, and instability versus stability.

Introversion-Extroversion

Introversion-extroversion is the first of two "superfactors" in personality variance defined by Eysenck and Eysenck (1968a, 1968b). Introversion describes traits such as introspection, orderliness, self-control, planfulness, and the like while extroversion is associated with an outgoing quality, impulsivity, lack of inhibition, aggressivity, and craving for excitement. In short, introversion refers to moving away from others while extroversion refers to moving toward others.

Neuroticism-Stability

Neuroticism-stability is the second personality "superfactor" of Eysenck and Eysenck (1968a, 1968b). This dimension involves the degree of emotional instability, the tendency for the person to display emotional overresponsiveness, vague somatic complaints, worry, and the tendency to experience stress-induced breakdown. The Eysencks's concept of "neuroticism" implies considerable underlying anxiety and disposition toward cycloid behavior, i.e., instability. Stability is, of course, the absence of these tendencies where the individual displays relatively normal levels of emotional resilience and, while some variation is customary, there is no demonstrated quality of overresponsiveness.

Conformity-Nonconformity

Conformity-nonconformity refers to the degree in which the patient accepts social values, standards, and customs of the prevailing general culture. In the United States, hard work, honesty, keeping one's word, devotion to family, paying one's debts, respecting the property of others, and the like are generally accepted as social values independently of whether any particular individual or subgroup adheres to them. The opposite pole is nonconforming where the individual does not understand these basic values or, if he does understand, ignores, perverts, or disrespects them.

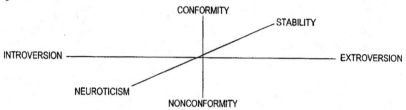

Figure 7.1. Three Dimensions of Personality Pathology Involved in Disorders of Simulation

Figure 7.1 illustrates these three dimensions of personality as intersecting continua. The relatively orthogonal position of neuroticism-stability and introversion-extroversion has been demonstrated to be a robust theoretical construct both in abundant research (Eysenck & Eysenck, 1968a) as well as in brief practical measurement instruments such as the Eysenck Personality Inventory (Eysenck & Eysenck, 1968b).

The Eysencks do not explicitly identify the conformity–nonconformity dimension that is subsumed under introversion-extroversion as well as neuroticism-stability. Amongst others, Mowrer (1950) implicitly advanced the concept of conformity-nonconformity in his discussion of developmental psychology and how early life experiences may lead to undersocialization. He postulated that extroversive types who are also high in "neuroticism" (and therefore unstable) tend to condition poorly in classical stimulus-response paradigms. That is, unstable extroverts do not learn well and fail to develop the conditioned responses that form the basis of social behavior. The result is often lack of social conformity that may extend as far as psychopathy. In contrast, unstable introversive types condition readily and overlearn, thereby frequently developing an overabundance of conditioned responses linked to early stimuli. The result is a restraining conditioned behavioral network that not only promotes social conformity but also neurotic symptoms as well.

The Eysencks define adequate life adjustment as an area bounded by low neuroticism (stability) and moderate to somewhat greater levels of extroversion. Since it is particularly relevant to Disorders of Simulation, the social conformity–nonconformity dimension is presented separately in the current conceptualization. As Eysenck & Eysenck (1968a) note, "the neurotic introvert might be characterized as being *oversocialized* and the neurotic extrovert as being *undersocialized*" (p. 7). Thus, both degree of socialization (conformity) and emotional overresponsivity are components of "neuroticism-instability" and, while obviously not perfectly orthogonal, the two dimensions are relatively independent. Fortunately, social conformity-nonconformity is relatively easy to assess through psychological tests, life history, and diagnostic criteria established by reference to Axis II of *DSM*, particularly with the assumption of relatively high levels of instability-neuroticism.

Normal individuals display personality traits that are nondiagnostic and, while not rising to the magnitude of formally diagnosable disorder, nonetheless reflect "enduring patterns of perceiving, relating to, and thinking about the environment and oneself that are exhibited in a wide range of social and personal contexts" (*DSM-IV*, p. 630). These traits reside near the "stability" end of the "neuroticism–stability" dimension, represent normal variation, and are easily portrayed by using attenuated descriptions derived from the formal Personality Disorders of *DSM*. Although traits have no official, taxonomic designation, they are nonetheless relevant to note when doing so provides information that is likely to assist the clinician in the formulation of treatment strategy and prognosis. "Axis II may also be used to indicate prominent maladaptive personality features that do not meet the threshold for a Personality Disorder" (*DSM-IV*, p. 27). Normal personality functioning, including the notation of normal variation in personality traits on Axis II, is the anchor point for the neuroticism–stability continuum of personality pathology.

As illustrated in Figure 7.2, if the axes of introversion-extroversion and conformity-nonconformity are represented as intersecting planes that are intersected by the third plane of stability-neuroticism, a three dimensional figure emerges. These three planes allow plotting a broad range of normal and abnormal personality configurations by adjusting the point of mutual intersection.

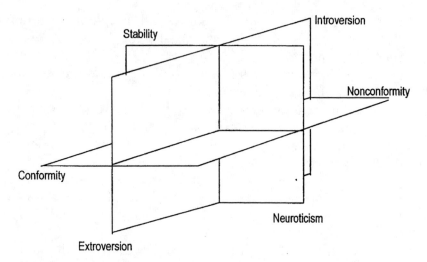

Figure 7.2. Three-dimensional Planes of Personality Pathology Involved in Disorders of Simulation

At one end, individuals who display highly stable personality structures reveal combinations of introversion-extroversion and conformity-nonconformity that fall within the general limits of normal personality functioning. As mutual intersection of the planes proceeds toward the neurotic (unstable) end, patients progressively display mild character traits, character neurosis, severe characterologic disturbance, and finally diagnosable Personality Disorder according to *DSM-IV*. Thus, as the intersection of planes slides from stability toward instability-neuroticism, personality traits become progressively more dysfunctional and finally reach a point where gross levels of dysfunction become evident.

Since Disorders of Simulation clearly represent abnormal behavior, the relevant plane described by introversion-extroversion and conformity-nonconformity is near the unstable end of the neuroticism–stability axis. That is, the current discussion refers to Disorders of Personality or very significant dysfunctional personality traits and, therefore, high "neuroticism" (instability) is implied. In order to simplify the three-dimensional representation in Figure 7.2, assume that the presence of high instability-neuroticism results in the two-dimensional diagram of Figure 7.3.

The combined 14 *DSM-III-R* and *DSM-IV* Personality Disorders may then be approximately placed, given the assumption that all the Disorders involve significantly greater than normal levels of instability and emotional responsivity.

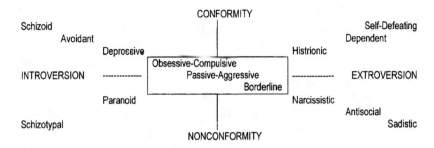

Figure 7.3. The Axis of Personality Pathology with *DSM-III-R* and *DSM-IV* Disorders Sorted According to Introversion-Extroversion and Conformity-Nonconformity with High Levels of Neuroticism-Instability Assumed

The descriptions of personality pathology in *DSM*, while modest in psychodynamic theory, commonly specify readily observable or historically relevant indices of interpersonal behavior. In Disorders of Simulation, both conformity-nonconformity and introversion-extroversion are important variables and, as Figure 7.3 illustrates, the *DSM-III-R* and *DSM-IV* Personality Disorders fall into five categories of personality pathology: conforming-introversive, conforming-extroversive, conflicted-ambivalent, nonconforming-introversive, and nonconforming-extroversive. Obviously, most disorders display the features associated with each quadrant in varying degree with the exception of the conflicted-ambivalent types. This latter group deserves a separate and more central designation since the Disorders within it partake of all four quadrants. Formal Personality Disorder or at least very strong personality trait disturbance must be present on Axis II of *DSM-IV* before a Disorder of Simulation can be diagnosed. This caution naturally follows from the preceding chapter that demonstrated the likelihood of very disturbed object relations in Disorders of Simulation.

FIVE TYPES OF PERSONALITY PATHOLOGY

Conforming–Introversive Personality Disorders

These Personality Disorders display levels of socialization indicating general conformance with and submission to accepted social patterns. Such individuals remain within the customary social context and require the presence of other persons although they may be quite introversively detached. While withdrawing from social contact, moving away from others and toward the self, they nevertheless display general awareness of social convention and almost never conflict with it except in a passive sense. Patients in this category rarely simulate illness or injury since, to do so, requires more extroversion than they can muster and brings them into uncomfortably close contact with others.

Avoidant personalities introversively experience social discomfort, fear of negative feedback, and interpersonal timidity, but remain exquisitely aware of the social context. Their pattern is one of withdrawal, lack of involvement, reticence, and infrequent social contact out of fear of embarrassment and uncertainty of social acceptance. Despite their appearance of cool detachment, such patients not only display social conformity but also yearn for social acceptance from a safe distance and a guarantee that others will not reject them. It is unlikely that such individuals will display Disorders of Simulation since to do so requires a great deal of personal contact, a condition they seek to avoid. That is, since Disorders of Simulation are an interpersonal phenomenon and since Avoidant Personality Disorders withdraw from interpersonal contact, it is quite uncommon to find disorders dependent upon the social context amongst Avoidants.

Depressive personalities customarily display introversive traits, tending to be passive, unassertive, and withdrawn. The general depressive aura suggests low self-esteem and relatively high levels of guilt. Low energy, feelings of inadequacy, and unworthiness lead to reduced socialization. Their harsh self-judgment and tendency to accent their failure as well as a disposition to underplay their own successes means they are more likely to follow than lead in interpersonal situations. The simulation of disorder is not likely in these patients, although some depressives may present with a plethora of somatic complaints that initially raise the specter of Simulation. However, upon examination it is clear that they have unconsciously transformed part of their depression into a variety of bodily aches and pains. Despite their depression, they nevertheless seek the company of others and tend to be conforming, albeit with a negative view of the present and future. It is not likely that such patients will display Disorders of Simulation given the outlay of energy required to establish and maintain a false persona.

Schizoid personalities display isolation in social relationships, neither seeking them out nor enjoying them. They are asocial loners, cold, aloof, indifferent, and clearly introversive. Schizoid patients are nonconforming by avoidance and neglect and seem unaffected by or indifferent to praise from others. They display social detachment and a deficient capacity to form social relationships but, to the extent that they do interact with others, they rudimentarily conform and may even maintain marginally adequate social adjustment. Like the Avoidant individual, Schizoid Personality Disorders find it difficult to tolerate the intense interpersonal contact required by Disorders of Simulation, including multiple psychological, psychiatric, and medical evaluations, a variety of treatments, attorney contacts, and other obligations that violate the precept of moving away from others rather than toward them.

Conforming–Extroversive Personality Disorders

These Personality Disorders display levels of socialization indicating general conformance with and submission to accepted social patterns. They move toward others extroversively in needful, dependent, or eye-catching ways. Such types remain within the customary social context, require the presence of other persons, and seek gregarious or submissive interpersonal contact. They uniformly display awareness of social convention and rarely conflict with it except in a passive sense. They may, however, exaggerate illness or injury, prolong its apparent effects, or otherwise marginally simulate. Patients falling into this personality-based category are more likely to display Compensation Neurosis than Factitious Disorder or Malingering.

Histrionic patients display adequate levels of socialization, are interpersonally needy, gregarious, tend to move toward others, and otherwise demonstrate general conformance with and submission to accepted social patterns. They are extroversive, constantly seek reassurance, approval, or praise from others, and may engage in flirtatious, flamboyant, seductive, or otherwise dramatic behavior in order to obtain these signs of interpersonal acceptance. They are frequently self-centered, display low frustration tolerance, and seek immediate gratification in an interpersonal contact. Histrionic patients border upon unconventional behaviors at times but generally remain within the social context. Compensation Neurosis may emerge under particularly stressful conditions but it is very difficult to distinguish from hysterical conversion phenomena without close attention to the axes of Behavioral Orchestration and Motivation. When patients diagnosed as Histrionic engage in Malingering or Factitious Disorder, it is generally because they are actually Borderline or Narcissistic but simply display a deceptively strong Histrionic veneer and defensive structure. Thus, because of its *polythetic* and atheoretical descriptive approach, *DSM-IV* may allow diagnosis of a Histrionic defense against a Narcissistic or Borderline personality as purely Histrionic.

Dependent personalities have a marked need for social approval and affection that is displayed in interpersonal conformity and submission. They require excessive advice and reassurance from others in the process of everyday decision making and, when they are unable to decide, they readily defer to others. They display extroversive traits since they experience discomfort when left alone, have fears of abandonment, and are easily hurt by criticism or disapproval, and may be manipulated into doing unpleasant tasks so that others will accept them. Rarely, others may manipulate individuals with this personality type into half-believing and half-feigning illness or injury on a protracted basis in order to please those upon whom they are dependent. Under such circumstances, Compensation Neurosis is most likely, Factitious Disorder highly unlikely, and Malingering is quite rare.

Self-Defeating personalities are masochistic. They display social conformity to such a pathological extent that they often allow or encourage others to reject or abuse them. Opportunities for interpersonal pleasure are perversely linked with internal suffering. They are extroversive because they are attracted to others who need a foil for the unempathic exercise of interpersonal hostility and aggression. In a covert, hostile, and passive way, such individuals exhibit the pathological extreme of social convention, turning it against themselves as they seek to fulfill their insatiable masochistic needs.

Malingering is not likely to occur in the Self-Defeating personality. Such patients frequently function in a manner that causes other persons to reject them, inviting degradation, humiliation, and abuse. Just as the Dependent seeks interpersonal contact as a source of nurturance, the Self-Defeating Personality Disorder goes one step further seeking others for masochistic purposes. That is, the Self-Defeating patient passively approaches others with the desire to extract the forbidden pleasures of rejection, suffering, and pain. Compensation Neurosis may occasionally occur for the same reasons as exist in the Dependent Personality but the expectation and pursuit of masochism is a veritable cornucopia for the development of Factitious Disorder. However, when Self-Defeating patients can be induced to simulate extensively, questions must be raised about the accuracy of the Axis II diagnosis. Patients whose ego strength is so weak, self-image so low, and object relations so impaired that interpersonal intimidation results in prolonged Simulation may be more appropriately diagnosed as falling within the lower levels of the conflicted-ambivalent category. It is important to note that masochistic features are not solely associated with the Self-Defeating individual but may simply be engrafted upon an underlying Borderline or Passive–Aggressive Personality Disorder.

Conflicted–Ambivalent Personality Disorders

These Personality Disorders display varying levels of socialization indicating general conformance with and submission to accepted social patterns on some occasions. At other times they appear undersocialized and rebel against or resist accepted social patterns. Thus, such individuals display conflict over the customary social context ranging from outward conformity with inward rebellion to passive negativism to overt acting-out. Conflicted–Ambivalent personality disorders are also ambivalent on the introversion–extroversion axis. They seek others but subsequently reject them, distrust others but have fears of abandonment. Patients with this personality type may erratically conflict with social convention in both an active and passive sense. Obsessive-Compulsives seem to strive for conformity while Passive-Aggressives react negatively to it and Borderlines display a chaotic and unstable pattern. In essence, these personality types alternate between withdrawal from others and needful dependency, between eccentricity and aggressivity. They also oscillate between moving toward the self and moving against the self, between moving toward others and against others. Patients in this group may display Disorders of Simulation since their interpersonal and social value structures are so highly conflicted.

Obsessive–Compulsive personalities display strong needs for perfection and are so conforming and socialized that they are often inflexible with regard to rules, regulations, organization, schedules, and the like. While professing to adhere closely to social convention, they usually display considerable interpersonal ambivalence, often with a hostile underlay. Their characteristic restricted affectivity, indecisiveness, and excessive devotion to productivity suggests introversion but their insistence upon conformity in others can be somewhat extroversive as well. While clearly oriented more toward "things" and "rituals" than people they do not display solely introversive and conforming traits and thus probably straddle the fence.

Because they present with a veneer of conformity, Obsessive-Compulsives are the least likely of conflicted-ambivalent personality types to simulate. Yet, with a reservoir of underlying anger and resentment, they may do so under particularly propitious conditions where they have the opportunity to ascribe their symptoms to some "legitimate" physical injury or illness. Thus, when Obsessive-Compulsives do simulate they are most likely to display Compensation Neurosis where extension or exaggeration of prior pathology is the rule. Malingering is less likely since the requirement for both overt symptom design and display runs headlong into their underlying guilt, fears of rule violation, and moralistic posture. They are not subject to Factitious Disorder. When either Factitious or Malingering varieties of Simulation occur in an Obsessive-Compulsive, the Personality Disorder diagnosis ought to be reconsidered since the patient may well be displaying an Obsessive–Compulsive defense against a malignant Passive–Aggressive or Borderline Disorder.

Passive–Aggressive individuals are substantially negativistic and display a pervasive pattern of resistance to social expectation. They obstruct traditional social convention by resistance, ineffectiveness, sulkiness, delay, and irritability. Passive–aggressive personalities are unpredictable, ambivalent, and emotionally immature, shifting between moving toward and moving away from others. They regularly cross the line between introversion and extroversion, rapidly oscillating but usually displaying a predominantly negative tone. They also vacillate between conforming and passively rebelling, at times submitting to authority but at other reacting with scorn, lack of respect, and criticism. They occupy the central position midway between introversion-extroversion and conformity-nonconformity. On the axes of personality pathology, the passive-aggressive is the most conflicted and likely to move in almost any direction with equal unpredictability. Equally, passive–aggressive patients are likely to unpredictably engage in any variety of Simulating Disorder.

The Simulation-prone dynamics underlying Passive–Aggressive Personality Disorder often find expression in bodily aches and pains as a thin cover for their vexatious, temperamental, and fractious behaviors as well as aggressive impulses. Such patients are infused with hostile desires for retribution over real or imagined slights, bitter resentment over past frustrations, and indignation that they failed to receive the special status or treatment they deserved. They may use complaints of illness or injury to exert control over others, extract dependency-fulfilling attention and support, or otherwise fail to conform to reasonable social and occupational expectations.

Consequently, most any variety of simulation will serve, although Factitious Disorder is the least likely. Factitious Disorder is most likely in particularly low-functioning types who, desperately needing nurturance and succor, attempt to recreate the early mother–child symbiotic relationship by seducing and entrancing doctors, nurses, and the entire health care system. Malingering provides a certain satisfaction to passive–aggressive types since the degree of control exerted over symptom design and display is inherently gratifying, especially if the ostensible target is a person or institution for whom the patient has smoldering rancor. Compensation Neurosis is favored as well since a minor injury or illness can be expanded and protracted into an enormously dependency-fulfilling disability where the patient becomes ever more dysfunctional thus "forcing" others to meet his every need.

Borderline patients are extremely unstable, chaotic, and intense. Interpersonal relationships are fraught with alternating overidealization and devaluation. Such patients oscillate between inappropriate outbursts directed at others and damaging actions directed at the self. They may frantically seek others and, having found them, engage in angry rejection. Thus, they customarily display angry introversive and extroversive trends in ever changing and unpredictable fashion. While aware of social convention in a general sense, they often rebel actively or passively. Because of high levels of internal ambivalence and conflict, they only erratically conform to social expectation.

The Borderline Personality Disorder is the most chameleon-like of all personality configurations, often masquerading as a broad variety of other, less severe characterologic or neurotic disorders. When the patient's Borderline pathology is relatively high functioning, the presentation may be quite neuroticlike including Dependent, Histrionic, Obsessive–Compulsive, and Narcissistic features. This mimicry frequently leads to misdiagnosis according to the *polythetic* standards of *DSM-IV* (APA, 1994) since the emphasis is far more upon observable behaviors than psychodynamic theory or developmental object relations. Low-functioning Borderlines are very disturbed since they may experience gross disorganization and brief psychotic symptoms under stress and may therefore sometimes be diagnosed as Paranoid or Self-Defeating.

Amongst low-functioning Borderlines, Factitious Disorder is quite likely to occur as a Disorder of Simulation. Social invalidism, acceptance of the role of the patient, diminished cognitive control, and pervasive object relations deficiencies are just the type of fertile ground upon which Factitious Disorder thrives. Indeed, it is likely that this particularly pathological variety of Simulation occurs predominantly within the low-functioning Borderline Personality Disorder group. Both low- and high-functioning Borderlines are susceptible to Malingering and Compensation Neurosis.

Those with a more nonconforming–extroversive veneer are more inclined to Malingering as the result of the sense of control and/or retribution it provides. Those Borderlines with a conforming–extroversive overlay are likely to engage in Compensation Neurosis because of the inherently dependency-fulfilling nature of this type of simulation.

Nonconforming Introversive Personality Disorders

These undersocialized patients display general variance with, rebellion against, or resistance to accepted social patterns. While retaining vague awareness of social convention, such Personality Disorders are introversively ambivalent and socially nonconforming. They may conflict with social convention, usually in a passive sense although the Paranoid may actively seek others in order to validate his own distorted perceptions. They move against the self and away from others, sometimes in odd, eccentric, or bizarre ways. Simulation of illness or injury amongst this group is rare and generally only occurs in Paranoid Personality Disorder under special conditions.

Paranoid individuals are acutely but suspiciously aware of social convention. They are wary, mistrustful, and rigidly edgy. Always certain that others have evil motives, they have a great need to maintain distance and avoid entangling interpersonal alliances. They are suspicious that others are attempting to deprive them of control and the ability to manage their own lives. They are remarkably self-contained and seem to need others only in a passive sense, as a screen for their projections and, therefore, they do not seek interpersonal contact. The therapeutic or evaluative encounter is usually intensely threatening to most Paranoid Personality Disorders and multiple doctor visits further threaten loss of control, suggest weakness, and frightening levels of dependency. Therefore, Disorders of Simulation are unlikely to be present in true Paranoids. However, under circumstances of threat, their superior air, hostile affectivity, and intimidating manner as well as their delusional tendencies to see mountains of conspiracy where only the molehills of incidental action exist, may lead them to outrageous claims of damage at the hands of others. Although litigation may result from their misperceptions, their claims usually have a peculiar and idiosyncratic quality where the patient is unshakably bent upon righting a wrong, receiving confirmation of their suspicions, or exacting revenge for real or imagined affronts. Such behaviors do not suggest Disorders of Simulation but rather the natural character armor of the Paranoid.

When strongly paranoid features serve as a defense against Narcissistic, Antisocial, Borderline, or Passive-Aggressive Personality Disorders, then Malingering, Compensation Neurosis, and even Factitious Disorder are certainly possible. However, the behavioral description approach of the *DSM-IV* (APA, 1994) may lead the clinician to diagnose these combinations solely as a Paranoid Personality Disorder. Thus, when a Paranoid Personality Disorder appears to engage in Simulation, it is particularly important to determine the motivational structure (level of object relations capacity). The Simulation may be no Simulation at all but rather the unconscious projection of a highly defensive and sometimes litigiously pursued belief that others are at fault or, through evil intent, have forced the patient into an untenable position where his or her innocence must be defended. In contrast, when clear control of symptom design and/or display is evident, it is likely that the apparent Paranoid Personality Disorder is actually a veneer or overlay engrafted upon a conflicted–ambivalent or nonconforming–extroversive personality type.

Schizotypal Personality Disorders fall at the outer limits of the nonconforming–introversive spectrum and, in all but degree, are virtually schizophrenic. They are odd, impoverished, introversive individuals who engage in clearly abnormal mentation and emotional life. Paranoid mentation, ideas of reference, bizarre preoccupations, and highly idiosyncratic thought patterns are typical. High levels of interpersonal misperception along with an unstable, chaotic internal organization invariably results in strange and eccentric social relations. Whether present in pure form or engrafted upon some other personality organization, patients with a quantum of schizotypy are quite unlikely to simulate. Effective Simulation requires at least a modicum of social understanding and, like their more socialized schizoid brethren, they find it difficult to tolerate the intense interpersonal contact much less generate the social context required to effectively display a Disorder of Simulation.

Nonconforming–Extroversive Personality Disorders

These patients not only display general variance with, rebellion against, or resistance to accepted social patterns but also tend to be extroversively aggressive, hostile, or manipulative. Nonconforming–extroversive types display indifference to social convention and frequently conflict with it in an active sense. These individuals have minimal to no regard for social relations and range from largely to fully interpersonally usurious. Thus, they move against others in aggressive and socially nonconforming ways. Narcissistic patients are grossly egotistical while Antisocial individuals are aggressively usurious and the Sadist can be cruel and intimidating. All the patients in this category actively violate, flout, manipulate, or ignore social convention, and display minimal capacities for empathy. The potential for Simulation of illness or injury is high amongst this group since they not only display an assaultive and arrogant quality but also view themselves as living above the rules that apply to others. The most likely diagnosis is Malingering although Compensation Neurosis occurs in a few cases. Factitious Disorder is rare since it involves self-injury in far greater degree than self-pleasure.

Narcissistic Personality Disorders are generally egocentrically grandiose and aggressive in seeking status, power, and prestige. Very calm and self-assured, lacking in humility, and having a sense of entitlement that is ineffectively restrained by ethics, humanity, or morality, such patients are inclined to be interpersonally usurious. They view themselves as superior with a sense of native endowment, demanding constant attention, expecting to be accorded special status, deserving of unceasing admiration, and not required to forbear the petty reciprocal exchanges of human interaction and shared living. They assume that others will defer or subjugate their needs in order to fulfill the Narcissist's desires for flattery, superiority, and reaffirmation of superior self-worth. Patients with this Personality Disorder are adept at rationalizing their excessive self-image, denying their deficits, and, upon occasion, aggressively projecting their own denied shortcomings onto others.

Narcissists come in several varieties including the high-functioning "phallic" type who are often bright, accomplished, and talented. Such individuals usually have achieved significantly and thus present with some evidence for their exhibitionistic claims of superiority. Therefore, they may be seen as more "neurotic" and slip through the Axis II differential diagnostic net. At somewhat more moderate levels of effectiveness, the "garden variety" Narcissist usually demonstrates grandiose fantasies considerably in excess of his actual accomplishments, desiring Nobel laureate status in exchange for pulp fiction performance. Low-level Narcissists may be more overtly concerned with manipulation, needfulness, demanding behavior, and dependent clinging. At the middle- to low-functioning level, the *DSM-IV* (APA, 1994) criteria make it difficult to distinguish between pure Narcissism, the Narcissistic defense against a Borderline Personality, and Antisocial Personality Disorder.

All varieties of Narcissistic disorder may display Malingering or Compensation Neurosis but not Factitious Disorder. The latter diagnosis requires too much self-abnegation, suffering, and pain to attract the simulating tendencies of the Narcissist. Malingering is the most probable Disorder of Simulation for high- and middle-functioning patients since it represents the shortest and least painful road to self-aggrandizement and success. As Millon (1981) notes, "narcissists may never have learned to be skillful at public deception; they usually said and did what they liked without a care for what others thought" (p. 168).

Those presenting with a Narcissistic Defense against a Borderline Personality Disorder may develop Compensation Neurosis because of its inherent dependency-fulfilling potential. The *DSM-IV* (APA, 1994) diagnostic protocol, however, may readily lead to Narcissistic Defense against a Borderline Personality Disorder being diagnosed as purely Narcissistic if the patient is reasonably well compensated and the Narcissistic defense is ascendant. But, if the patient has suffered stressors with subsequent decompensation into clinging dependency, the low-functioning aspect may first be evident leading to misdiagnosis as a purely Borderline Disorder. Masterson (1981) is quite helpful in making this critically important distinction.

Lower-level Narcissists may escape accurate detection to the extent that they present as apparently Antisocial and may be misdiagnosed as such. It is helpful to note that both the low functioning Narcissist and the Antisocial patient act out but do so in different ways. While both may qualify according to the Antisocial criteria of *DSM-IV* (APA, 1994), close inspection usually reveals that the acting out of the Narcissist is self-aggrandizing and self-centered while that of the Antisocial patient is vindictive, malevolent, and malicious. The low-functioning Narcissist may have some underlying dependency needs and is therefore prone to Compensation Neurosis while the true Antisocial Personality Disorder is often too impulsive and aggressively impatient to engage in the relatively long-term dependency machinations inherent in Compensation Neurosis.

Antisocial Personality Disorders display low frustration tolerance, impulsivity, and hostile affectivity. They have virtually no trust in others and therefore turn exclusively to themselves and their own mechanisms for gratification, irrespective of the needs, wishes, or feelings of others. Such patients are generally not willing to tolerate protracted periods of frustration, delay of gratification, or emotional discomfort. Consequently, they often act with an aggressive, invulnerable, and tough self-image, being drawn from one stimulating and exciting event to another without reflection, care, or concern.

Ruthless pursuit of untempered self-interest and power over others in the context of minimal capacity for delay of gratification makes the stereotypic Antisocial Personality one of the least sophisticated of simulators. Frequently, their fabrications reflect little forethought, are spontaneously produced, display little craft, are crudely justified, and directed toward enhancing their own control while abrogating the power of others. It is probably because their simulations are often relatively transparent upon clinical evaluation, and because such patients are usually conveniently grouped together (prison, drug clinics, etc.), that many authors identify Malingering as associated largely, if not wholly, with the Antisocial Personality Disorder.

However, Millon (1981) correctly notes that, "The *DSM-III* (APA, 1987) label of 'antisocial' as the designation for this personality syndrome places . . . too great an emphasis on the delinquent, criminal, and other undesirable social consequences often found among these patients" (p. 181). Indeed, the criteria for diagnosis are essentially a list of illegal, socially repugnant, or irresponsible behaviors. This view constitutes undue restriction of range since—like so many other Personality Disorders—the Antisocial configuration "contains many sub-categories of disorder which may vary a good deal in both clinical style and psychodynamics" (Masterson, 1981, p. 45). For example, some Antisocial individuals have been able to largely integrate their tendencies into socially acceptable form, engaging in no overt illegal activities but nonetheless displaying critical traits such as a lust for power and control, ruthless and vindictive interpersonal behaviors, blunting of conscience, aggressive manipulation, and contempt for those weaker than themselves.

At the least, Antisocial Personality Disorders are prevalent in two types. The low-functioning, aggressive, and essentially criminal element is well described in the *DSM-IV* diagnostic criteria and may be expected to engage in unsophisticated Malingering. Factitious Disorder demands prodigious capacity for self-inflicted pain and suffering while Compensation Neurosis requires strong dependency needs and capacity for delay of gratification; the low-functioning Antisocial has insufficient psychodynamic complexity for either of these Disorders of Simulation.

The high-functioning, assertive, and noncriminal Antisocial Personality Disorder is less likely to be diagnosed by *DSM-IV* criteria. The Antisocial dragnet rarely catches such individuals since it is difficult to obtain evidence of three or more behaviors from category A. Yet, upon careful evaluation, these patients clearly display evidence of a psychodynamically Antisocial Personality organization and, despite the fact that they are without documentable prior antisocial behavior, they may nonetheless simulate. Again, Factitious Disorder is unlikely for the same reasons as applied to the low-functioning variety. Higher-functioning Antisocials, however, may display Compensation Neurosis in addition to Malingering; they have usually developed enough social veneer and are sufficiently manipulative to pursue Compensation Neurosis despite low levels of dependency.

The diagnosis of Antisocial Personality Disorder is further complicated when significant Histrionic, Narcissistic, or Paranoid traits are also present. It is easy to misdiagnose one condition for another since the *DSM-IV* (APA, 1994) criteria for the latter three Disorders refer to behavioral and personality *characteristics* whereas the criteria for Antisocial Personality Disorder refer to behavioral *acts*. Thus, a patient who meets the criteria for Narcissistic Personality Disorder may also qualify as Antisocial by meeting the required three behaviors from category A. The result is Personality Disorder Not Otherwise Specified (Narcissistic and Antisocial) when—for reasons that at least include diagnosis of Disorders of Simulation—it is important to determine whether the patient is Narcissistic, Antisocial, or displays an Antisocial defense against a Narcissistic Disorder.

Sadistic Personality Disorders take the antisocial one step further. They are cruelly and unflinchingly aggressive, particularly if they believe they can act with impunity. Sadists seek to establish dominating, demeaning, overtly controlling relationships with others through belligerence, temper flares, and rageful behavior. They customarily resort to intimidation, harassment, threats, and physical violence when attempting to control others, although one variant is more likely to be voyeuristic than assaultive, finding gratification in witnessing acts of violence, collecting weapons or instruments of torture, and otherwise demonstrating involvement at a safe distance.

Obviously, such patients are cold-blooded and have little empathy, respect, or concern for human welfare since they take particular pleasure in watching or inducing suffering in others. The most common victim of the sadist is, of course, the Self-Defeating (Masochistic) Personality Disorder. The Sadistic has much in common with other nonconforming–extroversive types and frequently coexists with Narcissistic and/or Antisocial elements. They display similarity in hostility level, self-assured arrogance, lack of sentimentality, and high energy. At times the distinction between Antisocial and Sadistic Personality Disorders may be difficult since, as noted previously, Antisocial criteria are a series of behavioral acts which may occur—all or in part—in a number of other, more characteristically described Personality Disorders. However, there is first-degree kinship between Sadistic and Antisocial patients at psychodynamic and developmental levels and, therefore, the differential diagnosis is probably less critical when evaluating for Disorders of Simulation than, for example, the distinctions between Antisocial, Narcissistic, and Borderline Personality Disorders and their respective variants.

While attempts to injure and force humiliation upon others are often physical in nature, Sadistic individuals may also fabricate or exaggerate illness or injury if it serves their underlying desire for contemptuous and despotic interpersonal control. Malingering is therefore possible although Factitious Disorder and Compensation Neurosis are anathema since the latter two require self-immolating or dependent interpersonal postures. In Malingering, the sadist acts out of desires to humiliate or dominate others, exact revenge or retribution, or otherwise inflict pain and suffering that is qualitatively different from the acting out of Antisocial and Narcissistic patients. Narcissists simulate in ways designed to self-aggrandize while Antisocials are more likely to engage in unsocialized acting out.

SUMMARY AND CONCLUSIONS

The foregoing discussion described the *DSM-III-R* and *DSM-IV* Personality Disorders as falling within three-dimensional space defined by the axes of introversion-extroversion, conformity-nonconformity, and neuroticism-stability. With high levels of instability assumed, dimensions partitioned into only five sectors are sufficient to classify Personality Disorders in ways particularly relevant to Disorders of Simulation. Table 7.1 summarizes the axes of personality pathology as they customarily intersect with the Simulating Disorders.

It is also important to remember that, since *DSM* personality disorders are oblivious to object relations theory, some "unlikely" personality types may engage in simulation. Therefore, categorization in Table 7.1 according to likelihood is generally accurate but not invariant, especially in exceptional cases.

Table 7.1

Summary of *DSM-III-R* and *DSM-IV* Personality Disorders and Their Association with Disorders of Simulation

Personality Type	*DSM-III-R* and *IV* Personality Disorders	Motivational Structure Associated With		
		Malingering	Factitious Disorders	Compensation Neurosis
Conforming-Introversive	Schizoid	No	No	No
	Depressive[a]	No	No	No
	Avoidant	No	No	No
Conforming-Extroversive	Histrionic	No	No	Rare
	Dependent	No	No	Rare
	Self-defeating[c]	No	Rare	Rare
Nonconforming-Introversive	Schizotypal	No	No	No
	Paranoid	Rare	No	Rare
Conflicted-Ambivalent	Borderline	Yes	Yes	Yes
	Passive-Aggressive[b]	Yes	Yes	Yes
	Obsessive-Comp.	No	No	Rare
Nonconforming-Extroversive	Narcissistic	Yes	No	Yes
	Antisocial	Yes	No	Yes
	Sadistic[c]	Yes	No	No

[a] The Depressive Personality Disorder is located in "Criteria Sets and Axes Provided for Further Study" in *DSM-IV*.
[b] The Passive–Aggressive (Negativistic) Personality Disorder, fully accepted in *DSM-III-R*, was moved to Appendix B in *DSM-IV*.
[c] Both the Self-Defeating and Sadistic Personality Disorders existed as proposed rather than official categories in *DSM-III-R*. These disorders are plotted on the axis of Personality Pathology on a provisional basis. While they are sufficiently well described in *DSM-III-R* to allow some general categorization, they do not appear in *DSM-IV*.

8

Differential Diagnosis

> These tests, although they demonstrate either conscious malingering or unconscious hysteria, cannot in any way distinguish them. (MacLean, 1947, p. 1224)

In order to make a positive diagnosis of a Disorder of Simulation, it is important to consider the same complex array of variables as in the diagnosis of traditional disorders. The methods used in assessment of the patient should elicit information relevant to the tri-axial system.

AXIS I: BEHAVIORAL ORCHESTRATION—PART A: OBTAINING REPORTED DATA

Windows 1, 2, and 3 are best assessed by individual interviews with the patient. In the recent literature, several authors have compiled numerous protocols for interview techniques that may be quite helpful in obtaining this information (Hall & Pritchard, 1999; Rogers, 1988). Customarily, important information results from conjoint interviews with the patient and the patient's significant others, with and without the patient present. Review of records is an additional source of important data. It is often true that patients in whom a Disorder of Simulation is suspected will have a complex, extensive history that is revealed by study of medical and mental health records, school and employment records, military service records, legal records, treatment reports, family records, prior medicolegal evaluation, and similar sources.

AXIS I: BEHAVIORAL ORCHESTRATION—PART B: REPORTING OBTAINED DATA

The remaining three Windows may be most profitably assessed based upon patient behaviors as demonstrated during assessment and treatment. In Windows 4 and 5, examination of patient responses during mental status examination and individually administered intellectual, neuropsychological, personality, mental status, and other psychological assessments may be probed by testing the limits, process evaluation, and other supplemental methods as outlined for each test by various authors. If chronic pain or neuropsychological deficits are at issue, many authors have made suggestions for refining traditional tests to elicit indications of possible Simulation. There are also a few tests, which purport to assess Simulation directly, and, while the clinician should not rely upon them as either necessary or sufficient, they may provide important data that further diagnostic inquiry. Administering traditional personality assessment (e.g., MMPI, MCMI) and projective techniques (e.g., Machover Figure Drawings, Rorschach Psychodiagnostic) may discover additional indications of behavioral orchestration. It is also important to note that some of the observations under "Motivation" in chapter 6 may relate to the patient's response style. Window 6 is best assessed in treatment, and sufficient data are usually available after just a few sessions to determine how the patient is responding. For example, the patient's level of therapeutic engagement can certainly provide information about therapeutic alliance and response to confrontation or interpretation.

AXIS II: MOTIVATION—OBJECT RELATIONS

Since object relations is the product of formative early life experiences, supplemented and modified by succeeding years, the clinician must conduct an in-depth historical interview. In addition, clinical observation based upon assessment and/or treatment should examine for the patient's developmental level in as many ways as possible, as outlined in Table 6.3. Other significant object relations data may be inferred from traditional projective testing such as the Rorschach, Thematic Apperception Test, and the Machover Figure Drawings. In fact, any technique that elicits data regarding completion of rapprochement and developmental level is invaluable.

AXIS III: PERSONALITY PATHOLOGY—*DSM-IV*, AXIS II

The *DSM* provides concrete, specific criteria sets for the determination of Personality Disorder. Life history data, both from the patient and external sources, allow for proper formal diagnosis or the specification of significant subdiagnostic traits. Of course, traditional personality assessment techniques, both objective and projective, can contribute to the determination of personality type.

ADDITIONAL REQUIREMENTS FOR DIFFERENTIAL DIAGNOSIS

Multiple Data Sources

Comprehensive examination on all three axes should include as many outside sources as possible. It is critical to request and review every piece of historical information about the patient, including all prior reports, examination, depositions, hospital records, military files, occupational data, etc. Further, consultation and case review with allied health professionals are often productive.

The critical point to keep in mind when considering a diagnosis of Simulation is that no single data source—no single test or technique—is adequate to detect simulation. There is no substitute for the judgment of the clinician based upon a comprehensive compilation of data including, but certainly not limited to, "one-shot" tests for Malingering, specialized interview questions, subtle alterations in neuropsychological testing, lists of suspicious behavior, and similar popular approaches. Most methods suggested in the literature for detecting functional disorders are helpful but they cannot stand alone.

Syndrome Analysis

The most obvious illustration of the need for syndrome analysis is the formidable distinction between Malingering and Hysterialike Disorders. For at least one hundred years, authors have struggled to distinguish between these two clinical entities and attempts to do so have resulted in literally hundreds of clinical "tests" designed to detect simulation and distinguish it from other behaviors. Each health discipline has a well-developed body of literature specifying "one shot" techniques for detecting simulated symptoms. Ophthalmology, neurology, orthopedics, chiropractic, and every other discipline has its well-known means—usually named after their originator—that may be readily found in standard textbooks and journal articles.

For example, in orthopedics and neurology, when the complaint is paralysis of one leg, examination for Hoover's sign requires that the patient lie prone upon a table. The examiner places a hand beneath each heel and instructs the patent to try to raise the paralyzed leg. If he genuinely attempts to comply, the examiner should feel pressure from the patient's heel on the nonparalyzed side. The absence of pressure indicates that the paralysis is functional.

In psychology, certain combinations of validity and clinical scale scores on the MMPI suggest lack of genuineness in responding, perhaps even Malingering. On the MCMI, several bizarre questions are included and any patient who endorses one or more of the items is possibly untruthful.

Yet in each of these examples—and in every case with every test from every discipline—no examiner can observe one or two behaviors and distinguish with certainty between Malingering and Hysteria. As Jones and Llewellyn (1917) remarked nearly one century ago:

> Nothing . . . resembles malingering more than hysteria; nothing hysteria more than malingering. In both alike we are confronted with the same discrepancy between fact and statement, objective sign and subjective symptom—the outward aspect of health seemingly giving the lie to all the alleged functional disabilities. We may examine the hysterical person and the malingerer, using the same tests, and get precisely the same results in one case as the other. (p. 178)

This insightful statement is as true today as when it was written; the distinction between Malingering and Hysteria has never been easy and no single physical or mental test exists that reliably differentiates one from the other. One hundred years and thousands of professional articles later, the health disciplines remain unable to distinguish unequivocally between simulated and genuine symptoms by simply examining a quantum of behavior in isolation. The symptoms generated by both simulated and genuine-but-functional illness, injury, or stress are indistinguishable. For example, paralysis of the leg with a positive Hoover's sign occurs in both, distortion in psychological testing occurs in both, and double vision with one eye occluded occurs in both.

Therefore, diagnostic processes in addition to symptom analyses or behavioral observations are required in order to distinguish simulation from genuineness. In the modern rush to reduce the complexity of human functioning to simple behavioral rules, lists of suspicious behavior, cookbook recipes, and statistical comparisons, mental health professionals have often overlooked the most important distinguishing feature: *Disorders of Simulation, like all mental disorders, are coherent syndromes.*

That is, while human behavior is complex and convoluted, it is also coherent, lawful, and veridically integrated. Behavior follows a *pattern*. With the application of sound psychodynamic analysis, the meaning of a sample of patient behavior becomes apparent only in the context of the patient's *behavior pattern*. Analysis of behavior patterns is *syndrome analysis*. Mental disorder or even the meaning of a specific behavior cannot be determined from a single instance but must be analyzed as part of a pattern, the product of many factors demonstrated consistently over time. Thus, it is true now as it was in the past; attempts to determine whether any single behavioral act is hysterical or malingered are doomed to fail. The difference between genuineness and simulation can be established only through *syndrome analysis*.

Approach to Diagnosis

The *DSM* approach to diagnosis is polythetic and not consistently psychodynamic, but it is clearly presented, widely known, and broadly accepted. Although the present tri-axial approach to Disorders of Simulation is both behavioral and psychodynamic, it nevertheless follows the popular *DSM* format. It is important to keep in mind that much of the present tri-axial approach implies the application of psychodynamic theory, particularly with reference to crucial area of object relations (Axis II—Motivation).

MALINGERING

Diagnostic Features

As traditionally defined, Malingering is little more than immoral behavior: the intentional, voluntary production, exaggeration, or false attribution of symptoms that simulate physical or mental disorder. In the present formulation, an essential symptomatic feature of Malingering is behavioral orchestration characterized by intentional control of design *and* volitional control of display. Analysis of this feature requires close examination of patient behavior in each of six Windows of Opportunity (Criterion A).

Motivationally, most authors suggest that Malingering involves external gain, secondary gain, or external incentives, such as avoiding military duty, avoiding work, obtaining financial compensation, evading criminal prosecution, or obtaining drugs, often in a medicolegal setting. While these obvious motivations may be present frequently, they are neither necessary nor sufficient for making the diagnosis. Careful analysis of motivation indicates that a very primitive level of object relations capacity is involved, certainly prerapprochement, at Borderline levels or below as described by psychodynamic theorists (Criterion B).

While many who suffer from Malingering may display the traditionally designated *DSM* Antisocial Personality Disorder, Malingering is most likely to be associated with *either* formal Personality Disorder *or* very strong *DSM* personality traits in the Extroversive–Nonconforming quadrant (Narcissistic, Antisocial, Sadistic) and the conflicted–ambivalent category (Compulsive, Passive-Aggressive, Borderline) (Criterion C).

Associated Features and Mental Disorders

Malingering individuals may demonstrate any of the behaviors associated with the diagnosis of personality pathology on *DSM* Axis II. They generally display many of the hallmarks of deficient object relations associated with the motivational axis. History may reveal drug or substance abuse, disrespect for the rights or property of others, and erratic employment, a history of conflict with the law, marital difficulty, impulse control problems, a chaotic early life, and delinquent or undersocialized acts as a child and adolescent. They may also experience depression and anxiety disorders.

Associated Laboratory Findings

In some cases, laboratory findings are beyond the normal range since Malingering individuals may take opportunistic advantage of a genuine accident or other event that, in fact, produces some positive laboratory findings and symptoms that the patient grossly exaggerates. A presumably less common variety may have real illness, documented by medical studies, as the result of long-standing problems that the patient simply attributes to a wrongful cause. The rarest type of Malingerer stages events and thus has no injury or illness whatsoever as well as no real symptoms, although the patient may attempt to remedy this situation by falsifying records or laboratory results.

Prevalence

Most studies of Malingering in general clinical practice place the prevalence as very low, usually less than 1 or 2%. In civil litigation cases and in the military during wartime, the percentage may be higher, perhaps as much as 5 to 10%. It is generally believed, but has not clearly been demonstrated, that in criminal cases the percentage is considerably higher.

Age, Culture, and Gender Factors

Perhaps due in part to the historical association between Malingering and military service during wartime, the conventional wisdom suggests that Malingering is more prevalent in males than

females. However, there are no data in substantiation. The designation of a preadult as Malingering is inadvisable since many
disorders of childhood, such as Conduct Disorder, have greater
explanatory power. Malingering may occur at any adult age but
it is unlikely to emerge, fully formed, as a single behavior, without
a history. In general, the necessity for a Disorder of Personality
(or at least very strong traits) suggests that it is most likely to
first occur sometime near midadolescence. There are no data to
support the notion that Malingering occurs with greater frequency in some cultural or ethnic groups than in others.

Course

Course is difficult to specify since, in the past, once an individual
was identified as Malingering, he was generally dismissed as a
patient. However, given the primitive level of object relations inherent in Malingering and the historical tendency for the disorder to recur, it is prudent to consider it as an episodic condition
that may be evident throughout the patient's life span.

Subtypes

For purposes of clarity, the clinician should append specifiers to
indicate the processes involved in causal attribution and symptomatic production. Malingering may occur with exaggeration of
real symptoms, with fully simulated symptoms, or with a combination of real and simulated symptoms. Cause may be as simple
a false imputation of a preexisting condition or as complex as
wholesale event fabrication.

Differential Diagnosis

The distinction between Malingering and other Disorders of Simulation involves careful analysis of Behavioral Orchestration, Motivation, and Personality Pathology. However, there is always the
possibility of other physical or mental disorder instead of or in
addition to Malingering. That is, a patient suffering from Malingering may also have real physical disorders—perhaps exaggerated—that require treatment. Malingerers may also suffer from

additional mental disorders such as Impulse Control Disorder, Substance Abuse Disorder, Depression, or an Anxiety Disorder.

Table 8.1
Diagnostic Criteria for Malingering

A.   *Behavioral Orchestration* characteristic of Malingering that is nontrivial in at least:

      (1) Window 1, Self-as-Patient or Self-and-Other-as-Patient   and

      (2) Window 2 or Window 3   and

      (3) Window 4 or Window 5 or Window 6.

B.   *Motivation* characterized by object relations that are prerapprochement and at a level no greater than Borderline as described by psychodynamic theorists.

C.   *Personality Pathology* defined as the presence of formal disorder or the presence of very strong traits in one or more of the following *DSM-III-R* (APA, 1987) and *DSM-IV* (APA, 1994) Personality Disorder categories (Code on Axis II):

      Sadistic,   or

      Antisocial,   or

      Narcissistic,   or

      Passive-Aggressive,   or

      Borderline,   or

      Compulsive   or

      Not Otherwise Specified (combination of the above).

D.   *Specifiers:* Append to diagnosis.
    Symptoms:

      (1) *With Exaggeration of Real Symptoms.*

      (2) *With Fully Simulated Symptoms.*

      (3) *With a Combination of Exaggerated and Simulated Symptoms.*

    Causal Attribution:

      (1) *False Imputation Subtype.* (Preexisting pathology must result from a current accident, illness, or stressor *and* the patient must intentionally hide prior causation.)

      (2) *Event Fabrication Subtype.* (Events that never occurred or were staged must be intentionally alleged to have occurred and led to the symptoms as claimed.)

FACTITIOUS DISORDER

Diagnostic Features

Factitious Disorder has traditionally been defined as the intentional reporting of false symptoms or the actual self-induction of symptoms, usually accompanied by a need to assume the sick role. Unlike Malingering and Compensation Neurosis, however, Factitious Disorder invariably has been viewed as requiring a high level of psychopathology.

All varieties of Factitious Disorder demonstrate intentional design of symptoms, often in very complex and medically sophisticated ways. However, the actual display of the symptoms appears to be compulsive, driven, involuntary, and automatic. That is, Factitious Disorder patients cannot not simulate. Analysis of this feature requires close examination of patient behavior in each of six Windows of Opportunity (Criterion A).

Motivationally, Factitious Disorders have usually been defined as involving internal gain or internal incentives such as desiring to assume the sick role, discharging smoldering resentment for doctors, replaying an early dependent relationship with a nurturing caretaking figure, and similar motives. While these factors may occasionally be present, analysis of motivation indicates that a Borderline level of object relations capacity is involved. It is highly unlikely for Factitious Disorders to occur in postrapprochement individuals. Thus, Factitious Disorders display object relations that are prerapprochement, generally within the Borderline spectrum as described by psychodynamic theorists (Criterion B).

Although some patients may display no more than personality traits, most patients who suffer from Factitious Disorder display a formal *DSM* Personality Disorder. Predominately, Borderline or Passive–Aggressive Personality Disorders from the Conflicted-Ambivalent category are present. However, the Self-Defeating Personality Disorder may occur in some cases (Criterion C).

The false symptom reporting and active symptom induction varieties of Factitious Disorder are reported correctly in *DSM-IV* and, rather than repeating that information here, the reader is referred to Factitious Disorders: Subtypes (pp. 472–473). However, in coding the disorder, distinction should be made between the *False Reporting* variety in which symptoms are reported but no illness or injury exists and the *Active Induction* variety which includes real (albeit self-induced) pathology, sometimes of life-threatening magnitude.

Associated Features and Mental Disorders

An enormous variety of features may be associated with Factitious Disorder. The list of ways in which a patient may induce or falsely report symptoms in himself is limitless as the catalogs of colorful synonyms in Glossary tables 9.2 and 9.3 illustrate. Factitious Disorder may interfere with work, social, family, and marital relationships. The high frequency of physician and ER visits, often with minimal to no objective medical or etiologic findings, is usually frustrating to caregivers and may lead to discord between doctor and patient. Factitious Disorders may demonstrate any of the behaviors associated with the relevant Personality Disorder reported on *DSM-IV* Axis II.

Associated Laboratory Findings

In the False Reporting variety, laboratory findings are customarily negative since the patient simply reports nonexistent symptoms and usually has no illness as claimed. However, in the more virulent Active Induction variety, positive laboratory findings are customary with respect to the apparent condition but evidence of etiology may be strangely inconclusive.

Specific Age, Cultural, and Gender Features

There are no reliable data on age and sex ratios in Factitious Disorder. Data collection is difficult because Factitious patients tend to leave treatment when challenged and depart from hospitals against medical advice. As with Malingering, it seems unwise to diagnose Factitious Disorder in a child or young adolescent since many disorders of childhood have greater explanatory power.

Prevalence

No data are available on prevalence. It has often been assumed, but never clearly demonstrated, that the tendency for Factitious

Disorder patients to make multiple ER and hospital visits has led to overreporting the frequency of this disorder.

Course

Factitious Disorder is usually a chronic problem since its basis is in defective object relations. Unless the underlying problem is effectively treated, Factitious illness or injury is most likely a life-long problem.

Differential Diagnosis

The distinction between Factitious Disorder and other Disorders of Simulation requires careful analysis of Behavioral Orchestration, Motivation, and Personality Pathology. However, actual physical disorder is always possible, instead of or in addition to a diagnosis of Factitious Disorder, particularly because some Factitious patients actually induce illness in themselves or cause themselves physical injury. Factitious Disorders may also suffer from traditional mental disorders such as Impulse Control Disorder, Substance Abuse Disorder, Depression, or an Anxiety Disorder. Factitious Disorder patients are great imitators and diligent investigation may be required to separate these patients from others suffering from Somatoform Disorders and a wide variety of physical disorders.

FACTITIOUS DISORDER BY PROXY

Diagnostic Features

Factitious Disorder by Proxy involves the intentional induction or false reporting of physical or mental symptoms in another person, over whom the patient has influence, usually choosing the very young, debilitated, or infirm as the victim. The motivation traditionally ascribed is the need to assume the sick role by proxy. Unlike Malingering and Compensation Neurosis, however, Factitious Disorder by Proxy occurs in individuals with virulent levels of psychopathology.

Table 8.2
Diagnostic Criteria for Factitious Disorder

A. *Behavioral Orchestration* characteristic of Factitious Disorder that is non-trivial in at least:
    (1) Window 1, Self-as-Patient or Self-and-Other-as-Patient   and
    (2) Window 2 or Window 3   and
    (3) Window 4 or Window 5 or Window 6.

B. *Motivation* characterized by object relations that are prerapprochement at the Borderline level as described by psychodynamic theorists.

C. *Personality Pathology* defined as the presence of formal disorder or the presence of very strong traits in one or more of the following *DSM-III-R* (APA, 1987) and *DSM-IV* (APA, 1994) Personality Disorder categories (Code on Axis II):
    Borderline,   or
    Passive-Aggressive,   or
    Self-Defeating   or
    Not Otherwise Specified (combination of the above).

D. *Subtype* must be specified as:
    (1) *Predominately Psychological Signs and Symptoms, False Reporting Subtype.* (Psychological and/or physical symptoms must be falsely reported as occurring in the self, leading to unnecessary health-related attention and procedures. The reported symptoms must be specified.)
    (2) *Predominately Physical Signs and Symptoms, False Reporting Subtype.* (Physical symptoms must be falsely reported as occurring in the self, leading to unnecessary health related-attention and procedures. The induced symptoms must be specified.)
    (3) *Predominately Physical Signs and Symptoms, Active Illness Induction Subtype.* (Physical symptoms must be actively induced in the self, leading to unnecessary health related-attention and procedures. The induced symptoms must be specified.)
    (4) *Physical Symptoms Falsely Reported, Dual Factitious Subtype.*[a] (Psychological symptoms must be reported along with physical symptoms that are falsely reported as occurring in the self. The symptomatic presentation must lead to unnecessary health related-attention and procedures. The induced symptoms must be specified.)
    (5) *Physical Symptoms Actively Induced, Dual Factitious Subtype.*[a] (Psychological symptoms must be reported along with physical symptoms that are actively induced in the self. The symptomatic presentation must lead to unnecessary health related-attention and procedures. The induced symptoms must be specified.)

[a]Listed in *DSM-IV* as "With Combined Psychological and Physical Signs and Symptoms."

Symptomatically, Factitious Disorder by Proxy is character-ized by intentional design of symptoms, often in very complex and medically sophisticated ways, which the patient then attri-butes to or actually induces in the victim. The actual induction process, as opposed to symptom design, appears to be compulsive, driven, involuntary, and automatic. That is, Factitious Disorder by Proxy patients either induce or falsely report symptoms in another person, on an involuntary basis. Analysis of this feature requires close examination of patient behavior in each of six Win-dows of Opportunity (Criterion A).

Motivationally, Factitious Disorder by Proxy patients have usually been defined as desiring to assume the sick role by proxy, thereby discharging smoldering resentment for doctors, replay-ing an early dependent relationship with a nurturing caretaking figure, and similar motives. While these factors may be present in some cases, they are neither necessary nor sufficient for making the diagnosis. Analysis of motivation indicates that a Borderline level of object relations capacity is involved. Rarely, if ever, do Factitious Disorders by Proxy occur in individuals with a narcissis-tic or psychopathic object relations level. All object relations for the inducing or falsely reporting "by proxy" variant are prerap-prochement, and most likely limited to the Borderline spectrum as described by psychodynamic theorists (Criterion B).

Although some patients may display no more than personal-ity traits, most patients who suffer from Factitious Disorder by Proxy will display a formal *DSM* Personality Disorder. Predomi-nately, Borderline or Passive–Aggressive Personality Disorders from the Conflicted–Ambivalent category are present. However, the Self-Defeating or Sadistic Personality Disorders occur in a small number of cases (Criterion C).

With regard to false symptom reporting or active symptom induction varieties of Factitious Disorder by Proxy, *DSM-IV* is sub-stantially correct and, rather than repeating that information here, the reader is referred to Criteria Sets and Axes Provided for Further Study: Factitious Disorder by Proxy: Features (pp. 725–726). However, it is important to distinguish between the *False Reporting* variety (in which symptoms are reported but no illness or injury exists) and the *Active Induction* variety that in-volves real pathology, sometimes of life-threatening magnitude.

Associated Features and Mental Disorders

An enormous variety of features may be associated with Factitious Disorder by Proxy. The list of ways in which a patient may induce or falsely report symptoms in a victim is extensive and limited only by the medical knowledge and sophistication of the patient. Factitious Disorder by Proxy patients may display problems with work, social, family, and marital relationships. However, since the focus is upon the victim rather than upon themselves, many remain surprisingly functional and, at least initially, seem to be very supportive and concerned caretakers. The high frequency of physician and ER visits, often with minimal to no objective medical findings regarding the etiologic agent, is usually frustrating to caregivers and may lead to discord between doctor and patient. Factitious Disorder by Proxy patients may demonstrate any of the behaviors associated with the relevant Personality Disorder reported on *DSM* Axis II. The description under Associated Features in *DSM-IV* (APA, 1994) is very helpful and the reader is referred to Criteria Sets and Axes Provided for Further Study (p. 726).

Associated Laboratory Findings

In the False Reporting variety, laboratory findings are customarily negative since the patient simply reports nonexistent symptoms, and the victim usually has no illness as claimed. However, in the more virulent Active Induction variety, positive laboratory findings are customary with respect to the apparent condition but strangely inconclusive concerning etiology. Alternatively, when an etiologic agent is identified, the caregiver may become suspicious upon noting a high correlation between the presence of the "by proxy" Factitious patient and deterioration in the victim's condition.

Specific Age, Cultural, and Gender Features

There are no reliable data on age and sex ratios in Factitious Disorder by Proxy but the patient is customarily assumed to be far more often female than male since illness induction or false reporting is generally at the hand of the primary caretaker. The disorder seems to be more prevalent in young mothers than in older females.

Prevalence

No data are available on prevalence. There are reports in the literature that it may be more common than previously thought. Some authors have questioned whether, at least occasionally, Sudden Infant Death Syndrome is actually a tragic consequence of Factitious Disorder by Proxy.

Course

Factitious Disorder by Proxy is difficult to track but it is generally assumed that the disorder goes into remission when the victim reaches an age where he is able to function independently or becomes unavailable through death, divorce, or other circumstance. When a proxy victim is no longer available, patients may turn attention to themselves and convert to straightforward Factitious Disorder. There are some indications that family pets may serve as victim if no human victim is available. In any case, unless the underlying problem is effectively treated, Factitious illness or injury is most likely a lifelong problem.

Differential Diagnosis

The distinction between Factitious Disorder by Proxy and other disorders requires careful analysis of Behavioral Orchestration, Motivation, and Personality Pathology. The presumed patient is actually a victim and the caretaker is the one who carries the diagnosis. The Factitious Disorder by Proxy patient may, themselves, suffer induced or falsely reported pathology in addition to actually falsely reporting and/or inducing illness in others. Factitious Disorder by Proxy patients may also suffer from traditional mental disorders such as Impulse Control Disorder, Substance Abuse Disorder, Depression, or an Anxiety Disorder. Factitious Disorder by Proxy patients are often difficult to detect since, at least initially, attention is directed toward the putative patient who is, in reality, a victim instead.

Table 8.3

Diagnostic Criteria for Factitious Disorder by Proxy

A. *Behavioral Orchestration* characteristic of Factitious Disorder by Proxy that is nontrivial in at least:

    (1) Window 1, Other-as-Patient   and

    (2) Window 2 or Window 3   and

    (3) Window 4 or Window 5 or Window 6.

B. *Motivation* characterized by object relations that are prerapprochement at the Borderline level as described by psychodynamic theorists.

C. *Personality Pathology* defined as the presence of formal disorder or the presence of very strong traits in one or more of the following *DSM-III-R* (APA, 1987) and *DSM-IV* (APA, 1994) Personality Disorder categories (Code on Axis II):

    Borderline,   or

    Passive-Aggressive,   or

    Self-Defeating   or

    Not Otherwise Specified (combination of the above).

D. *Subtype* must be specified as:

    (1) *False Symptom Reporting.* (Psychological and/or physical symptoms must be falsely reported as occurring in another person leading to unnecessary health-related attention and procedures. Diagnosis is of the individual falsely reporting the symptoms. The reported symptoms must be specified and the identified patient [victim] recorded.)

    (2) *Active Symptom Induction.* (Psychological and/or physical symptoms must be actively induced in another person leading to unnecessary health related-attention and procedures. Diagnosis is of the individual actively inducing the symptoms. The induced symptoms must be specified and the identified patient [victim] recorded.)

    (3) *Concurrent Symptoms.* (Psychological and/or physical symptoms must be actively induced or falsely reported in both the patient and the victim. The induced symptoms must be specified for each party.)

COMPENSATION NEUROSIS

Diagnostic Features

Compensation Neurosis has never been well defined since the term emerged about one hundred years ago. Nevertheless, it has frequently been viewed as a bridge between Malingering on one side and genuine mental disorders on the other. Most authors have viewed Compensation Neurosis as involving claims of exaggerated symptoms, produced by secondary gain (frequently due to expectations of financial reward in litigation), that are likely to remit upon settlement of the claim. With the publication of *DSM-III* (APA, 1980), the diagnosis was apparently associated with Psychological Factors Affecting Physical Condition (PFAPC), and/or Psychogenic Pain Disorder, and/or Malingering. By *DSM-III-R* (APA, 1987) it was solely associated with PFAPC. One year later, Hyler, Spitzer, and Williams (1988) argued that the diagnosis ought to be discarded and it does not appear in *DSM-IV* (APA, 1994). Yet, contemporary authors continue to write articles about Compensation Neurosis (Hodges, Goode, & Masterton, 1996; Robinson, Rondinelli, Scheer, & Weinstein, 1997) and it continues as a topic of discussion in medicine, law, and mental health.

As presently defined, Compensation Neurosis is the volitional prolongation and/or exaggeration of genuine symptoms, unintentionally produced by an original accident, illness, or stress. It is not quite Malingering and not quite one of the traditional disorders with which it was replaced beginning with *DSM-III* (APA, 1980). Thus, Compensation Neurosis involves unintentional design of symptoms with volitional protraction and/or exaggerated display of those symptoms. Analysis of this characteristic requires close examination of patient behavior in each of six Windows of Opportunity (Criterion A).

Motivationally, Compensation Neurosis has traditionally been viewed as involving secondary gain such as obtaining compensation in a civil suit. While this factor may occasionally be present, it is neither necessary nor sufficient for making the diagnosis. Analysis of motivation indicates that a Psychopathic, Narcissistic, or Borderline level of object relations capacity is involved. It is important to note that the label *Compensation Neurosis* is not an accurate description of the condition but is simply a traditional term. The term *Compensation Neurosis* should not be taken literally because it is not simply motivated by compensation just as it is not a neurosis. In any case, all object relations capacities are pre-rapprochement as described by psychodynamic theorists (Criterion B).

Many patients who display Compensation Neurosis will not qualify for a formal *DSM-IV* (APA, 1994) Personality Disorder although all will display definite personality traits or combinations, predominately Antisocial and Narcissistic from the Extroversive–Nonconforming quadrant; Borderline, Passive-Aggressive, and Obsessive-Compulsive from the Conflicted-Ambivalent area; and Dependent and Self-Defeating from the Extroversive-Conforming quadrant (Criterion C).

Associated Features and Mental Disorders

Like other Disorders of Simulation, Compensation Neurotics may not be reliable historians and diagnosis usually requires diligent historical research as well as compilation of an extensive medical, occupational, and social history. Upon clinical interview and evaluation, Compensation Neurotics present similarly to the Somatoform Disorders. Their symptoms may be colorful, exaggerated, and out of proportion to the alleged cause or condition. Multiple visits to hospitals and physicians are common, as is an extensive past medical history. The apparent disability experienced by the patient may be quite extensive, interfering with social, recreational, vocational, and marital relations. The notion that the patient's disability disappears or greatly contracts in magnitude following the end of litigation is not a reliable index of Compensation Neurosis. Compensation Neurotics may also present with traditional mental disorders such as Depression, Panic Disorder, Anxiety Disorder, and iatrogenic substance abuse disorders, in a fashion similar to the Somatoform Disorders.

Associated Laboratory Findings

Prior laboratory studies may detect physical findings consistent with the alleged injury, accident, or stressor but current tests are usually within normal limits or reflect insufficient pathology to account for the patient's dramatic claims of dysfunction. This feature makes it particularly important to differentiate between the *DSM-IV* category of Pain Disorder and Compensation Neurosis, for example.

Specific Age, Cultural, and Gender Features

There is insufficient research to make any determination about associated features.

Prevalence

The prevalence is unknown but probably common.

Course

Studies of patients diagnosed as Compensation Neurotics (and closely related disorders) suggest that the claimed impairment is of substantial duration and the patient usually does not experience spontaneous remission at the end of any pending litigation. There are no data available on outcome with active mental health treatment but, given the similarity between Pain Disorder and Compensation Neurosis, the disorder probably has the best prognosis of any Disorder of Simulation.

Differential Diagnosis

The distinction between Compensation Neurosis and other Disorders of Simulation requires careful analysis of Behavioral Orchestration, Motivation, and Personality Pathology. In most cases, those suffering from Compensation Neurosis will have had a recent actual physical disorder induced by accident, illness, or stress. In both the Somatoform Disorders and Compensation Neurosis, symptoms have psychodynamic value and the patient's self-perception, as a genuine sufferer, is emotionally indispensable. In both, symptom magnitude is apparently in excess of reasonable expectations and symptom protraction is well beyond the normal length of recovery. However, an important distinction between Compensation Neurosis and similar *DSM* disorders, is that, in Compensation Neurosis, symptom prolongation is at the very least partially under volitional control. In contrast, most *DSM* Disorders are unintentional in design and involuntary in display. A diagnosis of Compensation Neurosis does not automatically rule out genuine physical disorder that requires treatment, although symptom display may be exaggerated.

Table 8.4
Diagnostic Criteria for Compensation Neurosis

A.   *Behavioral Orchestration* characteristic of Compensation Neurosis that is nontrivial in at least:
     (1) Window 1, Self-as-Patient   and
     (2) Window 2 or Window 3   and
     (3) Window 4 or Window 5 or Window 6.

B.   *Motivation* characterized by object relations that are prerapprochement and at the Narcissistic or Borderline level as described by psychodynamic object relations theorists.

C.   *Personality Pathology* defined as the presence of formal disorder or the presence of very strong traits in one or more of the following *DSM-III-R* (APA, 1987) and *DSM-IV* (APA, 1994) Personality Disorder categories (Code on Axis II):
     Antisocial,   or
     Narcissistic,   or
     Borderline,   or
     Passive-Aggressive,   or
     Obsessive-Compulsive,   or
     Dependent,   or
     Self-Defeating,   or
     Not Otherwise Specified (combination of the above).

D.   *Original Pathology* that produced the initial symptoms must be specified and coded on the appropriate axis.

DISORDERS NOT YET IDENTIFIED

If, after careful analysis, the patient does not fit the criteria for one of the customary *DSM* disorders or one of the Disorders of Simulation, an inaccurate diagnosis is likely. One of three errors

occurred somewhere in analysis of the case: a missed mental diagnosis, a missed physical diagnosis, or a new diagnosis.

A Missed Mental Diagnosis

An error may occur when the patient actually suffers from a traditional mental disorder that superficially resembles a Disorder of
Simulation. Somehow, the true diagnosis slipped through the diagnostic sieve and the patient was mistaken for an individual suffering from a Disorder of Simulation. Careful review of all case
material, another interview or testing session with the patient,
case consultation, rounds presentation, and other steps usually
taken in difficult cases may lead to a proper diagnosis.

A Missed Physical Diagnosis

Sometimes, it happens that the patient has actual physical pathology that has escaped detection upon medical examination. The
physician, finding nothing to account for the patient's complaints, makes a referral for psychological or psychiatric review
despite the fact that his physical pathology, if known, would fully
explain the patient's presentation. In order for the mental health
expert to make a proper diagnosis, it is important to thoroughly
examine the medical record. It may be necessary to request additional medical evaluations, suggest the use of medical diagnostic
procedures of greater sensitivity, obtain independent consultation and, in short, make a bold effort to rule out explanatory
physical pathology.

A New Diagnosis

Diagnostic error may occur when the patient suffers from some
disorder, either mental or physical, that is unknown to health
care professionals and that is not yet identified or classified. This
error is most likely when the clinician diagnoses by default. Since
there are undoubtedly a number of unknown physical and mental
disorders, diagnosis of simulation by default runs the risk of misla-
beling a serious but undiscovered disorder as simulation. It is
important to avoid the mistakes of the past where, for example,

Posttraumatic Stress Disorder was considered to be Malingering. To avoid this error, Disorders of Simulation must be affirmative diagnoses, made with positive criteria, and not by default.

CONCLUDING COMMENTS

Historically, Simulation is a phenomenon that has been viewed as either a moral–ethical act outside the province of psychology, or an indication of mental illness, or a behavior that may occur in anyone as the result of risk-benefit analysis. Understanding the problem of Simulation is not well served by any of these views. It is far more productive to view Disorders of Simulation as legitimate syndromes and patients who suffer from them as posing legitimate diagnostic questions. Individuals do not simulate merely for "convenience," "compensation," or other superficial reasons. The simulation of disorder is psychodynamically complex and does not occur on a "whim" or because the reinforcement contingencies are propitious. It occurs because Simulation is a developmentally suitable way of solving complex psychological and interpersonal issues. Disorders of Simulation should be fully included in the taxonomy of mental disorders, with specific diagnostic criteria, and be distinguished from the great body of "indefinite and unknown disorders." There are three distinct and recognizable diagnoses in Disorders of Simulation: Malingering, Factitious Disorder, and Compensation Neurosis.

In the literature on Simulating Disorders, the manner of symptom production has been the focus, usually designated as consciously as opposed to unconsciously produced. However, it is impossible to devise a behavioral test or observational method that will reliably and validly distinguish between conscious and unconscious processes, or detect Malingering, Factitious Disorder, or Compensation Neurosis, or determine if a patient is telling the truth, or responding validly to a test.

In the literature on Simulating Disorders, motivational factors have invariably been listed as few in number and superficial in content, invariably linked with greed, comfort, exculpation, desiring to be a patient, or shirking one's duty. These motivations are insufficient to explain why people simulate because they do not directly address the central motivational issue in Disorders of Simulation: developmental object relations capacity.

In the literature on Simulation, the issue of personality pathology has received little attention. Yet, a Disorder of Simulation is quite unlikely to occur in a person with complex, high-level personality development. The Simulating Disorders are primitive syndromes and occur in individuals who have primitively or poorly developed ego structures, significant enduring personality pathology, a psychodynamic structure consistent with primitive interpersonal relations, and a simple and unsophisticated approach to life's complex challenges.

The notion of Simulation as a simple behavioral act unattached to a syndrome is naïve because it defies all that psychology has learned about the veridical integration of human behavior. That is, human behavior must make sense in the context of the full range of psychodynamic factors operating within the individual, not just the need-press of the moment or a Baysean calculation of risk–benefit ratios. The notion of Simulation as a simple behavioral act is deceptive and promotes the notion that simple, quick tests or interview techniques can distinguish Simulation from "legitimate" disorders. The simple view of Simulation-as-behavior ignores the lesson learned from the historically impossible-to-test distinction between Hysteria and Malingering.

The notion of Simulation as a convenient behavior is antipsychodynamic because it suggests that Simulation is nonpathological and nonunique. It promotes the shallow view that Simulation may occur in any person, irrespective of his psychological complexity and developmental level. While Simulation as a simple behavior conforms to the *au currant* cognitive and behaviorally defined philosophies of psychopathology and psychotherapy, it is antipsychological because it promotes the false view that Simulation is a "brief encounter of the superficial kind."

The assessment of Simulation requires a complex, multiaxial formula. The first Axis involves six Windows of Opportunity for Simulation, ranging from identification of the patient to outcome of treatment. To be eligible for a diagnosis of Simulation and to assure that more than just a single behavior is involved, the patient must qualify in several Windows. The second Axis is motivational and, in Disorders of Simulation, motivation is synonymous with object relations. To be eligible for a diagnosis of Simulation, the patient's object relations capacity must be prerapprochement. The final axis involves personality pathology as specified by the *DSM*. To be eligible for a diagnosis of Simulation, the patient must have either a Personality Disorder *or* very significant personality traits in one or a combination of specified *DSM* Personality Disorder categories.

If a patient appears to be simulating but does not positively qualify under the diagnostic formula, he probably is not simulating. Instead, the patient is suffering from a customary *DSM* disorder which has been missed by the practitioner, *or* he is suffering from an unknown or undiscovered mental disorder which is superficially similar to a Disorder of Simulation, *or* he is suffering from a undiagnosed physical disorder which is superficially similar to a Disorder of Simulation. Patients should be positively diagnosed as suffering from a Disorder of Simulation—never as a simulator by default.

Finally, Disorders of Simulation should be dispassionately described and carefully researched, leaving the social, ethical, and legal judgments to bodies concerned with such matters. Patients who suffer from Disorders of Simulation should be considered to have a bona fide problem, one deserving mental health attention, understanding, analysis, and treatment.

Glossary

TABLE 9.1

Labels Often Used as Synonyms for Malingering

Brickibus Aureautus[a]	(Brussel, 1942)
California Syndrome	(Keltner, May, Johnson, & Post, 1985)
Constitutional Psychopathic Inferiority	(Brussel & Hitch, 1943)
Counterfeit Illness	(Rabin & Graham, 1984)
Degenerate Malingering	(Jones & Lewellyn, 1917)
Deliberate Malingering	(Wechsler, 1935)
Faking Bad	(Gudjonsson & Shackleton, 1986)
False Imputation	(original source unknown)
Fraudulent Malingering	(Wechsler, 1935)
Gold-Bricking[b]	(Waisman, 1965)
Gold-Digging	(original source unknown)
Goofing Off	(original source unknown)
Green Poultice	(original source unknown)
Leadswinging	(Anonymous, 1972)
Mild Malingering[c]	(Rogers, 1984a,b)
Moderate Malingering	(Rogers, 1984a,b)
Opportunism	(original source unknown)
Playing Sick	(original source unknown)
Positive Malingering	(original source unknown)
Pseudomalingering[d]	(Arnold, 1940; Schneck, 1970)
Psychoneurotic Malingering	(MacLean, 1947)
Pure Malingering	(Gill, 1941)
Sandbagging	(original source unknown)
Scrimshanking	(original source unknown)
Severe Malingering	(Rogers, 1984a,b)
Shamming Illness	(original source unknown)
Slacking	(original source unknown)
Shirking	(original source unknown)
Supratentorial Problems	(original source unknown)

249

True Malingering	(Wechsler, 1935)
Whiplash Syndrome	(MacNab, 1973)
Willful Malingering	(Collie, 1913)

[a] Quasi-Latin for goldbricking. Since World War II soldiers carried their chart from one medical clinic to another, pseudomedical terms were often used to camouflage the diagnosis from the patient's prying eyes. If the syndrome was very marked, "Maximus et extremus" or "Allergica ad bellum" was often appended.

[b] *Goldbricking, goofing-off,* and *scrimshanking* are properly used to indicate shirking one's duties but they are frequently encountered as synonyms for Malingering. Of the three terms, *scrimshanking* appears to be the closest to Malingering since it is frequently used to imply some conscious element.

[c] As used by Rogers, *mild Malingering* is essentially indistinguishable from the normal defensiveness that accompanies many mental disorders.

[d] Pseudomalingering and Pseudoneurotic Malingering have been used to designate partial Malingering or the conscious exaggeration of genuine disease but the former has also been applied to Ganser's Syndrome. Pseudomalingering has also been used to describe individuals who deliberately feign illness but who, much to their own dismay, later develop the very illness they attempted to simulate.

TABLE 9.2

Labels Used for Factitious Disorder with Predominantly Physical Signs and Symptoms

Ahasuerus' Syndrome	(Wingate, 1951)
Anticoagulant Malingerers	(Bowie, Todd, Thompson, Owen, & Wright, 1965)
Arteritis Factitia	(Manolis & Sanjana, 1987)
Artifactual Disease	(Carney & Brown, 1983)
Cardiopathica Fantastica	(Kounis, 1979)
Chronic Factitious Illness	(Spiro, 1968)
Compulsive Wandering	(Stendel, 1939)
Consultant Bafflers	(Naish, 1979)
Deception Syndrome[a]	(Hardie & Reed, 1998)
Dermatitis Autogenica	(Chapman, 1957)
Dermatitis Factitia	(Epstein, 1986)
Dermatitis Simulata	(King & Chalmers, 1984)
Dicumarol Eaters	(Bowie et. al., 1965)
Factitious Fever	(Petersdorf & Bennett, 1956)
Fraudulent Fever	(Hale & Evseichick, 1943)
Great Impostors	(Marsh & Johnson, 1983)
Great Pretenders	(Gruber, Beavers, & Amodeo, 1987)
Haematemesis Merchants	(Asher, 1951)
Haemoptysis Merchants	(Asher, 1951)
Hbg Munchausen $_{-2}{}^{\beta}{}_{2}{}^{6glu\text{-}glu}$	(Weaver, McMillan, Longmire, Yam, & Crosby, 1974)
Hemorrhagica Histronica	(Steinbeck, 1961)
Hosptial Frauds	(Sjoberg, 1951)
Hospital Addiction Syndrome	(Barker, 1962)
Hospital Hoboes	(Clarke & Melnick, 1958)
Hospital Vagrants	(Chapman, 1957)
Hyperpyrexia Figmentatica	(Petersdorf & Bennett, 1957)
Impersonators	(McGrath, 1972)
Impostor Patients	(Heym, 1973)
Ipsepathogenesis	(Marsh & Johnson, 1983)
Kopenikades[b]	(Sjoberg, 1951)
Laparotamophilia Migrans	(Asher, 1951)
Mania Operativa	(Chertok, 1974)
Mayhem Syndrome	(Flicker, 1942)
Metabolic Malingerers	(Gorman, Wahner, & Tauxe, 1970)
Munchausen's Syndrome	(Asher, 1951)
Neurologica Diabolica	(Asher, 1951)
Otolaryngologica Prevarica	(Pender & Pender, 1980)
Pathologic Malingering	(Shaw, 1964)
Pathomime	(Cramer, Gershberg, & Stern, 1971)
Pathomimicry	(D'Andrea, 1978)
Peripatetic Pseudoporphyria	(Williams, 1961)
Peregrinating Problem Patients	(Chapman, 1957)
Persistent Perplexing Pyrexia	(Molavi & Weinstein, 1970)
Professional Patients	(Powills, 1986)

Poly-Surgical Addiction	(Menninger, 1934)
Pseudopatients	(Vaisrub, 1975)
Scopophilia Meanderans	(Rhys-Evans, 1979)
S-H-A-F-T Syndrome[c]	(Wallace & Fitzmorris, 1978)
Surgical Addiction	(Menninger, 1934)
Thyrotoxicosis Factitia	(Marlotti et. al., 1982)
Van Gough Syndrome	(Abram, 1966)
VIP Syndrome	(Weintraub, 1964)
Wandering Jew Syndrome	(Wingate, 1951).

[a] Hardie and Reed (1998) proposed this term for those whose motivations are "internal" as opposed to "external" and it could therefore apply to Compensation Neurosis as well.

[b] A name by which such patients are known in Sweden, after the German town of Kopenick in which a famous hoax took place in 1906 (Clarke & Melnick, 1958).

[c] S-H-A-F-T is an acronym standing for "Sad, Hostile, Anxious, Frustrated and Tenacious."

TABLE 9.3

Labels Used for Factitious Disorder with Predominantly Psychological
Signs & Symptoms

Buffoonery Syndrome[a]	(original source unknown)
Cinderella Syndrome[b]	(Goodwin, Cauthorne, & Rada, 1980)
Ganser's Syndrome[c]	(Hyler & Spitzer, 1978)
Factitious Psychosis	(Pope, Jonas, & Jones, 1982)
Hysterical Psychosis[d]	(Hollender & Hirsch, 1964)
Hysterical Pseudodementia	(Wernicke, 1906)
Hysterical Pseudostupidity	(original source unknown)
Hystericomalingering	(original source unknown)
Mental Munchausen	(Cheng & Hummel, 1978)
Pseudodelirium	(Goldney & Lander, 1979)
Pseudodementia[e]	(Golden, 1948)
Pseudopsychosis	(Bishop & Holt, 1980)
Pseudomalingering	(Schneck, 1970)
Prison Psychosis	(original source unknown)
Psychiatrica Pseudopathica	(Sale, Burvill, & Kalucy, 1979).

[a] Buffoonery syndrome has often been linked with some variety of organic brain dysfunction and Ganser Syndrome, much as has been the case with pseudodementia.
[b] Cinderella occurs primarily in prepubescent children and is not really a ''by proxy'' variant but actually the reverse. In this syndrome, a child simulates or claims usually dramatic abuse that reflects negatively upon his caretaker.
[c] In *DSM-III* (APA, 1980) Ganser's Syndrome was considered a variant of Factitious Disorder but, in *DSM-III-R* (APA, 1987), the classification was changed to Dissociative Disorder, NOS (without criteria) and it remains in this category in *DSM-IV* (APA, 1994).
[d] Hysterical psychosis, hysterical pseudodementia, hysterical pseudostupidity, and prison psychosis have also been used to describe Ganser's Syndrome.
[e] Pseudodementia customarily refers to reduction in mental capacity as the result of severe depression, especially in the elderly. At times, it has been used to describe hysterical blocking that causes the patient to appear demented, at least temporarily. It has occasionally been used in the sense of factitiously presented cognitive or intellectual impairment.

TABLE 9.4

Labels Used for Factitious Disorder Not Otherwise Specified (Factitious
Disorder by Proxy)

Active Inducer	(Libow & Schreier, 1986)
Child Abuse	(Rogers et al., 1976)
Doctor Addict	(Libow & Schreier, 1986)
Hinterland of Child Abuse	(Meadow, 1977)
Malingering by Proxy	(Arnold, 1940)
Meadow's Syndrome	(Warner & Hathaway, 1984)
Medea Complex	(Lansky & Erickson, 1974)
Munchausen Syndrome by Proxy	(Meadow, 1977)
Polle Syndrome[a]	(Burman & Stevens, 1977)

[a] Polle Syndrome declined in popularity after Meadow and Lennert (1984) noted that the term was derived from incorrect information. Initially, it was thought that Polle Syndrome was descriptive for the child of a Factitious parent since the Baron's only child, Polle, died following a mysterious illness at one year of age.

TABLE 9.5
Labels Used for Compensation Neurosis

Accident Neurosis	(Bregler & Knopf, 1944)
Active Dependency Syndrome[a]	(Gordon et. al., 1973)
Acute Neurotic Reaction	(original source unknown)
Attenuated Malingering	(Jones & Llewellyn, 1917)
Attitudinal Pathosis	(Thorne, 1949)
Compensationitis	(Moorhead, 1944)
Compensation Hysteria	(Ferenczi, Abraham, Simmel, & Jones, 1921)
Conscious Symptom Exaggeration	(Clayer et al., 1984)
Covetous Neurosis	(Ferenczi, Abraham, Simmel, & Jones, 1921)
Desire Neurosis	(Brown, 1929)
Disability Neurosis	(Ford, 1976)
Fate Neurosis	(original source unknown)
Greenback Neurosis	(original source unknown)
Humpty Dumpty Syndrome	(Ford, 1977–1978)
Hysterical Malingering	(Braverman, 1978)
Hystericomalingering	(original source unknown)
Indemnity Neurosis	(original source unknown)
Industrial Neurosis	(original source unknown)
Insurance Hebephrenia	(original source unknown)
Justice Neurosis[b]	(Ramsay, 1939)
Litigation Neurosis	(Bailey, 1918)
Mediterranean Back	(Parker, 1970)
Mild Malingering [c]	(Rogers, 1984a,b)
Neurosis Following Accident	(Kennedy, 1946)
Neurosis Following Injury	(Foster, 1933)
Neurosis Following Trauma	(Kennedy, 1946)
Occupational Neurosis	(original source unknown)
Partial Malingering Neurosis	(Gill, 1941)
Pension Neurosis	(original source unknown)
Personal Injury Neurosis	(original source unknown)
Postaccident Anxiety Syndrome	(original source unknown)
Posttraumatic Hysteria	(original source unknown)
Profit Neurosis	(Nogales, 1934)
Psychotraumatic Malingering	(Braverman, 1978)
Quasi-Malingering	(Eisner, 1989)
Retirement Neurosis	(Bregler & Knopf, 1944)
Social Neurosis	(Eliasberg, 1941)
Secondary Gain Neurosis	(original source unknown)
Semimalingering Neurosis	(Southard, 1919)
Sinistrosis	(Arnold, 1940)
Telophrenia	(original source unknown)
Terror Neurosis (Schrekeneurose)	(original source unknown)
Traumatic Neurasthenia	(Huddleson, 1932)
Traumatic Neurosis[d]	(Oppenheim, 1889)
Triggered Neurosis	(original source unknown)

Unconscious Malingering[e]	(original source unknown)
Unconscious Exaggeration	(Baro, 1950)
Whiplash Neurosis	(Hodge, 1971)
Wish Neurosis	(original source unknown)

[a] Probably the most accurate and descriptive term but the use of *Compensation Neurosis* is traditionally preferred.

[b] Translation of the German term.

[c] Mild Malingering has been used by Rogers (1988) to signify normal defensiveness or Malingering of such slight effect that neither the diagnosis nor the outcome is materially changed. Presumably, Compensation Neurosis would fall into the same category although it may fall under Rogers' classification of "moderate Malingering" instead.

[d] Traumatic Neurosis is also the popularized name for the Posttraumatic Stress Disorder of *DSM-IV* (APA, 1994).

[e] Szasz (1961) mentions that this term has been used to describe hysteria as it emerged from the pre-Charcot grouping of all nonorganically ill patients as malingerers.

TABLE 9.6
Synonyms for Simulation

Amplification	Fictitious	Programmed
Contrived	Fraudulent	Pseudo (used as prefix)
Counterfeit	Hybrid Responding	Random Responding
Deception	Irrelevant Responding	Self-Administered
Exaggeration	Low Rate of Self-Disclosure	Self-Destructive
Fabrication	Maximization	Self-Inflicted
Faking Bad	Mendacity	Self-Mutative
False Attribution	Mimicking	Spurious
False Imputation	Mixed Deception	Supratentorial
Falsification	Other Deception	Surreptitious
Feigning	Pretended	Trickery

TABLE 9.7
Synonyms for Dissimulation

Cover-Up Malingering[a]	Low Rate of Self-Disclosure	Positive Dissimulation[b]
Decoy Malingering	Faking Good	Symptom Suppression
Diminution	Minimization	Reverse Malingering
Dissembling[c]	Negative Malingering	

[a] According to Arnold (1940), this variety of dissimulation is close to Schneck's pseudomalingering.

[b] The term *positive dissimulation* is obviously redundant and appears to have evolved in the mistaken belief that "dissimulation" refers to the simple act of faking and the direction must therefore be specified as positive (faking good) or negative (faking bad).

[c] Dissembling is defined as deception in the sense of hiding the truth rather than falsely imitating with intent to deceive. The term appears to be completely interchangeable with dissimulation (Oxford English Dictionary, 1971).

TABLE 9.8

Synonyms for Functional

Dissociative	Hysterical Overlay	Psychodynamic
Emotional	Irrational	Psychogenic
Emotional Overlay	Malingeringlike	Self-Deceptive
Functional Overlay	Neurotic	Subjective
Functional Underlay	Nonorganic Overlay	Subtentorial Problems
Hysteric	Pseudo (used as prefix)	Unconscious

TABLE 9.9

Synonyms for Organic

Affliction	Heredofamilial	Objective	Physical
Ailment	Illness (organic)	Organicity	Physiogenic
Disease (organic)	Infirmity	Organogenic	Sickness
Genetic Disorder	Malady	Pathophysiological	Structural

TABLE 9.10

Synonyms for *Vorbeireden*

Answering Past the Point	(original source unknown)
Approximate Answers	(original source unknown)
Balderdash Syndrome	(Gorman, 1982)
Buffoonery Syndrome	(original source unknown)
Gansering[a]	(original source unknown)
Gaslight Phenomenon	(Smith & Sinanan, 1972)
Hysterical Pseudostupidity	(Mathur, Rastogi, Singh, Singh, and Mathur, 1976)
Nonsense Syndrome	(Mathur, Rastogi, Singh, Singh, and Mathur, 1976)
Paralogia	(original source unknown)
Pseudodementia	(Good, 1981)
Psychological Past-Pointing	(original source unknown)
Talking Past the Point	(Ganser, 1898)
Vorbeigehen	(Ganser, 1898)
Vorbeireden	(Moeli, 1888 [as cited in Anderson, Trethowan, & Kenna, 1959])

[a] Terms for Ganser Syndrome are often used mistakenly and interchangeably with synonyms for *Vorbeireden*.

TABLE 9.11

Composite Index of "Suspicious Behaviors" Derived from a Review of the Literature.[a]

Referral
1. Medicolegal presentation, e.g., referral by an attorney to the physician for examination (*DSM-IV*).
2. The psychological setting in which the malingering occurs may be indicative (Davis & Weiss).

Reported History
3. A history of recurrent accidents or injuries (Yudofsky).
4. Will not acknowledge even minor inconsistency in reported history (e.g., minor deception, some lack of forthrightness) (Rogers).

Symptomatic Complaints
5. Claims a nonexistent problem (Hall & Pritchard).
6. Complaints unsupported by historical, physical examination, & diagnostic (Yudofsky).
7. Details of alleged frightening accident occurring in thoughts, dreams, & speech is likely neurotic (Davidson).
8. Eagerness for & satisfaction in reexamination by groups of doctors is more consistent with neurosis (Davidson).
9. Eagerness to discuss symptoms (Rogers).
10. An unlikely number of severe symptoms (Rogers).
11. Improbable or absurd symptoms (Rogers).
12. Rare symptoms or symptom sets (Rogers).
13. Vague, ill-defined symptoms which do not conform to known diagnostic entities (Yudofsky).
14. Causal misattribution of symptoms (Hall & Pritchard; Davis & Weiss).
15. Denial of ability to function (Hall & Pritchard).
16. Exaggeration of a real problem (Hall & Pritchard).
17. Minimizing of ability (Hall & Pritchard).
18. Excessive symptoms, overdramatization, theatrics, excessive suffering (Yudofsky; Davis & Weiss; Rogers).
19. Improbable responses to questions about everyday negative situations and problems (Rogers).
20. Inconsistently endorses symptoms (Rogers).
21. More blatant than subtle symptoms (Rogers).
22. Nonselective, nondiscriminatory symptoms (Rogers).
23. Overly specified symptoms (Rogers).
24. Sudden onset or resolution of symptoms (Rogers).
25. The organ system symptomatically involved may be instructive (Davis & Weiss).
26. Unlikely to copy symptoms they have seen in others during hospitalization, in contrast to neurotics (Davidson).

Behavior on Physical or Mental Testing
27. Behavioral approximation, Censoring (Hall & Pritchard).
28. Behavioral perseveration regardless of feedback (Hall & Pritchard).
29. Improbable failures, rare errors on easy test items, behavioral infrequency (Hall & Pritchard; Rogers).

30. Impulsivity on timed test items (Hall & Pritchard).
31. Insufficient effort, behavioral fractionalizing (Hall & Pritchard).
32. Marked discrepancy between claimed disability and objective findings (*DSM-IV*).
33. Psychological testing may help discriminate (Davidson).
34. Randomizing, inconsistent pattern of errors (Hall & Pritchard).
35. Resistance to or uncooperativeness with examination or treatment (*DSM-IV*; Yudofsky; Davidson).
36. Total inability to function, behavioral disengagement (Hall & Pritchard).

Egregious Behaviors
37. Unlikely to submit to apparently required surgical operation or to mental hospitalization (Davidson).
38. Drug screens detect unexplained toxic substances or nonprescribed medications (Yudofsky).
39. Tampering with medical records or diagnostic data (Yudofsky).
40. Self-inflicted injuries (Yudofsky).
41. Addicting or commonly abused drugs requested (Yudofsky).

Unobserved Activity
42. Functions well when he believes he is not being observed (Davidson; Rogers).
43. Able to play but unable to work (Davidson).

Primary and Secondary Gain
44. Determination of basic motives & whether symptom production is conscious or unconscious (Davis & Weiss).
45. The nature of secondary gain (Davis & Weiss).
46. Financial compensation or other gain as a result of the disorder (Yudofsky).
47. Symptoms allow avoidance of unpleasant situations such as pain, danger, anxiety (Yudofsky).
48. Symptoms allow avoidance of legal or social responsibility or penalties (Yudofsky).

Personality Variables
49. Antisocial Personality Disorder present (*DSM-IV*; Yudofsky).
50. Irresponsible, dishonest, inadequate features (members of the responsible-honest-adequate class are probably not simulating) (Davidson).

Treatment Results and Outcome
51. Reluctant to accept a favorable prognosis (Yudofsky).
52. Refuses an offer of employment which requires abilities or skills associated with unimpaired areas (Davidson)

ª Sources: four criteria from *DSM-IV* (1994, p. 683), 14 criteria by Yudofsky (1985, p. 1864), six general categories noted by Davis and Weiss (1974, vol. 3, p. 279), the 10 criteria of Davidson (1965, p. 220), the 15 assessment strategies of Rogers (1984a, pp. 261–262), and 12 faking styles from Hall and Pritchard (1996, p. 38).

References

Abram, H. D. (1966). The van Gogh syndrome: An unusual case of polysurgical addiction. *American Journal of Psychiatry, 123*(4), 478–481.

Alexander, F. G., & Selesnick, S. T. (1966). *The history of psychiatry*. New York: Harper & Row.

American Psychiatric Association (1952). *Diagnostic and statistical manual of mental disorders*. Washington, DC: American Psychiatric Association Press.

American Psychiatric Association (1968). *Diagnostic and statistical manual of mental disorders* (2nd ed.). Washington, DC: American Psychiatric Association Press.

American Psychiatric Association (1980). *Diagnostic and statistical manual of mental disorders* (3rd ed.). Washington, DC: American Psychiatric Association Press.

American Psychiatric Association (1987). *Diagnostic and statistical manual of mental disorders* (3rd ed. rev.). Washington, DC: American Psychiatric Association Press.

American Psychiatric Association (1994). *Diagnostic and statistical manual of mental disorders* (4th ed.). Washington, DC: American Psychiatric Association Press.

Anderson, E. W., Trethowan, W. H., & Kenna, J. C. (1959). An experimental investigation of simulation and pseudodementia. *Acta Psychiatrica et Neurologica Scandinavica, 132* (4 Suppl), 34, 1–42.

Andreasen, N. C. (1985). Posttraumatic stress disorder. In H. I. Kaplan & B. J. Sadock (Eds.), *Comprehensive textbook of psychiatry* (Vol. 4, 4th ed., pp. 918–924). Baltimore: Williams & Wilkins.

Andreyev, L. (1910). *The dilemma: A story of mental perplexity* (J. Cournos, Trans.). Philadelphia: Brown Bros.

Anonymous. (1972). Leadswingers. *South African Medical Journal, 46*(20), 598.

Arnold, F. O. (1940). The detection of malingering. *Medicolegal Criminal Review, 8,* 199–214.

Artingstall, K. (1999). *Practical aspects of Munchausen by proxy syndrome investigation.* New York: CRC Press.

Asher, R. A. J. (1951). Munchausen's syndrome. *Lancet, 10*(1), 339–341.

Bailey, P. (1918). Malingering in U.S. troops, home forces, 1917. *Military Surgery, 42,* 261–275.

Barker, J. C. (1962). The syndrome of hospital addiction (Munchausen syndrome): A report on the investigation of seven cases. *Journal of Mental Science, 108,* 167–182.

Baro, W. Z. (1950). Industrial head and back injuries: The neurological and psychiatric viewpoint. *Industrial Medicine and Surgery, 19*(2), 69–71.

Barton, W. A. (1985). *Recovering from psychological injuries.* Washington, DC: Association of Trial Lawyers of America.

Battie, W. (1758). *A treatise on madness.* London: J. Whiston.

Beard, G. M. (1880). *A practical treatise of nervous exhaustion (neurasthenia): Its symptoms, nature, sequences, treatment.* New York: William Wood.

Bishop, E. R., & Holt, A. R. (1980). Pseudopsychosis: A reexamination of the concept of hysterical psychosis. *Comprehensive Psychiatry, 21*(2), 150–161.

Blinder, M. (1973). *Psychiatry in the everyday practice of law.* Rochester, New York: Lawyers Cooperative.

Bools, C., Neale, B., & Meadow, R. (1992). Co-morbidity associated with fabricated illness (Munchausen syndrome by proxy). *Archives of Disease in Childhood, 67,* 77–91.

Bowie, E. J., Todd, M., Thompson, J. H. Jr., Owen, C. A. Jr., & Wright, I. S. (1965). Anticoagulant malingerers (the "dicumarol-eaters"). *American Journal of Medicine, 39*(5), 855–864.

Braverman, M. (1978). Post-injury malingering is seldom a calculated ploy. *Occupational Health and Safety, 47*(2), 36–40, 42–44.

Bregler, E., & Knopf, O. (1944). A test for the differential diagnosis between retirement neurosis and accident neurosis. *Journal of Nervous and Mental Disease, 100,* 366–380.

Breuer, J., & Freud, S. (1966). Studies on hysteria. In J. Strachey (Ed. & Trans.), *The standard edition of the complete psychological works of Sigmund Freud* (Vol. 2). London: Hogarth Press. (Original work published 1893–1895)

Brock, A. J. (1929). *Greek medicine.* London: J. M. Dent.

Brown, P. K. (1929). Desire or covetous neurosis. *Southwest Medicine, 13,* 356–359.

Brussel, J. A. (1942). Fact, functional or fake: Neuropsychiatric problem of the army. *Journal of the Medical Society of New Jersey, 39,* 442–445.

Brussel, J. A., & Hitch, K. S. (1943). The military malingerer. *Military Surgery, 93,* 33–44.

Burman, D., & Stevens, D. (1977). Munchausen family. *Lancet, 2*(8035), 456.

California Workers' Compensation Institute (1999). Website: http://www.cwci.org

Campbell, R. J. (1981). *Psychiatric dictionary* (5th ed.). New York: Oxford University Press.

Carney, M. W. P., & Brown, J. P. (1983). Clinical features and motives among 42 artifactual illness patients. *British Journal of Medical Psychology, 56*(1), 57–66.

Chapman, J. S. (1957). Peregrinating problem patients—Munchausen's syndrome. *Journal of the American Medical Association, 165*(8), 927–933.

Cheng, L., & Hummel, L. (1978). The Munchausen syndrome as a psychiatric condition. *British Journal of Psychiatry, 133,* 20–21.

Chertok, L. (1974). Mania operativa: Surgical addiction. *Psychiatric Medicine, 3*(2), 105–118.

Cheyne, G. (1733). *The English malady: Or, a treatise on nervous diseases of all kinds.* London: G. Strahan & J. Leake.

Clark, H. E., & Campbell, J. D. (1948). Self-inflicted gun-shot wounds—Surgical and psychiatric considerations. *American Journal of Psychiatry, 104,* 565–569.

Clarke, E., & Melnick, S. C. (1958). The Munchausen syndrome or the problem of hospital hoboes. *American Journal of Medicine, 25,* 6–12.

Clayer, J. R., Bookless, C., & Ross, M.W. (1984). Neurosis and conscious symptoms exaggeration: Its differentiation by illness behavior questionnaire. *Journal of Psychosomatics Research, 28*(3), 237–241.

Cocores, J. A., Santa, W. G., & Patel, M. D. (1984). The Ganser syndrome: Evidence suggesting its classification as a dissociative disorder. *International Journal of Psychiatric Medicine, 14*(1), 47–55.

Collie, J. (1913). *Malingering and feigned sickness.* London: Edward Arnold.

Cramer, B., Gershberg, M. R., & Stern, M. (1971). Munchausen syndrome: Its relationship to malingering, hysteria, and the physician-patient relationship. *Archives of General Psychiatry, 24*(6), 573–578.

D'Andrea, V. J. (1978). Cancer pathomimicry: A report of three cases. *Journal of Clinical Psychiatry, 39*(3), 233–240.

Davidson, H. A. (1965). Malingering. In *Forensic Psychiatry* (2nd ed., pp. 211–227). New York: Ronald Press.

Davis, D., & Weiss, J. M. (1974). Malingering and associated syndromes. In S. Arieti (Ed.), *American handbook of psychiatry* (2nd ed.), (Vol. 3, pp. 270–287). New York: Basic Books.

Diamond, B. L. (1956). The simulation of sanity. *Journal of Social Therapy, 2,* 158–165.

Doyle, A. C. (1894a). *Round the red lamp: Being facts and fancies of medical life.* New York: Appleton.

Doyle, A. C. (1894b). The adventure of the dying detective. In *The Complete Sherlock Holmes* (Vol. 2, pp. 932–941). New York: Doubleday.

Doyle, A. C. (1894c). The naval treaty. In *The Complete Sherlock Holmes* (Vol. 1, pp. 447–469). New York: Doubleday.

D'Souza, D. A., Bharucha, M. P., & Shah, M. V. (1977). Munchausen's syndrome (a case report with a review of the literature). *Journal of Postgraduate Medicine, 23*(2), 95–98.

Eckert, W. G. (1977). The pathology of self-mutilation and destructive acts: A forensic study and review. *Journal of Forensic Science, 22*(1), 242–250.

Ehlers, W., & Plassmann, R. (1994). Diagnosis of narcissistic self-esteem regulation in patients with factitious illness (Munchausen syndrome). *Psychotherapy and Psychosomatics, 62*(1–2), 69–77.

Eisner, D. A. (1989). Quasi-malingering: A proposal for a forensic diagnosis. *California Psychologist* (professional newsletter), *23*(11), 8–9.

Eliasberg, W. (1941). Challenge of social neuroses. *Journal of Nervous and Mental Disease, 94*, 676–687.

Enoch, M. D., & Trethowan, W. H. (1979). *Uncommon psychiatric symptoms* (2nd ed.). New York: John Wiley.

Epstein, E. Sr. (1986). Dermatitis factitia. *Cutis, 38*(1), 24.

Eysenck, H. J., & Eysenck, S. B. G. (1968a). *Eysenck personality inventory* (Manual). San Diego, CA: Education & Industrial Testing Service.

Eysenck, H. J. & Eysenck, S. B. G. (1968b). *Personality structure and measurement.* San Diego, CA: Knapp.

Feldman, M. D. (1994). Denial in Munchausen syndrome by proxy: The consulting psychiatrist's dilemma. *International Journal of Psychiatry and Medicine, 24*(2), 121–128.

Feldman, M. D. (1997). Concurrent factitious disorder and factitious disorder by proxy. Double jeopardy. *General Hospital Psychiatry, 19*(1), 24–28.

Ferenczi, S., Abraham, K., Simmel, E., & Jones, E. (1921). *Psychoanalysis and the war neuroses.* London: International Psycho-Analytic Press.

Flicker, D. J. (1942). The self-inflicted injury: A case report. *American Journal of Psychiatry, 99*, 168–173.

Flicker, D. J. (1956). Malingering—A symptom. *Journal of Nervous and Mental Disease, 123*, 23–31.

Ford, C. V. (1977–1978). A type of disability neurosis: The Humpty Dumpty Syndrome. *International Journal of Psychiatric Medicine, 8*(3), 285–294.

Foster, L. J. (1933). Traumatic neurosis. *American Journal of Roentgenology, 30*, 44–46.

Freemon, F. R. (1993). Detecting feigned illness during the American Civil War. *Journal of Historical Neuroscience, 2*(3), 239–242.

Galenus, C. (1929). How to detect malingerers. In A. J. Brock (Trans.), *Greek medicine* (pp. 225–228). London: J. M. Dent. (Original work published 150 A.D.)

Ganser, S. J. M. (1898). Uber einen eigenartigen hysterichen Dammerzustand (On a peculiar hysterical twilight state). *Archiv fur Psychiatrie und Nervenkrankheiten, 38*, 633–640.

Garner, H. H. (1965). Malingering. *Illinois Medical Journal,* *128*(3), 318–319.

Gavin, H. (1843). *On feigned and factitious diseases, chiefly of soldiers and seamen, on the means used to simulate or produce them, and on the best modes of discovering impostors.* London: John Churchill.

Gill, M. M. (1941). Malingering. *Bulletin of the Menninger Clinic,* *5*, 157–160.

Golden, M. (1948). A case history of pseudodementia. *Journal of Clinical Psychopathology,* *9*, 56–61.

Goldney, R., & Lander, H. (1979). Pseudodelirium. *Medical Journal of Australia,* *1*(13), 630.

Good, M. I. (1981). Pseudodementia and physical findings masking significant psychopathology. *American Journal of Psychiatry,* *138*(6), 811–814.

Good, R. (1942). Malingering. *British Medical Journal,* *26*(2), 359–362.

Goodwin, J., Cauthorne, C., & Rada, R. (1980). Cinderella syndrome: Children who simulate neglect. *American Journal of Psychiatry,* *137*, 1223–1225.

Gordon, R. E., Lyons, H., Muniz, C., Davis, H., Chudnowsky, N., White, R., Springer, P., Gagliano, T., & Haynes, K. (1973). Can compensation hurt the sick and injured? The active dependency syndrome. *Florida Medical Association Journal,* *60*(4), 36–39.

Gorman, C. A., Wahner, H. W., & Tauxe, W. N. (1970). Metabolic malingerers: Patients who deliberately induce or perpetuate a hypermetabolic or hypometabolic state. *American Journal of Medicine,* *48*(6), 708–714.

Gorman, W. F. (1982). Defining malingering. *Journal of Forensic Science,* *27*(2), 401–407.

Gruber, M., Beavers, F., & Amodeo, D. J. (1987). Trying to care for a great pretender. Nursing grand rounds. *Nursing,* *17*(5), 76–80.

Gudjonsson, G. H., & Shackleton, H. (1986). The pattern of scores on Raven's Matrices during "faking bad" and "non-faking" performance. *British Journal of Clinical Psychology,* *25*(1), 35–41.

Haddy, R. I., Diamond, E. L., Black, D. J., Upshaw, T. S., & Curry, R. W. Jr. (1987). Chronic factitious disorder with physical symptoms (Munchausen's syndrome): The early presentation. *Journal of Family Practice, 24*(2), 133–141.

Hale, V., & Evseichick, O. (1943). Fraudulent fever. *American Journal of Nursing, 43*(11), 992–994.

Hall, H. V., & Pritchard, D. A. (1996). *Detecting malingering and deception: Forensic distortion analysis.* Delray Beach, FL: St. Lucie Press.

Hardie, T. J., & Reed, A. (1998). Pseudologia fantastica, factitious disorder and impostership: A deception syndrome. *Medicine, Science and the Law, 38*(3), 198–201.

Heym, H. H. (1973). The impostor patient: Munchausen's syndrome with report of a case. *Delaware Medical Journal, 45*(6), 155–160.

Hodge, J. R. (1971). The whiplash neurosis. *Psychosomatics, 12,* 245–249.

Hodges, A., Goode, H., & Masterton, G. (1996). Psychodynamic factors in the aetiology of compensation neurosis. *Medicine, Science and the Law, 36*(1), 77–79.

Hollender, M. H., & Hirsch, S. P. (1964). Hysterical psychosis. *American Journal of Psychiatry, 120*(11), 1066–1074.

Hoskins v. I.A.C. (1963). 28 C.C.C. 69.

Huddleston, J. H. (1932). *Accidents, neurosis and compensation.* Baltimore: Williams & Wilkins.

Hutchinson, K. A. (1992). *An integrated theory of developmental object relations.* San Francisco, CA: Professional School of Psychology (dissertation).

Hyler, S. E., & Spitzer, R. L. (1978). Hysteria split asunder. *American Journal of Psychiatry, 135*(12), 1500–1504.

Hyler, S. E., Williams, J. B. W., & Spitzer, R. L. (1988). Where, in DSM-III-R, is "Compensation neurosis"? *American Journal of Forensic Psychiatry, 9*(1), 3–12.

Ingraham, M. R., & Moriarty, D. M. (1967). A contribution to the understanding of the Ganser syndrome. *Comprehensive Psychiatry, 8*(1), 35–44.

Jacoby, G. A. Jr., & Hyslop, N. E. Jr. (1979). Case records of the Massachusetts General Hospital. Weekly clinicopathological exercises. Case 35–1979. *New England Journal of Medicine,* *301*(9), 488–496.

Jamieson, R., McKee, E., & Roback, H. (1979). Munchausen's syndrome: An unusual case. *American Journal of Psychotherapy, 33*(4), 616–621.

Jonas, J. M., & Pope, H. G. Jr. (1985). The dissimulating disorders: A single diagnostic entity? *Comprehensive Psychiatry, 26*(1), 58–62.

Jones, A. B., & Llewellyn, L. J. (1917). *Malingering or the simulation of disease.* London: William Heinemann.

Jones, R. M. (1995). Factitious disorders. In H. I. Kaplan & B. J. Sadock (Eds.), *Comprehensive textbook of psychiatry* (4th ed., Vol. 1, pp. 1271–1279). Baltimore: Williams & Wilkins.

Justus, P. G., Kreutziger, S. S., & Kitchens, C. S. (1980). Probing the dynamics of Munchausen's syndrome. Detailed analysis of a case. *Annals of Internal Medicine, 93*(1), 120–127.

Kaplan, H. I., & Sadock, B. J. (Eds.). (1995). *Comprehensive textbook of psychiatry* (6th ed.). Baltimore: Williams & Wilkins.

Keen, W. W., Mitchell, S. W., & Morehouse, G. R. (1864). On malingering, especially in regard to simulation of diseases of the nervous system. *American Journal of Medicine and Science, 48,* 367–394.

Keltner, J. L., May, W. N., Johnson, C. A., & Post, R. B. (1985). The California syndrome: Functional visual complaints with potential economic impact. *Ophthalmology, 92*(3), 427–435.

Kennedy, F. (1946). Mind of the injured worker: Its effect on disability periods. *Compensation Medicine, 1,* 19–24.

Kernberg, O. (1975). *Borderline conditions and pathological narcissism.* New York: Jason Aronson.

King, C. M., & Chalmers, R. J. (1984). Another aspect of contrived disease: "Determatitis simulata." *Cutis, 34*(5), 463–464.

Kohut, H. (1977). *The restoration of the self.* New York: International Universities Press.

Kounis, N. G. (1979). Munchausen syndrome with cardiac symptoms. Cardiopathia fantastica. *British Journal of Clinical Practice, 33*(3), 67–72, 79.

Krupinski, M., Tutsch-Bauer, F., Frank, R., Brodherr-Heberlin, S., & Soyka, M. (1995). Munchausen syndrome by proxy. *Nervenarzt., 66*(1), 36–40.

Lansky, S. B., & Erickson, H. M. (1974). Prevention of child murder: A case report. *Journal of the American Academy of Child Psychiatry, 13*, 691–698.

Lasky, H. (1980). Psychiatry and California workers' compensation laws: A threat and a challenge. *California and Western Law Review, 17*(1), 1–25.

Lasky, H. (1988). *Guidelines for handling psychiatric issues in workers' compensation cases.* Los Angeles, CA:Lex-Com Enterprises.

Lehmann, H. E. (1985). Unusual psychiatric disorders, atypical psychoses, and brief reactive psychoses. In H. I. Kaplan & B. J. Sadock (Eds.), *Comprehensive textbook of psychiatry* (4th ed., Vol. 4, pp. 1224–1238). Baltimore: Williams & Wilkins.

Libow, J. A., & Schreier, H. A. (1986). Three forms of factitious illness in children: When is it Munchausen syndrome by proxy? *American Journal of Orthopsychiatry, 56*(4), 602–611.

Liddon, S. C. (1970). Conversion hysteria versus malingering: A personal confession. *Military Medicine, 135*(1), 286–288.

Linn, L (1985). Clinical manifestations of psychiatric disorders. In H. I. Kaplan & B. J. Sadock (Eds.), *Comprehensive textbook of psychiatry* (4th ed., Vol. 4, pp. 550–590). Baltimore: Williams & Wilkins.

Lipsitt, D. R. (1986). The factitious patient who sues. *American Journal of Psychiatry, 143*(11), 1482.

Lorei, T. W. (1970). Staff ratings of the relative importance of the consequences of release from or retention in a psychiatric hospital. *Journal of Consulting and Clinical Psychology, 34*(1), 48–55.

Mackay, C. (1852). *Extraordinary popular delusions and the madness of crowds.* London: Office of the National Illustrated Library.

MacLean, A. R. (1947). The paradox of psychoneurotic malingering. *Journal of the Indiana State Medical Association, 40*(12), 1223–1226.

MacNab, I. (1973). The whiplash syndrome. In Congress of Neurological Surgeons (Ed.), *Clinical neurosurgery* (pp. 232–241). Baltimore: Williams & Wilkins.

Manolis, A. S., & Sanjana, V. M. (1987). Cardiopathia fantastica and arteritis factitia as manifestations of Munchausen syndrome. *Critical Care Medicine, 15*(5), 526–529.

Marlotti, S., Martino, E., Cupini, C., Lari, R., Giani, C., Baschieri, L., & Pinchera, A. (1982). Low serum thyroglobulin as a clue to the diagnosis of thyrotoxicosis factitia. *New England Journal of Medicine, 307*(7), 410–412.

Marsh, A. P., & Johnson, B. E. (1983). The great impostor. Munchausen's syndrome and other factitious disease. *Journal of the Kansas Medical Society, 84*(1), 147–151, 161.

Masterson, J. (1981). *The narcissistic and borderline disorders: An integrated developmental approach.* New York: Brunner/Mazel.

Mathur, S., Rastogi, C. K., Singh, Y. D., Singh, R. N., & Mathur, G. P. (1976). Ganser's syndrome: A rare psychiatric disorder. *Indian Pediatrics, 13*(12), 947–948.

Mauran, L. (1995). Troubles nerveux et pithiatisme chez les soldats francais, pendant la Grande Guerre (Nervous and hysterical problems amongst French soldiers during the Great War). *History of Science and Medicine, 29*(1), 63–69.

McCahill, M. E. (1995). Somatoform and related disorders: Delivery of diagnosis as first step. *American Family Physician, 52*(1), 193–204.

McGrath, W. B. (1972). Impersonation. *Arizona Medicine, 29*(10), 782–783.

McMahon, C. E. (1975). The wind of the cannon ball: An informative anecdote from medical history. *Psychotherapy and Psychomatics, 26,* 125–131.

McMahon, C. E. (1984). Nervous disease and malingering: The status of psychosomatic concepts in nineteenth century medicine. *International Journal of Psychosomatics, 31*(3), 15–19.

M'Naughten. (1843). 10 Clark & Fin. 200.210 (8 Eng. Rep. 718, 722).

Meadow, R. (1977). Munchausen syndrome by proxy: The hinterland of child abuse. *Lancet, 2*(8033), 343–345.

Meadow, R., & Lennert, T. (1984). Munchausen by proxy or Polle Syndrome: Which term is correct? *Pediatrics, 74*(4), 554–546.

Meloy, J. R. (1989). The forensic interview, part IV: The presence of distortion. *The California Psychologist, 23*(2), 7, 13.

Mendelson, G. (1982). Not "cured by a verdict": Effect of legal settlement on compensation claimants. *Medical Journal of Austria, 2*(1), 132–134.

Menninger, K. A. (1934). Polysurgery and polysurgical addiction. *Psychoanalytic Quarterly, 3,* 173.

Menninger, K. A., Mayman, M., & Pruyser, P. (1963). *The vital balance.* New York: Viking Press.

Merrin, E. L., Van Dyke, C., Cohen, S., & Tusel, D. J. (1986). Dual factitious disorder. *General Hospital Psychiatry, 8*(4), 246–250.

Miller, H. (1961a). Accident neurosis: Lecture 1. *British Medical Journal, 1,* 919–925.

Miller, H. (1961b). Accident neurosis: Lecture 2. *British Medical Journal, 8,* 992–998.

Millon, T. (1981). *Disorders of personality: DSM-III, Axis II.* New York: Wiley.

Mills, M. J., & Lipian, M. S. (1995). In H. I. Kaplan & B. J. Sadock (Eds.), *Comprehensive textbook of psychiatry* (6th ed., Vol. I, pp. 1614–1622). Baltimore: Williams & Wilkins.

Molavi, A., & Weinstein, L. (1970). Persistent perplexing pyrexia: Some comments on etiology and diagnosis. *Medical Clinics of North America, 54,* 379–396.

Moorhead, J. J. (1944). Traumatic neurosis. *Medical Clinics of North America, 28*(3), 663–703.

Mowrer, O. H. (1950). *Learning theory and personality dynamics.* New York: Ronald Press.

Nadelson, T. (1979). The Munchausen spectrum: Borderline character features. *General Hospital Psychiatry, 1*(1), 11–17.

Naish, J. M. (1979). Problems of deception in medical practice. *Lancet, 2*(8134), 139–142.

Nogales, P. (1934). Aspecto medicolegal del la Neurosis de Renta (Medicolegal aspects of profit neurosis). *Siglo Medicine, 93,* 374–377.

Oppenheim, H. (1898). *Der traumatische neurosen.* Berlin: Hirschwald.

Ostfeld, B. M., & Feldman, M. D. (1996). Factitious disorder by proxy: Awareness among mental health practitioners. *General Hospital Psychiatry, 18*(2), 113–136.

Oxford English Dictionary, Compact Edition. (1971). New York: Oxford University Press.

Parker, N. (1970). Accident neurosis. *Medical Journal of Australia, 22*(2), 362–365.

Parker, N. (1977). Accident litigants with neurotic symptoms. *Medical Journal of Australia, 2*(10), 318–322.

Parker, N. (1979). Malingering: A dangerous diagnosis. *Medical Journal of Australia, 1*(12), 568–569.

Pender, D. J., & Pender, V. B. (1980). Otolaryngologica prevarica: Munchausen's syndrome update and report of a case. *Laryngoscope, 90*(4), 657–660.

People v. Drew. (1978). 22 Cal. 3rd (September 16).

Petersdorf, R. G., & Bennett, I. L. (1957). Factitious fever. *Annals of Internal Medicine, 46,* 1039–1062.

Pope, H. G. Jr., Jonas, J. M., & Jones, B. (1982). Factitious psychosis: Phenomenology, family history and long-term outcome of nine patients. *American Journal of Psychiatry, 139*(11), 1480–1483.

Power v. WCAB. (1966). 51 C.C.C. 114, 117.

Powills, S. (1986). Professional patients drain hospital funds. *Hospitals, 60*(13), 116.

Pritchard, J. C. (1835). *A treatise on insanity and other disorders affecting the mind.* London: Sherwood, Gibert & Piper.

Rabin, P. L., & Graham, B. S. (1984). Counterfeit calculi. *South Medical Journal, 77*(3), 304–307.

Raff, M. J., Stodghill, W. B., & Royal, T. M. (1975). Fraudulent feculent fever in a female fabulist. *South Medical Journal, 68*(3), 360–362.

Ramsay, J. (1939). Nervous disorder after injury: Review of 400 cases. *British Medical Journal, 2,* 385–390.

Raspe, R. E. (1948). *The singular travels, campaigns, and adventures of Baron Munchausen.* London: Cresset Press.

Ray, I. (1838). *A treatise on the medical jurisprudence of insanity.* Boston: Charles Little & James Brown.

Reich, J. D., & Hanno, P. M. (1997). Factitious renal colic. *Urology, 50*(6), 858–862.

Rhys-Evans, P. H. (1979). "Scopophilia Meanderans"—An unusual presentation of Munchausen's syndrome. *Journal of Laryngology and Otology, 93*(1), 67–74.

Robinson, J. P., Rondinelli, R. D., Scheer, S. J., & Weinstein, S. M. (1997). Industrial rehabilitation medicine. 1. Why is industrial rehabilitation medicine unique? *Archives of Physical Medicine and Rehabilitation, 78*(3 Suppl), S3–S9.

Rogers, D., Tripp, J., Bentovim, A., Robinson, A., Berry, D., & Goulding, R. (1976). Non-accidental poisoning: An extended syndrome of child abuse. *British Medical Journal, 1,* 793–796.

Rogers, R. (1984a). *Rogers Criminal Responsibility Assessment Scales (RCRAS) and Test Manual.* Odessa, FL: Psychological Assessment Resources, Inc.

Rogers, R. (1984b). Towards an empirical model of malingering and deception. *Behavioral Science and the Law, 2*(1), 93–111.

Rogers, R. (Ed.). (1988). *Clinical assessment of malingering and deception.* New York: Guilford Press.

Rogers, R., & Cavanaugh, J. L. (1983). "Nothing but the truth" . . . a reexamination of malingering. *Journal of Psychiatry and the Law, 11*(4), 443–459.

Rosen, G. M. (1996). Posttraumatic stress disorder, pulp fiction, and the press. *Bulletin of the American Academy of Psychiatry and the Law, 24*(2), 267–269.

Rosenhan, D. L. (1973). On being sane in insane places. *Science, 179,* 250–258.

Sale, I., Burvill, J., & Kalucy, R. (1979). Munchausen syndrome in a psychiatric setting: Three case reports. *Australia and New Zealand Journal of Psychiatry, 13*(2), 133–138.

Saluki, A. (1978). Munchausen: Fact and fiction. *Journal of the Royal College of Physicians London, 12*(3), 286–292.

Schneck, J. M. (1970). Pseudo-malingering and Leonid Andreyev's "The Dilemma." *Psychiatric Quarterly, 44*(1), 49–54.

Schreier, H. A., & Libow, J. A. (1993). *Hurting for love: Munchausen by proxy syndrome.* New York: Guilford Press.

Scott, R. (1584). *The discoverie of witchcraft.* London: E. Cotes.

Shaw, R. S. (1964). Pathologic malingering: The painful disabled extremity. *New England Journal of Medicine, 271*(1), 22–26.

Sheridan, J. S. (1995). MSBP in context II. In A. V. Levin & M. S. Sheridan (Eds.), *MSBP: Issues in diagnosis and treatment* (pp. 90–92). New York: Lexington.

Shipley, J. T. (1961). *Dictionary of word origins.* Patterson, NJ: Littlefield, Adams.

Shontz, F. C. (1965). *Research methods in personality.* New York: Appleton-Century-Crofts.

Sjoberg, S-G. (1951). Munchausen's syndrome. *Lancet, 1,* 1073.

Slovenko, R. (1973). *Psychiatry and law.* Boston: Little, Brown.

Smith, C. G., & Sinanan, K. (1972). The "Gaslight phenomenon" reappears: A modification of the Ganser syndrome. *British Journal of Psychiatry, 120*(559), 685–686.

Southard, E. E. (1919). *Shell-shock and other neuro-psychiatric problems.* New York: Arno Press.

Spiro, H. R. (1968). Chronic factitious illness: Munchausen's syndrome. *Archives of General Psychiatry, 18*(5), 569–579.

Sprenger, J., & Kramer, H. (1928). *Malleus Maleficarum* (M. Summers, Trans). London: John Rodker. (Original work published 1484)

Steinbeck, A. W. (1961). Haemorrhagica histronica—The bleeding Munchausen syndrome. *Medical Journal of Australia, 48*, 451–456.

Stendel, E. (1939). Studies in the psychopathology of compulsive wandering. *British Journal of Medical Psychology, 18*, 250–254.

Sussman, N., & Hyler, S. E. (1985). Factitious disorders. In H. I. Kaplan & B. J. Sadock (Eds.), *Comprehensive textbook of psychiatry* (4th ed., Vol. 4, pp. 1242–1245). Baltimore: Williams & Wilkins.

Swezey, C. L. (1968). Emotional disorders as industrial injury in California. *Lincoln Law Review, 3*, 112–123.

Sydenham, T. (1697). *Discourse concerning hysterical and hypochondriacal distempers: "Dr. Sydenham's complete method of curing almost all diseases, and description of their symptoms" to which are now added five discourses of the same author concerning the pleurisy, gout, hysterical passion, dropsy, and rheumatism* (3rd ed). London: Newman & Rich Parker.

Szasz, T. S. (1961). *The myth of mental illness.* New York: Harper & Row.

Tarsh, M. J., & Royston, C. (1985). A follow-up study of accident neurosis. *British Journal of Psychiatry, 146*, 18–25.

Thorne, F. C. (1949). The attitudinal pathoses. *Journal of Clinical Psychology, 5*, 1–6.

Travin, S., & Protter, B. (1984). Malingering and malingering-like behavior: Some clinical and conceptual issues. *Psychiatric Quarterly, 56*(3), 189–197.

Vaisrub, S. (1975). Pseudopatients and pseudoresearch. *Journal of the American Medical Association, 232*(1), 59.

Veith, I. (1955). On malingering. *Bulletin of the Cleveland Medical Library, 2*, 67–73.

Waisman, M. (1965). Pickers, pluckers and imposters: A panorama of cutaneous self-mutilation. *Postgraduate Medicine, 38*(6), 620–630.

Wallace, P. F., & Fitzmorris, C. S. (1978). The S-H-A-F-T syndrome in the upper extremity. *Journal of Hand Surgery (Am.), 3*(5), 492–494.

Warner, J. O., & Hathaway, M. J. (1984). Allergic form of Meadow's syndrome (Munchausen by proxy). *Archives of the Diseases of Childhood, 59*(2), 151–156.

Weaver, J. W., McMillan, R., Longmire, R. L., Yam, L. T., & Crosby, W. H. (1974). Scientific notation for hemoglobin Munchausen. *Journal of the American Medical Association, 229*(8), 1045.

Wechsler, I. S. (1935). Trauma and the nervous system—With special reference to head injuries and a classification of post-traumatic syndromes (analysis of one hundred cases). *Journal of the American Medical Association, 104*(7), 519–526.

Weiner, H., & Braimann, A. (1955). Ganser Syndrome: Review and addition of some unusual cases. *American Journal of Psychiatry, 3*, 767–783.

Weintraub, W. (1964). The VIP syndrome: A clinical study in hospital psychiatry. *Journal of Nervous and Mental Disease, 138*, 181–193.

Weintraub, W. (1989). *Verbal behaviors in everyday life.* New York: Springer.

Wernicke, C. (1906). *Grundriss der Psychiatrie.* Leipzig.

Weyer, J. (1991). *De Praestigiis Daemonum* (J. Shea, Trans.). Binghamptom, NY: Medieval and Renaissance Texts and Studies. (Original work published 1563)

Whitlock, F. A. (1967). The Ganser syndrome. *British Journal of Psychiatry, 113*(949), 19–29.

Whytt, R. (1777). *Observations of the nature, causes and cure of those disorders which have been commonly called nervous, hypochondriac or hysteric.* Paris: Chez P. Fr. Didot.

Williams, C. B. (1961). Peripatetic pseudoporphyria: Report of a case. *New England Journal of Medicine, 264*, 925–927.

Wingate, P. (1951). Munchausen's syndrome. *Lancet, 1*, 412–414.

Woodyard, J. E. (1982). Diagnosis and prognosis in compensation claims. *Annals of the Royal College of Surgery England, 64*(1), 191–194.

Yudofsky, S. C. (1985). Malingering. In H. I. Kaplan & B. J. Sadock (Eds.), *Comprehensive textbook of psychiatry* (4th ed., Vol. 4, pp. 1862–1865). Baltimore: Williams & Wilkins.

Subject Index

Author Index

References citations are in **boldface**

283

Author Index

References citations are in **boldface**